Welcome to the world of St. Piran's Hospital

Next to the rugged shores of Penhally Bay lies the picturesque Cornish town of St. Piran, where you'll find a bustling hospital famed for the dedication, talent and passion of its staff—on and off the wards!

Under the warmth of the Cornish sun, Italian doctors, heart surgeons and playboy princes discover that romance blossoms in the most unlikely of places…

You'll also meet the devilishly handsome Dr. Josh O'Hara and the beautiful, fragile Megan Phillips…and discover the secret that tore these star-crossed lovers apart.

Turn the page to step into St. Piran's— where every drama has a dreamy doctor… and a happy ending.

Dear Reader,

Having written *Spanish Doctor, Pregnant Midwife*, which was based in Penhally Bay, I was delighted to be asked to contribute to the new series set in and around St. Piran's Hospital.

I was especially pleased to spend some time with the characters on the rugged coast of Cornwall, a part of the world I love, and which is very similar to the West Coast of Scotland where I live now.

This is the story of extreme sport fanatic Mac, who is a doctor with the Royal Cornwall Air Ambulance Service, and Abby, single mum and air ambulance paramedic.

When committed bachelor Mac meets Abby he is immediately attracted to her. Soon after he finds out that Abby has a secret that is about to turn his life upside down, and he learns that loving involves taking risks too.

I hope you enjoy reading Mac and Abby's story.

Anne Fraser

ST. PIRAN'S: DAREDEVIL, DOCTOR...DAD!

Anne Fraser

HARLEQUIN®

entertain, enrich, inspire™

Recycling programs for this product may not exist in your area.

ISBN-13: 978-0-373-06852-4

ST. PIRAN'S: DAREDEVIL, DOCTOR...DAD!

First North American Publication 2012

Copyright © 2012 by Harlequin Books S.A.

Special thanks and acknowledgment are given to Anne Fraser for her contribution to the St. Piran's Hospital series

Recent titles by Anne Fraser

SPANISH DOCTOR, PREGNANT MIDWIFE

MISTLETOE, MIDWIFE...MIRACLE BABY

PRINCE CHARMING OF HARLEY STREET

**These books are also available in ebook format
from www.Harlequin.com.**

Dedication

To my lovely editor, Joanne, with heartfelt thanks
for her support and guidance.

ST. PIRAN'S HOSPITAL

Where every drama has a dreamy doctor...and a happy ending.

Last month there was a real treat in store—the first two St. Piran's stories in one month!

Nick Tremayne and Kate Althorp finally got their happy-ever-after in

ST. PIRAN'S: THE WEDDING OF THE YEAR
by Caroline Anderson

Then Dr. Izzy Bailey was swept off her feet by sexy Spaniard Diego Ramirez:

ST. PIRAN'S: RESCUING PREGNANT CINDERELLA
by Carol Marinelli

And there's plenty more romance brewing in St. Piran's!

The arrival of Italian neurosurgeon Giovanni Corezzi will make you forget the cold this month in

ST. PIRAN'S: ITALIAN SURGEON, FORBIDDEN BRIDE
by Margaret McDonagh

And daredevil doc William MacNeil unexpectedly discovers that he's a father in

ST. PIRAN'S: DAREDEVIL, DOCTOR...DAD!
by Anne Fraser

The new heart surgeon has everyone's pulses racing in November in

ST. PIRAN'S: THE BROODING HEART SURGEON
by Alison Roberts

And fireman Tom Nicholson steals Flora Loveday's heart in

ST. PIRAN'S: THE FIREMAN AND NURSE LOVEDAY
by Kate Hardy

And finally in December, newborn twins could just bring a marriage miracle for Brianna and Connor Taylor in

ST. PIRAN'S: TINY TWIN MIRACLES
by Maggie Kingsley

Not to mention playboy Prince Alessandro Cavalieri's arrival in St. Piran's in

ST. PIRAN'S: PRINCE ON THE CHILDREN'S WARD
by Sarah Morgan

The St. Piran's books will also be available in ebook format from www.Harlequin.com from this month onward.

CHAPTER ONE

ABBY sank onto the sofa transfixed by what was happening on the TV screen. At the end of a rope, a man was being lowered out of a Royal Navy helicopter. Abby held her breath as the figure swirled precariously in the buffeting wind. She had put on the TV to catch the weather report but now she couldn't tear her eyes away from the drama unfolding in front of her.

Beneath the helicopter a boat was listing dangerously to one side, obviously in serious trouble. The reporter covering the story was telling the viewers that the Royal Navy rescue service had been called out to the stricken vessel. 'The family of four were on a sailing trip when they got into trouble off the Cornish coast. Heavy seas pushed their boat onto rocks and it is now taking on water rapidly. We have heard that the helmsman took a heavy blow to his head and is unconscious. His wife, who radioed for help, and their two young children, are still on board.'

Although the newscaster's expression was calm, Abby could detect suppressed tension in her voice. 'The helicopter crew has only a short time to get everyone off before the boat sinks. We understand that there is a doctor helping from the Royal Cornwall Air Ambulance Service.'

The man at the end of the winch dropped onto the listing boat, unhooked himself from the line and slithered his way across the deck. Within minutes he was being lifted back on board the helicopter, with two small figures attached to him like clams.

He swiftly dropped down to the boat again, retrieving another person from the stricken yacht. Heart in her mouth, Abby leaned forward. The injured skipper was still on the boat! Could he be rescued before the yacht sank, taking him and his rescuer along with it? If he had a head injury, as the newscaster was suggesting, then it would be dangerous to move him. But what other option was there? To leave him would be unthinkable.

The downdraught from the helicopter whipped the sea into a frenzy. Nearby, a coastguard rescue boat was making valiant attempts to approach the yacht but the heavy waves were preventing it from getting anywhere close. Abby squeezed her eyes closed. She could hardly bear to watch.

'A second man is being lowered onto the boat.' The newscaster's voice dropped to a whisper. 'We understand he's a doctor.'

Abby opened her eyes. Sure enough, she could just make out the letters on the fluorescent jacket of the second man.

The line attached to the helicopter was swinging wildly as the pilot struggled to keep the aircraft level. The small boat rose up to meet the man on the end of the winch then dropped away again. The figure swung first to the right then to the left as the deck kept veering away. Abby knew there was a real possibility that the rescuers might lose their own lives in the attempt to reach the injured skipper.

Suddenly the doctor was on the deck. Quickly he released himself from the harness and the line was reeled back into the helicopter.

Almost unable to breathe, Abby watched him pick his way across the slippery deck, almost losing his balance as the boat shifted wildly in the heavy seas. Moments later another man dropped down from the helicopter, this one with a stretcher. Abby lost sight of the first man as he disappeared from view. Had he slipped overboard?

While she'd been watching, Emma had come into the room. Seeing Abby staring at the screen, she unplugged herself from her MP3 player and sat down next to her.

'Is that what you're going to be doing?' Emma asked. 'In your new job?'

'Sometimes,' Abby admitted. Although she hoped to hell she wouldn't be involved in anything quite as dangerous as what was going on in front of her. It was one thing being trained to be winched up and down from a helicopter in calm conditions—this was something altogether different.

Emma looked at her wide-eyed. 'Cool,' she said.

Thankfully her daughter didn't seem to appreciate the danger the men were in. That was good: Abby didn't want Emma worrying about her.

It seemed like hours but it could only have been a few minutes before the stretcher, now loaded with the injured skipper, was being attached to the winch. Abby knew the danger was far from over. The yacht was sinking rapidly. She was amazed that it had managed to stay afloat as long as it had.

Then the men with the stretcher were being lifted back onto the helicopter. As soon as they were on board the aircraft swung away. Seconds later the boat tipped up and with a final surge was engulfed by the waves. Any sooner and it would have taken the three men with it.

'I understand the mother and two children have been taken to hospital where they are being treated for hypothermia and shock,' the reporter continued. 'At this time we have no details about the condition of the skipper except that he is stable. But right now we can give you a live interview with some of the men involved in the daring rescue.'

The drama over, Emma went back to her music and left the room. Before Abby could switch the television off, the camera panned out slightly, revealing two men. One, a man in his fifties, was wearing the jumpsuit of the Royal Navy, the other the fluorescent jacket of a rescue doctor. Both men were smiling broadly, as if what they had just done had been exhilarating—and no more dangerous than a routine training exercise.

But as the camera zoomed closer, it was the younger man, the doctor, that made Abby's heart leap in her chest. Underneath his five-o'clock shadow there was something disturbingly familiar about his hooked nose and wide grin. But before Abby could get a better look at him the camera, frustratingly, focussed solely on his colleague.

'I have Sergeant Lightbody with me, who was the winchman involved in the rescue,' the reporter said.

The older man shifted slightly, looking uncomfortable to find himself on TV.

'Sergeant Lightbody,' the newscaster continued, 'can you tell the viewers at home what it was like out there today? From what I could see, it seemed that you just managed to get the victims off the boat in the nick of time.'

Sergeant Lightbody looked even more ill at ease. 'It was certainly a little breezy out there. I guess it was one of the more difficult situations we've been involved in for a while.'

'A little breezy? A bit of an understatement, surely? If you and your men hadn't been able to get these people off, it could've ended in tragedy. That all the family members survived is testament to the skill and courage of your team.'

'It's what we do.' Sergeant Lightbody shrugged. 'Anyway, if it hadn't been for Dr MacNeil here, we might not have got the skipper off without further injury—if at all.'

The camera shifted to the younger man. He was shaking his head. Despite the hat pulled low on his brow, shadowing his eyes, Abby realised with a jolt that she did recognise him. She didn't need to check the photograph she had kept for all these years to know that Dr MacNeil was Mac—her dead sister's lover and Emma's father!

Her legs shaking, Abby got up and retrieved the remote then froze the screen. She was breathing rapidly as she studied the fuzzy picture. It was him! He was older, yes; there were faint smile lines on either side of his mouth and radiating from the corners of his ice-blue eyes. He had filled out a little, and his hair was shorter, although still sun-bleached at the tips. Still, she would know that wide smile and glinting, expressive gaze anywhere.

She pressed the remote and the picture moved again.

'Dr MacNeil, could you tell us what happened back there? I understand you work with the Royal Cornwall Air Ambulance team. Is this just another typical day for you?'

Abby's heart was pounding so hard she could almost hear it. She had found Mac! And not just found him, she was actually going to be working with him. She sank back down on the sofa as her legs threatened to give way beneath her. Thank God Emma had left the room. She would have known immediately that something was wrong, and right now Abby needed to make sense of what she was seeing.

Mac grinned into the camera. Unlike Sergeant Lightbody, he seemed completely at ease. 'Not exactly a typical day but, yes, the Royal Cornwall Air Ambulance teams up with other rescue services when required. We believe that having immediate medical attention on the scene can often make the difference between life and death.'

'Even if it means putting your own life at risk?' The stunning blonde reporter was almost whimpering with admiration.

'I'm pretty certain the Royal Navy wouldn't let anything happen to me,' Mac replied lightly. 'Besides, they are the real heroes. They do this sort of thing day after day. If it wasn't for the pilot of the helicopter and his team, we would have never been able to get to the casualties.'

Abby still couldn't believe what she was seeing. It was ironic, really. Abby had tried desperately to find this man years before without any success, and now he was here, in Penhally, and she'd be working with him!

Incredible to think that the reason they were here in the first place was because Emma didn't have a father.

A few months ago, just before Emma's eleventh birthday, Abby had asked her whether she wanted to invite her schoolfriends over for a party. To Abby's horror, Emma had burst into tears. When she'd eventually managed to calm her down, Emma had admitted that the children at the school had been ostracising her for the last couple of weeks. Only her best friend had still talked to her.

'But why, darling? Has something happened? You used to have loads of friends.'

Between tears and sobs of anguish Emma had explained that one of the girls had started taunting her about not having a dad.

'I told them that of course I had a dad,' Emma had said, indignant. 'So they asked where he was. When I told them I didn't know, they made fun of me. They said that I was lying or else I must be a rubbish daughter that my dad didn't want to know me. I tried to ignore them but they kept coming after me, saying these horrible things.' She'd looked up at Abby, her blue eyes swimming with tears. 'I know you're not my real mum, Mum.' She'd smiled, realising what she'd said. 'I mean, you're my real mum, but not my birth mum. But you've never told me who my father is. Why doesn't he care about me? Why *hasn't* he ever come to see me?'

Abby's heart had ached for her child. Although, as Emma had put it, *she* wasn't her biological mother, Emma was hers in every way that counted. She couldn't love her more had she given birth to her, and Emma being her twin sister Sara's child simply made the bond closer.

'I want to know who my dad is,' Emma had continued quietly. 'All the other girls at school know who their dad is, so why can't I?'

Abby had looked into the stormy blue eyes that were so like Sara's and a lump had formed in her throat. She'd known only too well how Emma had felt.

'My darling, he probably doesn't even know you exist.'

'How can he not know? How could my real mum not have told him?'

Abby winced before she'd begun speaking. 'Sara was very happy you were going to be born. I guess she didn't want to share you.'

The truth was that Sara hadn't wanted Emma's father to know about the pregnancy. At least not until she discovered that she was going to die. It was only then that she told Abby that Emma's father was Mac, the windsurfing instructor they had met while on holiday in Mykonos. When Emma was just three months old Abby went back to the Greek island to try to track him down, but it was hopeless. The summer season was over, and the visitors as well as the instructors had long since packed up and left. No one could tell her anything about Mac. Who he was or where he'd gone.

Before Sara died, Abby promised she would raise her daughter as her own. She had kept that promise and even though it hadn't always been easy, Abby had no regrets. Emma brought such joy to her life.

'I don't want to stay at that school, Mum. Please. Can't I go to a different school when I go to secondary?'

'It's not that easy, sweetie. Here in London it's difficult to find a good school within walking distance. Let me try and sort things out with the school first.'

But despite several visits to the school, the bullying continued. It both angered and saddened Abby to see Emma withdraw more and more into herself, so when Abby saw an ad for an experienced paramedic for the Royal Cornwall Air Ambulance Service, after talking it over with Emma, she decided to apply. Cornwall would be perfect for them. It was near the sea and would suit Emma's love of the outdoors much better. They were both thrilled to leave London and its sad memories behind. Abby had promised Emma that as soon as they were settled in their new home and she in her job she would continue the search for her father. Little did Abby know then that fate was going to throw them directly in his path, sooner than either of them could possibly have imagined.

Abby retrieved the tattered holiday snap from the sideboard drawer. It had been taken on the last night of her and Sara's holiday on Mykonos and Abby studied it for what must have been the hundredth time. It was a group photograph, taken on the beach. Mac had his arm draped around Sara, who was laughing up at him. She herself was at the end, a solemn figure with mid-length hair, her eyes hidden behind sunglasses. She doubted if Mac had even been aware that she was there. They had been introduced, of course, but his glance had slid almost immediately straight past Abby to her much more glamorous and fun-loving sister.

She turned to stare at the TV again, almost expecting him to reappear. She still had a week of training to complete before she started her job, so she had some time to think before she came face to face with Dr William MacNeil.

What was she going to tell Emma?

What was she going to say to Mac when they met?

What the hell was she going to do?

CHAPTER TWO

ABBY'S stomach fluttered nervously as she stepped into the base of the Royal Cornwall Air Ambulance Service. Although she had been a trained paramedic for almost twelve years, this would be an altogether different experience. She would be *flying* to rescues and despite the intensive training she had just undergone, she worried how she would cope with being lowered from a helicopter, particularly in gusty weather. But she was here now and those concerns paled into insignificance in comparison to her anxiety about meeting Mac again.

Ever since she'd seen him on television she'd been agonising over what to do. What if he was married and had a family of his own? What if Mac didn't want to know about his daughter? That hurt would be too great for the little girl. In which case should she even tell

Emma that Mac was here? Did she have the right to keep the truth from Emma?

In the end she decided she wouldn't say anything to Emma until she'd had a chance to suss Mac out for herself. After all, a bad father was worse than no father at all.

The air ambulance leader, who had interviewed Abby when she'd applied for the job, met her at the door. Paul was in his early fifties with an easy smile and a relaxed and welcoming manner.

'Abby, we've been looking forward to you joining us,' he said. 'Did you enjoy your training? The course leader spoke highly of you.'

The course leader might have spoken highly of her, but that meant zilch. How she would cope in a real-life rescue would be what counted.

'What do think of Penhally Bay?' Paul continued.

'It's lovely. I haven't had too much time to explore yet—what with the course, getting my daughter settled into school and all the unpacking. But I promised Emma that on my first day off we'll have a proper look around.'

'It's a great place for a child to grow up,' Paul said. 'My kids have long since flown the coop, but they come back whenever they can. Is Emma liking Penhally High? Mine went there and they loved it. I can't imagine it's changed too much.'

Abby nodded, managing a small smile. If nothing else, their move here had been the right thing for Emma, at least as far as her new school went. Although her daughter had only been at Penhally High for a short while, she had quickly made new friends and already seemed much happier and settled.

So she was here to stay, and if life had thrown her a curve ball by flinging her directly in Mac's path, so be it. There was no going back. But until she decided what, if anything, to tell him, she would play her cards close to her chest.

Nevertheless her heart was pounding uncomfortably at the thought of meeting him again. Would he recognise her after all these years? It was unlikely. Her appearance had changed quite a bit and he hadn't paid her much attention twelve years ago. He had been far too caught up in her twin sister, the glamorous, effervescent Sara.

'Come up to the office and meet everyone,' Paul interrupted her thoughts. 'They're looking forward to meeting you.'

Her legs like jelly, Abby followed him up a steep flight of steps and into a large room where a number of people were chatting and drinking coffee.

Immediately her eyes were drawn to Mac. He was sitting, his long legs stretched out in front of him, his arms cradling the back of his head as he chatted to a colleague. Like most of the others in the room, he was dressed in an orange jumpsuit, but his was unzipped almost to the waist, revealing a dazzling white T-shirt underneath. There was no disguising his powerful build and Abby felt as if a bird were trapped in her chest.

'Everyone, I'd like you to meet our latest recruit, Abby Stevens,' Paul introduced her.

This was the moment she had been dreading. Would Mac remember her? Would he recall Sara's last name? Had he even known what it was? Although everyone turned to look at her, Abby was unable to stop herself from watching Mac's reaction. Blue eyes narrowed for a moment as if she had triggered a memory, but then he grinned and jumped to his feet. His eyes swept over her body.

'I'm Dr William MacNeil. But everyone calls me Mac.' His grip was firm and to her dismay it felt as if she had touched a live wire. Abby withdrew her hand quickly and turned to greet the other members of the team but not before she'd seen Mac's puzzled frown.

Abby forced herself to concentrate as she was introduced to the others in the room. Apart from Paul, there were two paramedics, Mike and Jim, a pilot—an older man called Greg—as well as Lucy, another doctor, and Kirsten, whose job it was to take the calls and keep in touch with the ambulance throughout the rescue. They all smiled welcomingly.

Instinctively Abby knew she would enjoy working with this group of people—with one possible exception.

'Would you mind showing Abby around, Mac?' Paul asked. 'I have some paperwork to attend to and Lucy and Mike have just popped in to give us a report on yesterday's callout.' Paul turned to Abby. 'I'll see you all later.'

'A car accident on the coastal road,' Lucy explained as Paul left the room. She was small and plump with bright, intelligent eyes. 'The driver was going too fast for these roads and hit another car head on.'

'Any fatalities?' Abby asked.

'Surprisingly not. Luckily the oncoming car managed to swerve in time. The fire brigade had to use the jaws of life to get the driver out. It took hours and we had to keep him ventilated by hand. He's still on the critical list, but he's damned lucky to be alive.' Lucy glanced at her watch. 'Time for me to go!' She held out her hand again. 'It's good to have another woman on board, Abby. Kirsten and I get a little overwhelmed by all the testosterone around here, don't we, Kirsten?'

Kirsten grinned back. 'Don't let Lucy kid you—she's a match for the guys any time.'

Abby glanced across at Mac, who had remained silent throughout the exchange. He was studying Abby as if she puzzled him.

'Hey, have we met before?' he asked.

Abby's pulse beat even faster. Although she and Sara hadn't been identical twins there had been similarities between them—hazel eyes, straight noses and curvy mouths. But Sara had cropped her hair short and bleached it platinum blonde for their Greek holiday. In contrast, Abby had kept her shoulder length caramel hair tied back in a ponytail and at that time had worn glasses. The two sisters could hardly have looked more different and unsurprisingly Mac had barely glanced at Abby back then. Even if he did recognise her, this was hardly the time or place to tell him about Sara and Emma. Not that she had decided *what* to tell him.

She forced a smile. 'I don't think so.'

He lost the frown and grinned at her. 'You're right,' he said, lowering his voice. 'I would have remembered you. I don't tend to forget beautiful women.' He winked at her.

'And unless you're losing it, they don't tend to forget you either. That's what you mean,' chipped in Lucy. She turned to Abby, her eyes twinkling. 'Watch out for our Mac here. We love him to bits, but he's a heart-breaker. Luckily I'm too old for him and Kirsten's already taken.'

'You know I'd take you to dinner any day of the week, Lucy. Just say the word.' Mac grinned back.

'Ah, if only,' Lucy sighed theatrically. She picked up her handbag. 'I'm out of here.'

'Me too,' Kirsten said. 'I've got work to do around here!'

Left alone with Mac, Abby felt as if she had a coiled spring somewhere in her chest. He was still looking at her through half-closed eyes as if she puzzled him. 'Dr MacNeil,' she said stiffly. 'I think we should get on with that tour, don't you?'

Again there was that heart-stopping grin. 'Call me Mac. Everyone else does.'

* * *

Mac stood back to let Abby go in front of him. He whistled under his breath as he watched the way her bottom swayed as she walked. On anyone else the orange uniform tunic top and matching trousers would have been unflattering, but it could have been tailor made for Abby. And, even apart from her figure which looked as if it had been designed with him in mind, she was a stunner. A man could drown in those eyes and as for the high cheekbones, emphasised by the hint of colour his remarks had brought to her cheeks, he had dated models who would scratch their eyes out for bone structure like that. Even the spattering of freckles over her nose didn't detract from her beauty—if anything, it made her cuter. He had already checked the third finger of her left hand. No wedding ring. Good. This was going to be interesting.

Mac had only just started showing Abby the little office where Kirsten and her small team fielded the calls when the telephone rang.

Kirsten held up a finger, asking for silence. They listened as she entered a few details into the computer.

'Try not to worry, love. We'll have someone there as soon as possible. Stay on the phone while I talk to the doctor.'

She swivelled around in her chair until she was facing Abby and Mac.

'I have a lady on the line. She's thirty-four weeks pregnant but thinks she's gone into early labour. She can't get herself to the hospital because she's on a farm and her husband is away with the car.' Kirsten covered the mouthpiece with her hand. 'She also tells me she has placenta praevia and was due to be admitted for a Caesarean section in a couple of weeks.'

'Where is the farm?' Mac asked. Gone was the laconic man of earlier. In his place was someone who was entirely focussed.

Kirsten pointed to a map. 'Over here.'

'What about the local road ambulance?' Abby asked.

Kirsten shook her head. 'It's at least an hour away on these roads and, besides, the woman—she's called Jenny Hargreaves—says the track to the farm is pretty impassable for anything except a four-by-four. We've had some heavy rain over the last fortnight.'

'We need to get her to the maternity unit as fast as possible,' Mac said. 'Okay, Kirsten, get Greg to fire the 'copter up and tell Jenny we're on our way. Is there anyone with her who can help? A friend? A neighbour?'

Kirsten shook her head. 'She's on her own, apart from her nine-year-old son.'

'Get him on the line and keep him there. Then phone St Piran's and bring them up to speed. Could you make sure we have an incubator for the baby on board, too? C'mon, Abby. I guess you're on. Let's go and get kitted up.'

As Abby raced after him down the steps and into the cloakroom where their gear was kept, she ran through what she knew about placenta praevia. And what she did know didn't make her feel any better.

'Not good news, is it?' she said as Mac passed her a jacket.

'Tell me what you know about the condition.'

'Placenta praevia is where the placenta is lying in front of the baby, blocking the birth canal. I know it can cause massive, even fatal bleeding if left untreated. If she's already in labour, we don't have much time.' Although they had covered complications of childbirth in their training, until Sara it hadn't crossed Abby's mind that it could really happen. Now she knew better. Please, God, don't let this first call end in disaster.

'Do we have an obstetrician on call?' she asked.

'At St Piran's. Kirsten will patch us through as soon as we're airborne. There's no time to wait, though.' Mac stopped for a moment and rested his hands on her shoulders. He looked directly into her eyes. 'Are you going to be okay?' His look was calm, reassuring. Everything about him radiated confidence and Abby relaxed a little.

'Sure.' She kept her voice light. 'All in a day's work.'

They piled into the helicopter and lifted off, heading towards the coast.

'ETA twenty minutes,' Greg's voice came over the radio. 'It's a bit breezy where we're heading so it might get a little bumpy.'

'Do you think we'll be able to put down?' Mac asked.

'There's a good-sized field behind the farmhouse, but I guess it depends on how soggy the ground is. We won't know until we get there.'

Abby and Mac shared a look.

'Have you ever done an emergency section before?' Abby asked. If they couldn't get mother and baby to hospital, it would be their only chance. But such a procedure would be tricky even for a qualified obstetrician in a fully equipped theatre. Her heart started pounding again. Confidence was one thing, but did Mac have the skill needed to back it up?

'I have.' He leaned across and flashed Abby another wicked grin. 'But don't worry, I have every intention of letting the obstetricians do it.' He held up a finger and listened intently.

A quiet voice came over the radio. 'Hello, Mac. Dr Gibson here. What do we have?'

'A thirty-four-weeker with placenta praevia who has gone into early labour. Control has her son on the phone. Mum tells him she thinks her contractions are coming about five minutes apart. The mother's name is Jenny Hargreaves. She tells us she was due to be delivered by section at St Piran's so you should have her case notes there.'

There was a short silence. Abby guessed Dr Gibson was bringing up Jenny's record on her computer screen.

'I'll make sure neonatal intensive care is standing by and that we have a theatre ready. How long d'you think before you'll have her here for us?'

'Another ten minutes until we land. If we can. Say another ten to examine our lady and get her loaded and twenty back. Do you think we'll make it?' Again there was that easy smile as if this was just another everyday callout.

'If anyone can, you can,' came back the reply. 'But if she's gone into active labour she could be bleeding massively and you may have to section her there and then. It won't be easy.'

'Hell, whoever said anything is easy in this job? But trust me.' He turned and winked at Abby. 'If I can get her to you without having to section her, I will.' He flexed long fingers. 'Been a long time since I did one of those.'

'Good luck,' Dr Gibson said calmly.

A short while later they reached the farm. To Abby's relief the pilot had been able to find a spot to land. The helicopter rotors had barely slowed when Mac hefted the large medical bag over his shoulder.

'Okay, we're on. Remember to keep your head down.' Abby took a deep breath, sent a silent prayer towards heaven, and followed him out of the helicopter.

Mac sprinted towards the farmhouse, carrying the medical case that weighed at least ten kilos as if it were nothing. Abby ran after him, doing her best to keep up.

A child with wide, frightened eyes was waiting for them by the doorway.

'Please hurry, my mum is bleeding,' the boy said.

This was the worst possible news. Jenny

being in labour was one thing, but they had banked on having enough time to get her to hospital. If she had started bleeding it meant that the placenta was beginning to detach. As it did, the baby's life support system became compromised and the life of the mother was in jeopardy. It would have been dangerous enough in hospital, but all Abby and Mac had was some morphine and basic equipment. It wasn't good. Abby's heart jumped to her throat.

Mac paused by the doorway and hunkered down so that he was at eye level with the boy. He placed a hand on the child's shoulder.

'What's your name, son?'

'Tim.'

'It's going to be all right, Tim, I promise. Now, if you could take us to your mum, we'll look after her.'

Whatever Tim saw in Mac's eyes seemed to reassure him. He nodded and led them inside the farmhouse and into a bedroom. On the bed, a woman lay writhing with pain. She was pale and her eyes were stretched wide with fear.

Abby and Mac rushed to her side.

'Jenny, isn't it?' Mac said as he laid the medical case on the floor. 'I'm Dr MacNeil and this is Abby Stevens. We're going to do everything we can to look after you and your baby.'

Abby felt Jenny's pulse.

'Over one hundred and thready,' she told Mac as she unwrapped the stethoscope from around her neck.

'How long have you been bleeding? And when did the contractions start?' Mac asked.

'I just started bleeding a few minutes ago. The contractions started about an hour ago. I phoned the hospital and they said they would get an ambulance.' Jenny reached out a hand and squeezed Abby's fingers hard. 'You have to save my baby. Please. You've got to help us.'

'We are going to do everything possible,' Abby replied with what she hoped was a confident smile.

She checked Jenny's blood pressure. As expected, it was low. Jenny was already bleeding heavily.

'I'm just going to give you some fluids through a needle in your vein,' Mac explained as he swabbed a patch of skin near Jenny's elbow. 'Then we're going to get you onto a stretcher and into the air ambulance, okay?'

'What about Tim? I can't leave him here by

himself. My husband isn't due back until to-morrow morning.'

'Is there a neighbour we could call for you?'

Jenny shook her head. 'We only moved here a couple of months ago. I don't know anyone yet. I've been so busy getting ready for the new baby.'

'In that case, Tim can come in the helicopter with us. How about it, Tim?' Mac turned to the little boy who had remained by the door, taking everything in with wide eyes.

'Wicked,' he said. Now adults were taking control, the colour had returned to his face.

Mac finished setting up the drip.

'Okay, Jenny. The helicopter's just outside waiting to take you to hospital. We're going to get you on board as quickly as we can.'

Jenny clutched her stomach as another con-traction took hold. 'Just get me to the hospital,' she said through gritted teeth. Then she forced a smile and turned to her son. 'Tim will help, won't you, love?'

Tim's terror had disappeared. Whether it was because they were there helping his mother or whether it was the excitement of the helicopter ride, Abby didn't know or care. All that mattered was that the boy was calm.

It would help Jenny and give them one less thing to worry about.

Abby draped a blanket round her patient before strapping her into the stretcher. As they carried her outside, Abby tried not to wince when a contraction gripped the mother and she squeezed Abby's fingers with ferocious strength.

Please let her hang in there, Abby prayed silently. At least until they got her to hospital. She slid a glance at Mac. Nothing in his demeanour indicated that at any time they could be dealing with a life-and-death scenario. Was he really as calm as he appeared?

Inside the helicopter they attached Jenny to the on-board monitoring equipment and pumped fluids into her. Abby checked the fetal heartbeat again. So far so good.

As soon as they had Jenny settled and the helicopter was heading towards St Piran's, Mac raised his thumb to Tim. Greg had given the boy a helmet and earmuffs to deaden the noise.

Tim returned the salute, unable to hide his excitement.

Abby slid a glance at Mac as he leaned over Jenny. He puzzled her. Everything about him contradicted the image of him she had held in her head for the last twelve years. Whenever she'd thought about him, she'd imagined an ageing Lothario chatting up young women on the beach under the pretext of teaching them how to windsurf, not this caring and utterly professional doctor.

Even if it was obvious from his behaviour when they'd met as well as Lucy's comments that he still was a blatant flirt she liked the way he had taken the time to reassure Tim.

Her thoughts were interrupted as the helicopter touched down on the hospital landing pad. Abby breathed a deep sigh of relief. They had made it!

'Stick close to me,' Mac said to Tim after removing the young lad's helmet.

The helicopter's rotors hadn't even stopped when the hospital staff were there to take charge of Jenny. The transfer was quick. Mac and Abby updated the hospital staff as they ran next to the trolley with Tim following closely behind.

'Thanks, guys. We'll take it from here,' the doctor Mac had addressed as Dr Gibson said.

They watched as Jenny disappeared from view.

'C'mon, Tim. Why don't we get you a drink or something?' Abby offered, knowing that

now the excitement of the helicopter journey
was over the boy would start fretting again.
'And in the meantime we can try and get your
dad on the phone and either me or Dr MacNeil
here will speak to him. How does that sound?'

'Sounds okay. When can I see Mum?'

'Not for a little while,' Abby said. 'But while
Dr MacNeil is speaking to your father, I'll find
somewhere where you can wait.'

Tim's face crumpled. 'I don't want to stay
on my own. I want my dad.'

Abby felt terrible for the little boy. If something happened to her, she'd hate for Emma to
be left alone. But what could they do? They
had to get back to the air ambulance base.
There could be another call at any time.

But Mac seemed to have his own ideas. 'Tell
you what,' he said. 'When I speak to your dad,
I'll suggest you come back with Abby and me
to the air ambulance headquarters. How about
it? You could have a look around see all the
stuff we use. We have some cool things we
can do with our computers. I'll let the staff
here know where we are and as soon as they
have any news about your mum they can let
us know. What do you say?'

Tim's face brightened. 'Could I? No one
will mind? I promise I won't get in the way.'

Once more, Abby was pleasantly surprised. Mac could easily have left the child here. After all they had done their job and Tim wasn't their responsibility. She really had underestimated him. Nothing about him made sense. Her head was beginning to ache. Right now she would have given anything for some time on her own to think, but she had promised Tim a drink while they waited for Mac to speak to his father and do the handover.

Spotting a vending machine against the wall inside the A & E department, Abby scrabbled in her pocket for some change and fed it into the slot. To no avail—the wretched machine stubbornly refused to part with its goods. Banging with the flat of her hand against the side had no effect either.

'Here, let me help.' A woman who looked as if she had stepped out of a magazine came across. She fiddled with the machine and a can rolled out.

'It just takes a certain knack.' She held out a manicured hand. 'You must be new. I'm Rebecca O'Hara, my husband Josh is one of the A & E consultants.'

'Abby Stevens. First day with the Air Ambulance Service.'

'Pleased to meet you, Abby. Where are you

from? I can tell by your accent that you're not from here.'

'I've been living in London for the last few years.'

'London?' Rebecca looked wistful. 'Don't you miss it?'

'I love it here,' Abby said honestly. She glanced across the room to where an anxious Tim was waiting for her. Although she had the distinct impression Rebecca wanted to chat, Abby didn't like to leave the boy any longer than she had to.

Just then Mac appeared. 'Oh, hello, Rebecca.' He smiled. 'If you're waiting to see Josh, I'm afraid he's up to his neck with patients at the moment.'

Rebecca looked dejected. 'I'll have a cup of coffee with the nurses while I'm waiting.'

She turned back to Abby. 'Lovely to meet you. Perhaps we could have a coffee some time?' And then with a flutter of slim fingers she headed towards the staffroom.

Back at base, no one seemed particularly surprised to see Tim. Mac gave him the promised tour after which he settled Tim in front of the computers and started explaining how the system worked.

A little while later, Dr Gibson phoned to say that they had sectioned Jenny and although she had lost a great deal of blood, she and her new baby son were going to be fine. Tim was ecstatic about having a brother, but as it was going to be a couple of hours before Jenny would come around properly from the anaesthetic, they decided to keep him with them a bit longer. Tim's father was on his way to the hospital.

'I'll drop Tim back at the hospital later,' Mac said to Abby. 'I'm due to do some teaching there this afternoon.'

Abby raised an eyebrow.

'I keep my hand in at the hospital when we're not busy. It helps keep me up to date and it only takes me a couple of minutes to get back here if we get a callout.' He smiled. 'You don't fancy a drink later, by any chance? I can tell you all about Penhally.' His expression was teasing, his eyes glinting.

Abby was horrified to feel a tingle run down her spine. Damn it! Why did she have to find him so damn sexy? Even sexier and better looking than twelve years ago. And the fact that he had a caring side made him all the more attractive. What was she thinking? There was no way she could be attracted to her dead sister's ex-lover; it was too weird. What was more, she had to remember that Mac was the type of man for whom flirting was as natural as breathing. It didn't mean anything. Wasn't the way he'd treated Sara evidence of that?

He was looking at her, waiting for her reply, certain she would say yes. He was so supremely confident she would love to turn him down. And she would have, if it wasn't for Emma. Her antennae, honed by years of being let down by men just like him, were on red alert. Of all the men in all the world, why did she have to be working with him?

Despite every nerve cell in her brain telling her to keep her distance from this man, for her daughter's sake, she needed to learn more about him. Emma was going to a friend's after school and wouldn't be home until seven. Abby made up her mind.

'I'll tell you what,' she said. 'I like to go for a walk after work. You can join me if you want.' She shrugged. 'It's up to you.' Smiling to herself as she saw the look of surprise in his eyes, she whirled on her heel, ignoring the feeling that two blue eyes were watching her speculatively.

* * *

Mac watched Abby's retreating back until she was out of sight. He would have bet a hundred bucks she had been about to turn him down, and her acceptance had taken him by surprise. Not that a walk was what he had in mind and not that he would have let one refusal put him off. In fact, it would have heightened the excitement of the chase. He tried to ignore the unpleasant feeling lurking somewhere deep down that felt uncomfortably like shame. Should he really be going after Abby? Although she intrigued and excited him, there was a certain wariness about her that suggested she had been hurt before, perhaps badly. And then there was the odd way she had kept looking at him during the call-out. For someone as experienced as she was supposed to be there was an edginess about her that, while not quite alarming him, concerned him a little.

There was something else about Abby that was niggling him. He could have sworn he had met her before, but he had to be mistaken. He might have been with a lot of women in his life, but he would never have forgotten someone like her.

What was her story anyway? Not that it really mattered. He liked women, enjoyed their company and had a lot of respect for them, but he had no intention of having a long-term relationship with one. Once they made demands on him, he couldn't help but lose interest. But he was getting way ahead of himself. This was simply a walk with a colleague, albeit a beautiful one. What was the harm in that? Nevertheless, however much he tried to dismiss the feeling of unease, he couldn't quite shake it. A sixth sense he had relied on all his life was telling him that something extraordinary had arrived in the form of Abby Stevens and he wasn't sure he liked the feeling one little bit.

CHAPTER THREE

Mac was leaning against the side of a four-by-four, looking relaxed, when Abby eventually emerged at the end of her shift. After changing out of her jumpsuit, she had taken a few moments to put on some lipstick and brush her hair. She told herself that she wasn't preening herself for Mac, it was simply that she needed the confidence of make-up as well as the time to get her thumping heart rate under control. But she knew deep down that wasn't the whole truth. Wasn't there just a tiny part of her that liked it that he had made it clear he was attracted to her? She dismissed the thought immediately. This wasn't about her. It was about Emma.

Mac was wearing a pair of faded jeans and a white T-shirt under a well-worn leather jacket. His teeth flashed in a wide grin when he saw her. Surely it was anxiety over what she had to tell him that made her stomach flip?

He opened the passenger door of the Jeep with a flourish.

'There's an interesting cliff walk about ten minutes' drive from here. There's a fantastic fish restaurant nearby. We could have something to eat after our walk and I'll drive you back here so you can collect your car.' He paused. 'Unless you want to leave your car at your house? I could follow you home and we could leave from there. Where is it you live, anyway?'

Something in the way his eyes were glittering made Abby wonder if he was imagining an ending to the evening that included him and her in bed together. Little did he know there was a greater chance of hell freezing over.

'I'm renting a cottage in Penhally Bay while I look around for a place to buy. But I'd rather follow you in my own car. And as for supper...' she shook her head '...sorry, I have other plans.' A walk was one thing, a meal *à deux* quite another.

Mac frowned and Abby felt a small stab of triumph. He was clearly a man who was used to getting his own way. Well, he'd find out soon enough that she liked having her way, too.

She followed his four-by-four, uncomfortably aware of the anxiety that was coiling in her chest. He had no idea about the bombshell she was soon going to be dropping into his life. For a second she felt sorry for him, but only for a second. Emma was the only person who mattered in this whole sorry mess.

The sun was slipping lower, streaking the sky with gold, but it would be light for another hour or two. There was still a hint of warmth in the air, and the earlier wind had subsided. It was a perfect October evening, with just a hint of summer still.

The hordes of tourists had long since left and there was only one other car in the car park as they parked their cars side by side.

'The walk I had in mind is a couple of miles each way,' Mac said. 'That's not too far for you, is it?'

'I like walking,' Abby said. 'As long as I'm home for seven.'

She had to walk rapidly to keep up with Mac's long strides. He glanced down and checked his pace so it matched hers.

'How are Jenny and the baby doing?' she asked. As promised, Mac had taken Tim back to the hospital where his father had been waiting for him.

Mac frowned. 'Last I knew, mother and baby were doing fine. Why, did you hear something?' There was no mistaking the concern in his eyes.

'No, I haven't heard anything.' Abby said. 'I just thought you might have popped in to see her when you were at the hospital.'

Mac looked puzzled. 'Why would I do that?'

'Don't you follow up on your patients? Aren't you curious to know how everything turned out?'

He shook his head. 'I treat them, look after them as best I can, then let the hospital staff do their bit. All I care about is giving the best treatment I am capable of. I don't see the point in getting too involved with patients. We have to know when to let go, so we can move on to the next one.'

Abby was dismayed. Once again it seemed she had got this man wrong. Could he really be as disinterested in his patients as he seemed? Abby couldn't imagine not following up on her patients. Most of the time, out there on a rescue, she formed a strong bond with the people whose lives depended on her. It was part of who she was.

'So tell me, what brings you here, to Cornwall and Penhally Bay in particular?' Mac changed the subject. 'Someone mentioned you'd been working with the London ambulance service for the last eleven years. What happened? Did you get tired of the big city?'

Anxiety raced along her spine. It was the perfect moment to tell him about Emma, but she wasn't ready. Not yet. Not until she knew more about him. Once she told him there would be no going back.

'My daughter needed a change of air,' Abby said evasively. 'And I needed a change of scenery.'

'You have a daughter? I didn't know.' He sounded surprised...and regretful.

Abby suspected he wouldn't have been so keen to ask her out if he'd known she had a child. Most of the men she had dated in the past had reacted the same way. They all backed off when she told them and if they didn't, her refusal to put them before Emma usually made them give up on her sooner or later. And that was fine. She didn't need or want a man in her life who couldn't accept Emma. Not even this one. *Particularly* not this one.

He flicked his eyes to her left hand again. 'You don't wear a ring so I'm guessing you're not married.'

'I'm a single mum.' Let him make of that

what he would. He would know the truth soon enough. First she had some questions of her own.

'What about you? I assume you're not married?'

'Nope. Not the marrying kind, I guess.'

'Children?' Abby held her breath as she waited for his reply.

'No, none of them either. Not the father kind.'

Little did he know.

'How long have you worked for the air ambulance?' Abby asked.

'Two years. I completed my specialist training in anaesthesia, then I did a course in medical emergency retrieval in Glasgow. But unfortunately the surfing conditions aren't great there, so when I found they were looking for a rescue medic here, I jumped at the chance. It means I can kite board when I'm not working.'

So his sport was as important as his job. Maybe more so. Abby was disappointed. Minute by minute she was having to revise her opinion of the man who was Emma's father.

'Although I can tell you're Scottish from your accent, it doesn't sound very Glaswegian,' Abby probed. The more she knew about this man, the better.

'I was brought up on Tiree. It's an island off the west coast of Scotland. I lived there until I went to medical school in Glasgow when I was eighteen. I don't go back to Tiree very often.' His mouth tightened and as Abby glanced at him she could have sworn she saw anger behind his eyes, but it disappeared so quickly she couldn't be sure. Did Mac have secrets of his own?

She was about to question him further when he stopped in his tracks. She followed his gaze to see what had caught his attention. To their left, close to the edge, a man was pacing frantically up and down, shouting a boy's name.

'Something's wrong,' Mac said. 'I'm going to take a look-see.'

As Mac called out, the man turned to them, relief evident under his panic.

'It's my son,' he said. 'I can't find him! One minute he was here, and then the next he was gone. I only meant to close my eyes for a minute, but I must have dropped off. You've got to help me find him. He's only eight.' The man's eyes were darting around while he was speaking.

Mac placed a hand on his shoulder. 'Stay

calm and tell me everything. What's your name?'

'Dave. My son's called Luke.'

'Where did you last see Luke?'

'He was over there.' The man pointed behind him. 'He wanted to go down to the beach but I told him there was no path. I said I'd take him there tomorrow. Oh, my God. What if he tried to go down by himself and fell?'

'Have you phoned for help?'

'No, I haven't had time. I've been too busy looking for him.'

Mac's eyes raked the side of the cliff. Something caught his attention and he stopped and sucked in a breath. Abby followed his gaze. Near the edge, a piece of the cliff had broken away. From the look of it, it had only happened very recently. Seeing the troubled look in Mac's eyes, she knew he was thinking the same thing. There was a good chance the boy had got too close to the edge and slipped over. If they were right and the boy had fallen, he could be badly hurt, or worse.

'Abby. Phone 999 and get them to alert the coastguard and the rescue services. Dave, I'm just going to have a look over this cliff and see if I can see him. You stay back, okay?'

Abby touched Dave's shoulder reassuringly

as she used her mobile. It was still possible the boy had wandered off and was nowhere near the cliff but they couldn't take the chance.

Mac walked close to the cliff then dropped to his stomach to peer over the edge. 'I think I can see him,' he called. 'Is he wearing a red jacket?'

Luke's father rushed forward. Mac jumped to his feet and barred his way.

'You have to stay back,' Mac warned. 'The edge here is already unstable. If you come any closer you could slip or a bit of the cliff could crumble and fall on your son.

'I'm going to climb down there and see how he is, okay?' Mac added quietly.

'Shouldn't we wait for the rescue services?' Abby said. 'The operator said they shouldn't be more than ten minutes. If you go down there, you could fall, too.'

Mac dug in his pocket and pulled out his car keys. He tossed them to Dave. 'Dave, go back to the car park. My car is the Jeep. In the boot you'll find a red medical case, a rope and a yellow jacket. Could you fetch them?'

Dave hesitated and Mac gave him a gentle push. 'Go! It's the best way to help Luke. Be as quick as you can.'

As soon as Dave had set off at a run, Mac

turned back to Abby. 'We don't have time to wait for help.' While he was talking he had removed his jacket. 'I'm going to go down. When Dave returns I might need you to lower my medical bag on the end of the rope. Okay?' He moved towards the cliff.

'Shouldn't you at least wait for the rope?' If Mac fell they would have two victims to rescue. Even in her anxiety, the irony wasn't completely lost on her. She had just found Emma's father. If he fell now, Emma might never get to know him.

Mac turned around and grinned. 'Hey, I was brought up near cliffs. Never met one yet I couldn't beat. I'll be okay. As soon as you hear the rescue 'copter, let off a flare. Keep Dave occupied by telling him to search for a good place for the helicopter to land.'

Before she could protest further, he disappeared over the edge.

Abby's heart banged against her ribs. What was Mac thinking? Although if it had been Emma down there, she would have gone herself. Fear of heights or not.

She tiptoed over to the edge, following Mac's earlier example, and lay flat on her stomach and peered over. Although Mac was picking his way carefully down the cliff he was moving faster than she would have thought was safe. From this vantage point she could see that although the cliff was steep, it didn't fall away as sharply as she'd thought. Relief swept through her. Perhaps Luke had a chance.

As Dave returned with the bag, rope and Mac's fluorescent jacket she became aware of a whooping sound in the distance. Shielding her eyes against the sinking sun, she could just about make out the large yellow shape of a Sea King helicopter. Thank God! They would have proper equipment and hopefully a way to get both Mac and Luke up.

'Come on.' She jumped up and shouted across to Dave. 'We need to find a decent landing place to direct the pilot to land.'

'How is my son? Could you see him? Is he okay?'

Abby moved towards open ground and yelled back over her shoulder. 'Mac will be with him in a few minutes. He's a doctor. He'll do everything he can to help Luke.'

Without waiting to see whether Dave was following or not, she raced over to the flat piece of ground. It was just about big enough for the helicopter to land and thankfully the previous days' rain had run away, leaving it solid underfoot.

Abby waved Mac's jacket and immediately the helicopter headed in their direction. Dave was standing behind her, looking lost and terrified. She summoned up a smile. 'I promise you, your son is in good hands.' And she believed it. 'Stay back until they land, then tell them everything. Okay? I'm going to lower the medical bag down to Mac.'

She ran back to the cliff edge and dropped on to her front again. Mac was at the bottom now and kneeling next to the prone figure of the boy. At least he had made it down in one piece. But Mac couldn't risk moving the child on his own. If Luke had survived the fall, there was every chance he had serious neck and head injuries and any movement could mean the difference between a full recovery and life in a wheelchair.

Mac glanced up and gave her a thumbs-up. Luke must still be alive. She tied the medical bag to the rope and lowered it down but it snagged on the jagged rock face. The incline may have helped Mac reach the boy, but it was hampering her efforts to get the bag down to him. Almost crying with frustration, she was only vaguely aware of a hand touching her shoulder. She looked up into calm green eyes of a crew member from the helicopter.

'Miss, you have to stand away from the edge.' Before she could protest, the man took her arm and raised her to her feet. 'We'll take it from here.'

'Mac—Dr MacNeil—is down there with the boy. Mac's a doctor with the air ambulance. He needs his bag.'

'Mac, as in Daredevil Mac?' A broad smile spread across the man's craggy face. 'Well I'll be bug—blown. We know him well, and if he's onto it, everything will be A-okay. Don't worry, I'll get the bag down to him.'

Pulling the case back up, the man, whose name badge said Roberts, took it and ran back to the helicopter. Seconds later the Sea King took off again.

Abby joined Dave, knowing that for the time being there was little she or the anxious father could do. She hooked her arm in his as they watched the helicopter hover over the cliff. A couple of tense minutes passed before a figure, clutching a stretcher and the medical bag, was lowered from the side of the helicopter. Abby's heart thudded painfully. In many ways she would have preferred to be down there helping. This waiting was worse than anything.

Minutes crawled like hours. Then suddenly the crewman came back into view. He was holding onto the stretcher, which now contained a figure. Immediately after the winchman and the stretcher were pulled on board, the helicopter lowered the rope again and after a few moments Mac appeared above the top of the cliff. He, too, was pulled into the waiting Sea King.

Instead of flying off, the helicopter landed again. Abby grabbed Dave's hand and ran towards it. Roberts had barely pulled her and Dave in before the helicopter banked away. Roberts passed her a helmet with a radio attached.

With a brief word to Dave to stay where he was, Abby hurried over to Mac, who was bent over the stretcher.

'He has a compound fracture of the femur. I can't rule out internal injuries and of course we have to suspect head and spinal injuries. I've given him IV morphine for the pain.'

Mac attached his patient to the pulse oximeter while Abby checked Luke's vital signs.

Although Luke's blood pressure was low and his pulse elevated, and he wasn't out of the woods yet, he was a very lucky boy. His leg would take time to heal and would have hurt like crazy before the morphine took effect, but as long as he didn't have internal injuries he'd probably be able to leave hospital in a week or two. Abby shuddered when she thought what might have happened if she and Mac hadn't come across Dave when they had. She was even more confused about Mac than ever. He had risked his life for Luke, he had been thoughtful with Tim, yet he had made it clear that he didn't believe in getting involved with patients. Which one was the real Mac?

Luke tried to sit up, but Abby pushed him gently back down.

'Dad?' he asked. 'Where's my dad?'

Abby beckoned to Dave to come forward. Anything to help the child stay calm was good.

'He's right here,' Abby said gently. She moved away slightly so Luke could see his father. Both father and son started to cry. 'Dave, you need to move away again so we can work on your son, okay? Try not to worry, I'm sure he's going to be okay.'

When they touched down at St Piran's the staff from A & E were waiting for them.

'Status update?' the A & E consultant, bearing the name badge Dr Josh O'Hara, asked.

Abby had only the briefest impression of dark hair and deep blue eyes before Luke was rushed inside.

Abby, her part in the drama over, went in search of Dave. He would be desperate for news of his injured child. She found him sitting outside Resus, his head in his hands.

She tapped him gently on his shoulder. 'Dave.'

He looked at her with red-rimmed eyes. He tried to speak, but couldn't. He shook his head, almost as if he were too scared to ask after his son.

'How is he?' he managed after clearing his throat.

Abby sat next to him and took his hand in hers.

'I think he'll be fine, Dave. It was good we found him when we did, and that we were able to start giving him medical treatment straight away. All that will make a big difference to his recovery.'

They sat in silence for a moment. 'Is there anyone I can call for you? Luke's mother? She'll need to know he's in hospital.'

Dave took a deep shuddering breath. 'She's dead.' He buried his face in his hands. 'She died from breast cancer six months ago.'

'I'm so sorry,' Abby said.

Dave's eyes were bleak. 'She'd never forgive me if I let something happen to our child. I promised her I'd look after him and I fell asleep. What kind of father am I?'

'You're human. It can be difficult, bringing up a child on your own. You can't watch them all the time.'

Dave raked a hand through his hair. 'But I fell asleep! I've been working overtime so I could afford to take Luke away on holiday. So he and I could spend more time together. He needs something to cheer him up. The loss of his mum was a terrible blow. To both of us.' Abby was only dimly aware of Mac coming to stand next to them. 'And I could have lost him, too.'

'You've not lost him,' Mac said quietly. 'He's got to go to Theatre to get his leg pinned where it was broken, but he's going to be fine.'

'He's going to be okay?' Dave said almost as if he didn't dare allow himself to believe what Mac was telling him. The relief in Dave's eyes brought a lump to Abby's throat.

'Yes, he is. I promise you,' Mac said firmly. 'You can see him for a few moments before he goes to Theatre, if you like.'

Dave sprang to his feet. He clasped Mac's

hands in his. 'How can I ever thank you? I know you put your own life in danger and I'll never forget you for that. Either of you.' Without giving them a chance to reply, he rushed away to see his son.

'Another satisfied customer,' Mac said wryly. 'Perhaps he'll take better care of his son after this.' He rubbed a hand across his chin. 'What the hell was he thinking? Having a nap while his eight-year-old played near a dangerous cliff. Some people just shouldn't have children.'

Abby rounded on him. 'He's doing the best he can. Do you know he only fell asleep because he's been working all hours to give his son a holiday? Luke's mother died recently and Dave has been doing the best he can to care for him. Being a single parent isn't easy. We all make mistakes. It's just by the grace of God, most of the time, things turn out all right.' What the hell did Mac know about being a parent, the demands, the worry?

Mac held up his hands as if to ward off her words. He looked stunned and contrite. 'Hey, I had no idea.'

'You shouldn't be so quick to judge, Mac. As the saying goes, you don't know what a person's life is like until you've walked in their shoes.'

Mac narrowed his eyes, his expression unreadable. 'I have no intention of ever walking in his shoes, as you put it.' The clouds cleared from his face. 'But I didn't know his circumstances,' he said. 'If I had, I wouldn't have been so quick to make assumptions.' He smiled ruefully. 'I stand corrected.'

Their eyes locked and Abby's heart somersaulted. She had the strangest feeling that he knew every thought that was rattling around her confused brain. Dismayed, she pulled her eyes away from his searching gaze and glanced at her watch. She had to get back for Emma, but her car was still miles away where she had left it when she and Mac had set out on their walk.

Mac caught her look of alarm. 'What is it?'

'I need to get home,' she said. 'Like now. But my car's on the other side of Penhally, still in the car park.'

'Mine, too,' Mac glanced up as Josh emerged from Resus.

'Know where I could borrow a car, mate?' Mac asked.

Josh dug in his pocket and fished out a set of keys. He tossed them at Mac, who caught them.

'Take mine,' Josh said. 'Just make sure you bring it back in one piece.'

'Hey.' Mac pretended to look offended. 'Don't I always?'

Josh raised an eyebrow. 'You know it's only a matter of time if you continue to drive like the devil.'

'I only drive fast when I'm on my own. And when the road allows. Your car will be perfectly safe.' Mac turned to Abby. 'I'll drop you off at your house then collect your car.'

Abby wasn't at all sure she wanted to be in a car with Mac after hearing Josh's comments, but she did have to get home. Emma was too young to be left on her own, even for a short while. 'What about yours?' Abby protested.

'Don't worry about mine. It's not a problem. I can get it any time.'

Inside Josh's car, Abby glanced at her watch again. She should make it before Emma. With a bit of luck.

'You did a brave thing back there,' she said as they drove down the narrow lanes in the direction of Penhally Bay.

Mac grinned at her and her pulse scrambled. He was having the strangest effect on her. As if she didn't have enough to contend with. Leftover adrenaline, she told herself.

'As I said before, it was a piece of cake. Where is your house?'

Abby gave him the address and he nodded. 'I think I know where you are.'

'But don't you think you were a little reckless?' Abby persisted. 'You could have been killed, or fallen and then we would have had two bodies to rescue.' *And Emma wouldn't have a father, suitable or unsuitable.*

Mac slid her a glance. 'Where's the fun in life if you can't take risks?' he said. 'You might as well be dead if you don't. And, anyway, I knew I could climb down to him. Believe me, it wasn't nearly as dangerous as it looked. At least, not for me. Free climbing is one of my hobbies.'

Abby frowned. She didn't like the sound of this free climbing, whatever it was.

'Which means what exactly?'

'It's a form of climbing where you don't use ropes. Great fun.'

Oh, dear Lord. Emma's father was an adrenaline junkie who didn't seem to care whether he lived or died. Could it get any worse?

'Oh, and by the way,' Mac said, following her pointed finger, as he pulled up in front of the small two-up, two-down where she and Emma lived. 'You owe me a date. And one thing you should know about me is that I always collect my debts.' His diamond-coloured eyes locked onto hers and once again Abby had the strangest feeling he could see into her soul.

The blood rushed to her cheeks. It was as if someone had lit a fire just below her skin and it was smouldering away. Any minute now she'd go up in a puff of smoke. She was out of the car almost before it had come to a complete stop. So far none of this was going the way she'd planned.

Shortly after Mac left, Emma came running into the cottage and flung herself down on the sofa. She beamed happily at Abby.

'Hey. I gather you had a good time?' Abby asked.

'It was great. A few of the other girls came over and we had the coolest time trying on each other's clothes and make-up. Not one of them asked me anything about my dad. I don't think they care at all.'

'Those girls in your other school were the exception, Emma. They just had to make themselves feel good by putting you down.' She ruffled her daughter's hair. Whatever happened with Mac, they had made the right decision coming here. In the last few weeks Emma had changed back from the subdued, under-confident girl she had become in London to the lively fun-loving kid she had always been before that.

Emma jumped up from the sofa and hugged Abby fiercely. 'You're the best mum in the world,' she said.

Abby's heart twisted. All she had ever wanted was to give Emma the security and love she and Sara had never experienced. There was nothing she wouldn't do for Emma. Not even risk losing her to her father. If that father could make her happy. What she was not prepared to do now that Emma was just getting back to her bright usual self was risk her daughter being rejected. Abby knew only too well how that felt.

'Sara loved you as much as I do. You'll never forget that, will you?'

'I know. You tell me that almost every day.' Emma looked sad for a moment. 'I really wish I could have known her.' But in the way kids did, her face brightened almost immediately. 'At least I have you to tell me all the stories about her. I love hearing the ones about how you both kept getting into trouble. They make me laugh.'

'Yes, but, remember, I only tell you some

of these stories as a warning about how easily you can get into trouble.' Abby was stricken. What if Emma tried to copy some of the pranks she and Sara had got up to? It didn't bear thinking about.

Emma grinned. 'You are so easy to tease, Mum. I get you every time.'

'Why don't you have your shower while I get supper ready?' Abby suggested. 'Then afterwards there's a movie on TV we can watch together.' Mac would be back any minute with her car, and she wasn't ready for child and father to meet.

And that wasn't the only thing she wasn't prepared for, Abby admitted to herself as she set about preparing supper. She hadn't expected to find herself reacting to him the way she did. The way her heart kept misbehaving every time he was around wasn't just down to her anxiety about Emma and was an unwelcome complication in a situation that was already complicated enough. Damn it, why did he have to be so infuriatingly gorgeous?

As she'd hoped. Emma was still in the shower when Mac arrived with her car. In her haste to have him gone before Emma came downstairs, she practically grabbed her car keys from his hand. All this emotional turmoil was exhausting. She knew she couldn't keep father and daughter apart for ever. Sooner or later, she would have to tell them the truth.

CHAPTER FOUR

BACK at work, Mac didn't mention another date. Abby wasn't sure if she was relieved or offended. For her second shift, she worked with Lucy, attending a car accident as well as a child with breathing difficulties. Although she enjoyed working with Lucy, she had to admit she was disappointed that she wouldn't always be working with Mac. She told herself it was simply because she was trying to figure him out and nothing to do with the fact she felt alert, more alive somehow, when he was around.

Every now and again she would look up to find his eyes on her. He would grin as if he'd caught her out and she would look away quickly, terrified in case he noticed the blush stealing up her cheeks.

'What do you say we go for a walk down on the beach?' Abby suggested to Emma one day after work. Although it was after five, it was unseasonably warm for October.

'Great. Can I go swimming?' Emma asked, and before Abby could reply she was off upstairs to her small bedroom. Emma had to be constantly on the go.

Abby fetched her own costume from the bedroom opposite Emma's. She slipped into her bikini before pulling on a long, silky cardigan to cover her until they got to the beach. Their rented home was tiny, having once been a fisherman's cottage. It had a sitting room and a small kitchen downstairs and two bedrooms upstairs with a small bathroom separating them. Abby would have preferred something bigger, but her salary as a paramedic didn't stretch very far. After rent and food, anything left over went on clothes and outings for Emma. Sometimes it was a struggle to make ends meet, but if the alternative had been not having Emma in her life, Abby knew it was no contest. Over the years she had scrimped and saved until she had some savings in the bank. Enough to put a deposit down on a small house when they found the right place. At least here in Penhally they had a chance of getting on the housing ladder. In London, it had been impossible.

'I'm ready. Let's go,' Emma called to Abby.

The beach was a ten-minute walk from their house. Although the tourists were away, the sun still warmed the air and there were plenty of locals making the most of the last few warm evenings.

As they walked, Emma asked Abby about her job.

'I love it. The rest of the team seem really nice. I went on my first rescue on Monday with one of the doctors. We managed to get a woman to hospital so her baby could be born safely. We also had to rescue a boy who had fallen down a cliff. Being here has different dangers from those in London. Ones that you might not even think about. So, please, Emma, you need to be very careful when you're out with your friends.'

'You worry too much, Mum. Nothing will happen to me.'

Abby smiled at her daughter. 'I know it won't. And I know I'm a worry wart. But just promise me you'll always be careful.' She couldn't bear it if anything happened to her.

'I might be a pilot when I grow up,' Emma said, dismissing Abby's fears. 'I think I would like flying off to help people in trouble.'

Trust Emma to be drawn to that kind of career. The little girl loved nothing better than taking on anything that was exciting. It struck Abby that she shared at least one trait with Mac. The worst possible, in Abby's opinion. How many more would there be? 'You can be anything you like, darling. As long as you stick at school and do your best.'

Emma stuck out her tongue. 'C'mon, Mum. I'll race you to the sea.' And with that she was off, long legs flying across the sand and her blonde hair streaming behind her. Abby laughed and raced behind her daughter, her heart feeling as light as it had for as long as she could remember.

The shore was busy with people either walking their dogs, playing ball games or paddling. To one side, in an area cordoned off, were the surfers, windsurfers and kite boarders. Abby had watched them once or twice before, impressed at their skill.

The wind down at the shore was gustier than it had been at the cottage and the surfers were taking full advantage of the substantial waves. Further out, where the waves were even bigger, was a kite boarder. Abby and Emma stopped paddling to watch as the boarder let his parachute pull him into the air. There was a collective gasp from other people who had stopped to watch as he somersaulted in the air before landing perfectly on the water. He caught the wind in his parachute to propel him across the water, faster than Abby had ever seen anyone move without the use of an engine. Just as she thought he was going to crash onto the beach, he flipped in the air again, this time landing so he faced in the opposite direction. Abby had never seen anything quite as graceful before. Although the figure was tall, well over six feet, his movements in the air were almost balletic.

'I want to learn how to do that,' Emma said, her eyes wide with admiration. 'It looks so cool.'

Over my dead body, Abby thought grimly. It was far too dangerous. But she didn't say anything. Experience of her headstrong daughter had taught her that the more Emma was told not to do something, the more she wanted to do it. In that way she was very like Sara.

'I think you have to learn to surf or windsurf first, before you can move onto something like that,' Abby said mildly. With a bit of luck it would take Emma years to master the basics. And by that time she would have forgotten her interest in kite surfing.

The kite surfer was racing back towards the

shore. When he was only a metre or so away, he turned his board sideways and jumped off. He seemed to have given up for the day.

As he walked up the beach, Abby's breath caught in her throat. It was Mac. He shook the water from his hair before peeling his suit down to his waist. Abby sucked in her breath. His chest was as muscled as she'd remembered, the six pack of his abdomen even more defined than twelve years earlier. All at once a memory of the first time she had seen him came flooding back.

It had been the first full day of their holiday on Mykonos and Abby had been looking forward to relaxing in the sun with Sara. The last few years had been tough. Since their mother had more or less evicted them from the family home, Sara's behaviour had become wilder and wilder. Although Abby had trained as a paramedic, Sara had not found a job she'd wanted to do for more than a few weeks. More interested in partying than working, Sara had lost more than one job for failing to turn up for work after a late night. Abby had hoped that their holiday would give her a chance to talk to Sara and make her see that sooner or later she had to settle down.

As they'd made themselves comfortable on

their sun-loungers, Abby's attention had been caught by a tall windsurfing instructor who had been giving lessons to a group of beginners on the beach close by. His height alone would have caught her attention, but his tanned and toned physique had made him stand out like some Greek god. His sun-bleached hair had reflected the sun and when he'd grinned, which had been often, his eyes glinted. Abby had never seen anyone whose presence had been so immediate before and her stomach had flipped. He must have felt the intensity of her gaze as he'd looked up from what he was doing and, catching her eye, had winked with a wide smile. Abby had blushed and dipped her head.

Sara had noticed and followed her gaze to where Mac had returned his attention to his class and had been demonstrating how to move the sail on the board in order to catch the wind.

'Now, that's what I call hot,' Sara said appreciatively. 'I think I've just signed up to windsurfing classes.' Not having a shy bone in her body, Sara sauntered over to join the group, and that was more or less the last Abby saw of her for the rest of the holiday. Instead of the girly chats Abby had envisaged, from that moment Sara spent every spare minute with Mac, leaving Abby to amuse herself.

Abby was forced back to the present as Mac noticed them standing on the beach and walked up to them. He smiled widely.

'Fancy meeting you here,' he said to Abby. His eyes glinted as they lingered on her bikini-clad figure and Abby resisted the impulse to wrap her arms around her body to shield herself from his appreciative gaze.

'We were watching you out there. Pretty impressive.' Abby's heart was in her throat. This wasn't how she'd planned father and daughter would meet.

'Yes. It was really wicked,' Emma piped up.

He turned his gaze to Emma and raised a quizzical eyebrow at Abby.

'This is my daughter, Emma. Emma, this is Dr William MacNeil, my colleague.' *And your father.*

'I'm pleased to meet you, Emma,' Mac said with a tip of his head.

'How did you learn to do that?' Emma said, unable to hide her admiration.

'Many, many years of practice.'

'Could you teach me?'

'Emma,' Abby said warningly. 'I don't think it's fair to ask.'

Mac caught Abby's eyes over the top of Emma's head.

'Why not? I'd have to teach you how to windsurf first. And I could teach Abby, too.' He raised a challenging eyebrow.

Emma's face lit up. 'Would you? That would be amazing! My dad was a windsurfer. Mum, would that be okay? Please say yes.'

Abby suppressed a groan. Emma's dad was a windsurfer right enough. This one standing in front of them. And here he was, offering to give lessons to the child he had no idea was his daughter. Under any other circumstances, Abby would have smiled. In many ways, this was exactly what she had hoped for. Daughter and father getting to know each other, but it was all happening too fast. Abby hated to refuse Emma anything, but she *had* to tell her and Mac the truth before they met again.

'We'll see. But the weather's going to start getting colder soon and then it will be winter. Perhaps it would be better to leave it until next year?' she hedged.

'But that's ages away,' Emma protested. 'I can wear a wetsuit. That'll keep me warm, won't it, Dr MacNeil?'

'Let's just see how we get on. You might decide you hate it after a go or two and that's okay. Not everyone sticks it out.'

'I will. Mum always says I stick to everything once I make up my mind, isn't that right?'

Abby ruffled her hair. 'It's true.'

'Okay, then. How about next Saturday? If the weather holds. I can pick you and your mum up.'

Emma squealed with delight before remembering she was trying to be cool these days. She clamped her hand over her mouth. 'Can I, Mum? Please say yes.'

Abby hated to refuse Emma anything and right now she couldn't think of a single reason to say no. She could always cancel the lesson later. If she had to. She shivered as the sun dropped below the horizon. 'Okay, but we'd better let Dr MacNeil get on. And I should be getting supper ready.'

'Why don't I take you girls out for something? My treat,' Mac suggested.

Behind Emma, Abby shook her head at him. The last thing she wanted right now was to have these two spending time together. At least, not until she had told them the truth.

Emma's face dropped. 'I said I would go

round to Sally's house to watch a film. Her mother said she'd order pizza in for us.'

'In that case...' Mac grinned at Abby '...there's no reason why we can't go, is there?'

Abby wanted to refuse, but now that Emma and Mac had met she knew she had to speak to Mac. Putting it off would just make it harder.

'I'll have to drop Emma off at her friend's and get changed first,' she said.

'No problem. I need to go home, too. What about if I pick you up in an hour's time? We could go to the restaurant I mentioned the day we went for a walk.' Without waiting for a reply, he picked up his sailing gear and walked away, whistling.

CHAPTER FIVE

Abby was breathing so fast that too much oxygen was making her knees weak. She would have to find the words to tell Mac that Emma was his daughter. And after that she would have to tell Emma. There was no way she could let this windsurfing lesson go ahead without both of them knowing who the other truly was.

Emma chatted about Mac and kite boarding all the way back to their little cottage. 'I can't wait to learn how he does that. How long do you think it will take me to learn? I can't believe you're working with someone as cool as him. Just wait until I tell my friends.'

Abby ached for her child. Even before knowing Mac was her father, Emma was clearly starstruck. And Abby couldn't blame her. But the very things that made him an exciting figure were the very things that could make him totally unsuitable as a father. For the umpteenth time, Abby wondered if she were about to make a dreadful mistake. Now Emma had met Mac, she'd be even more devastated if Mac wanted nothing to do with her. Whichever way Abby looked at the problem, there was no obvious right answer.

After dropping Emma off at her friend's, Abby jumped into the shower. Then she attacked her wardrobe, pulling out one outfit after another before discarding them on the floor. She told herself she wanted to look good because she needed the confidence to face Mac with her news.

Eventually she settled on a pair of dark trousers and a deep red silk blouse. A slick of dark eye shadow and the merest hint of lipstick completed her make-up. She brushed her hair until it shone and left it loose around her face, studying herself critically in the mirror. Her eyes were bright, and two spots of bright colour on her cheeks stood out against her pale skin. Suddenly she had to laugh. When Mac saw her, no doubt he would think it was the thought of going out with him that was making her look like an over-excited schoolgirl. She had to relax. Cool, calm and collected was what the occasion demanded and she knew only too well how to do cool, calm and collected. She must never let herself forget, not even for a second, that Mac was Emma's father. That fact alone made him totally out of bounds.

Hearing a knock on the door, she ran downstairs, grabbing her raincoat from the peg beside her door.

Mac smiled broadly at her when she opened the door. He had changed into dark jeans and a white shirt, which accentuated his tanned skin and the dazzling blue of his eyes. A shot of electricity ran up her spine. Despite the warning signals her brain was firing at her, her body clearly wasn't listening.

Tonight he was driving a low-slung sports car instead of the Jeep. Abby looked at him questioningly.

'The Jeep's my day car,' he said carelessly. 'This one I save for night-time. What?' He laughed, catching her look. 'I like cars. You know—boys' toys.'

He drove the same way he did everything else—fast, but with total concentration. Thankfully he slowed down on the narrow coastal roads where visibility was limited. Nevertheless, Abby found herself gripping her seat and pumping an imaginary brake pedal as if she could slow him down.

He caught her doing it, and grinned wickedly, but he slowed the car down even further.

'Isn't it beautiful?' Abby pointed to the horizon where the sinking sun was turning the sea red. Despite the way her heart was hammering, the sight had a calming effect on her. Abby relaxed into her seat. Why *did* he have to be so attractive? She had thought he was the sexiest man she'd ever seen the first time she'd ever set eyes on him, and she still thought that. Boy, she should have got out more.

'I find everything about it beautiful,' Mac said slowly, turning his head to look at her. 'Quite stunning.'

She couldn't think of a reply, let alone force the words past a throat suddenly as dry as dust. Thankfully moments later they drew up outside a quaint-looking building. It was single storey with thick stone walls. It had been built close to the sea and as Abby stepped out of the car she gasped with pleasure. Stretching before her, as far as the eye could see, was the ocean. It was bluer than Mac's eyes and crests of white tipped the waves, which boomed like thunder as they crashed onto the shore.

Mac came to stand beside her. 'You like?'

he asked, his ready smile back in place. 'See that little cove down there?' He pointed to a sandy area to Abby's left. 'That's one of my favourite places to go kite boarding.'

'You mean you surf out there? Where all those rocks are? Isn't it dangerous? Not to say foolhardy?'

Mac's grin got wider. 'Safe is boring.'

Abby craned her neck to see down to the bay. As far as she could tell, there was no path down.

'How do you get down there? I don't see a path.'

'There isn't one—that's part of the attraction. It means I always get the place to myself.'

'So how do you get to it? By boat?'

'Sometimes. Sometimes I climb down. It's more fun. It's not really that difficult—as long as you know what you're doing. One day I'll show you.'

Abby shivered at the promise behind the words. He was making it clear he found her attractive and that he expected to see more of her. Soon he would learn that it was probably going to happen, but not for the reasons he thought.

His daredevil attitude worried her. What if Emma found her father only to lose him in some reckless escapade? She was beginning to appreciate where her daughter had got her own love of risky sports from. She'd always assumed it was from Sara, but now she knew it was from both her parents. It didn't bode well for the future. She shivered again.

'You're cold. I'm sorry. Let's get inside.' He sniffed the air. Wood smoke mingled with the scent of the sea. 'Smells as if they have a fire going inside. We're early enough to grab a table that's near the fire and also has a view of the sea.'

Abby was glad he'd put her shiver down to the cold. She was already beginning to dread telling him about Emma. What if he refused to accept she was his daughter? If he did, at least this way Emma would never need know. At least, not until she was eighteen and perhaps by then she'd be able to deal with her father's rejection. But she was getting way ahead of herself. Unlikely though it seemed, perhaps he'd be pleased to find he had a child. He had been good with Tim and Luke. There was only one way to know for sure and no point in putting it off any longer.

Nevertheless, she waited until they had ordered. Mac was looking at her with the same air of puzzlement that he had shown when they'd been first introduced.

'I can't get it out of my head that we've met before. We haven't, have we? You know…' He had the grace to look embarrassed. 'No, of course we haven't. As I said, I would have remembered you.'

Abby took a deep breath. 'I lied that first day at work. We have met before. Almost twelve years ago. On Mykonos.'

Mac's frown deepened and he looked at her intently. 'Mykonos? I was there as a windsurfing instructor, but I don't… Wait a minute. I do remember you. Your hair was shorter and you wore glasses. But of course. You were there with your sister, Sara.' He leaned back in his chair and whistled. 'You've changed.'

To her fury, Abby blushed under his frank admiration. Of course he hadn't remembered her. Nobody had ever given her a second glance. Not when Sara had been around. Sara had been confident, keen to meet new people and to try out new experiences. She had thrown herself into life almost as if she'd known she wasn't long for the world. Abby had always taken on the big sister role, even though she'd only been the elder by a couple of minutes, and had never minded always being in Sara's shadow. All she'd ever wanted had been for Sara to be happy.

Abby opened her handbag and pulled out the photograph she'd put in it. She handed it to Mac. 'That's my twin, Sara. Non-identical, obviously. You have your arm around her shoulder. The one at the end is me.'

'I remember now. Hell, I haven't thought about that summer in years. Imagine you carrying that photo around all this time' He looked at her, his dark brows drawing together. 'Why?' He half smiled. 'Don't tell me you had a crush on me and I didn't know. If so, I'm sorry. One thing's for sure, no one could fail to notice you now.'

Once again he sent her a look that gave her goose-bumps and infuriated her at the same time. Did the women he knew really fall for that kind of patter?

'How is Sara?' he continued, grinning. 'If I remember correctly, your sister knew how to have fun! Has she settled down? Sorry. That was a stupid question. Of course she has. She must be what, thirty—thirty-one?'

'Sara's dead,' Abby said bluntly.

There was no mistaking the shock on Mac's face. 'Dead! I am so sorry. When? What happened?'

'She died just over eleven years ago. About nine months after the holiday where you met.' It still sent a stab of pain through Abby whenever she had to say the words. Would she ever get used to it?

'I can't believe it! She was so full of life.' He pushed his half-eaten food away. 'I liked her very much. She was a lovely person.' Clearly he hadn't fully grasped the implication in her words.

'So fond of her you never tried getting in touch after she left?' Abby couldn't keep the bitterness from her voice. Mac had taken advantage of her sister. He had used her. Although they had both been young, he must have known that there had been a chance Sara could fall pregnant. Or had he simply not given a damn?

'Hey, I did try to get in touch, once or twice,' Mac said. 'But the phone number she left with me was never answered.' He leaned across the table, his eyes unfathomable. 'We were both young. We both accepted it was a holiday romance. Nothing more.' He placed his hand on top of Abby's. She snatched it away. Whether it was because she was still angry with him or whether it was because his touch sent little sparks of electricity shooting up her arm, she didn't want to think about.

'How did she die?' he asked softly. 'Was it an accident?'

This was the hard part. This was where she had to tell him about Emma. But suddenly she couldn't. Not yet.

'Could we talk about something else?' she asked softly. 'Even though it's been years, it still hurts too much.'

Mac was immediately contrite. 'Sure.' He leaned back in his chair and studied her intently. 'Tell me about you. How come you ended up here? Penhally is quite a change to London.'

How could she explain the change without mentioning Emma?

'I'd rather talk about you,' she said evasively. 'When we met back on Mykonos you were a windsurfing instructor. It was a bit of a shock to find you are a rescue medic.'

Mac grinned. 'Yeah, well. Back then I'd just graduated and I wanted one summer off before I started my first house job. I was fortunate. I managed to get an instructing job every summer while I was a medical student. It helped pay the bills.' For a moment his eyes darkened and he lost his ready smile. Then just as quickly the grin was back in place. 'If I couldn't be a doctor, I probably would have been a professional windsurfer. Luckily I got into medical school. Better pay and much more satisfying.'

He paused as a couple took a table close by. 'Tiree has an international reputation for some of the best surf in the world. I couldn't grow up there and not do a watersport of some description.'

'Don't tell me that's what brought you to Penhally Bay.' She didn't even attempt to hide her incredulity. What kind of doctor took a job because of the surfing conditions?

He looked amused. 'Partly. Glasgow is a great city, but I couldn't live in a place I can't kite board regularly. But I also came here because there was an opening for a medic in the air ambulance service. The job here is exactly what I always wanted.'

'You love it, don't you? The excitement and the danger. I saw the rescue you did with the family on the boat on television. You risked your life to save those people. Just as you did with Luke.'

Mac grinned again. 'It's part of the job. But you're right. I feel more alive when I battle the elements—beat the odds. But what about you?

Do you think you'll cope? It must be different from what you've been used to.'

How deftly he had turned the conversation away from himself again.

'Some of it does frighten me. Especially the thought of being lowered by a winch in blustery conditions. I think it has something to do with being a mum. You know that you have a child waiting for you at home. Someone who needs you to be around for a long time, and it makes you think twice about taking risks.'

'I wouldn't know about that.' Although he smiled, a shadow crossed his eyes. 'One of the benefits about being single is that I don't have anyone who needs me. Luckily.' Abby suspected she was being warned. *Don't expect too much. I'm not in it for the long term.*

So far nothing Mac had said was what she wanted to hear.

Sensing that Mac was about to ask about Emma, Abby added quickly, 'What about your parents? Brothers? Sisters?' It wasn't just that she wanted to keep the conversation away from Emma for the time being at least, she was intensely curious. She told herself it was purely because Mac's family would be Emma's family, too.

It was as if the shutters had come down. Mac's blue eyes grew cold and distant.

'I'm an only child. I have no idea who or where my father is,' he said shortly. 'My mother still lives in Tiree. I see her when I can.'

Abby felt a tug of sympathy—and recognition. Whenever she was asked about her parents, she gave pretty much the same reply. Her father had disappeared after she and Sara had been born. He had never come back to see his daughters and the only contact they'd ever had with him had been the odd birthday card. He had died years ago, and their mother had only thought to tell Sara and Abby long after the funeral had taken place.

'But let's not talk about the past.' Mac leaned forward. 'It's the here and now that matters. I want to know more about you.'

'And the future?' Abby persisted. 'Doesn't that matter?'

Mac grinned and narrowed his eyes speculatively. 'The only thing about the future that interests me right now is when you're going to come out with me again.'

Abby returned his look coolly. Her brown eyes were reproving, almost accusing. Mac could have kicked himself. He should have known the usual direct approach wouldn't work with this woman. Instinctively he knew that Abby was someone who would expect to be courted slowly and seriously. But he didn't feel like taking things slowly with Abby. If he could have taken her home with him tonight and made love to her, he would have without a moment's hesitation.

And he didn't do serious. Abby was a woman with a child. A mother, and a protective one at that. Everything he had learned about her so far told him that she wasn't the kind of woman to have casual affairs. Why, then, was he ignoring the alarms bells that were jangling in his head?

The faint scent of her perfume drifted across at him and before he could stop himself he leaned across the table and took a lock of her thick caramel hair between his fingers. It was heavy and silky. He swallowed a groan as an image of Abby naked beside him, her hair touching his skin as she leaned over to kiss him, flashed into his head. He knew without a shadow of doubt he would never be satisfied until he had this woman in his bed.

A range of emotions he couldn't quite place

crossed Abby's face. He would bet his life, though, that she felt the attraction, too.

'But the future does matter, Mac. So does the past.' She fiddled with her napkin. 'Emma...' she started. 'Sara...' She took a deep breath. Some of the colour had left her face.

'Sara died following childbirth. She developed an infection a few days after she delivered Emma. The doctors did everything they could but it was no use.' Her enormous brown eyes swam with unshed tears.

'After Emma was delivered?' Mac echoed. 'I thought Emma was your child.'

'She is. But I'm not her birth mother. Sara was. After she died, Emma came to live with me.'

Mac was puzzled. Why was she telling him this? It did explain, however, why there was no father in the picture. Despite everything he'd just told himself, he couldn't help feeling glad.

'Sara delivered Emma nine months after she returned from Mykonos.' Abby caught her bottom lip between her teeth.

Did she have any idea how cute she looked when she did that?

'Mac, Emma is your daughter.'

Emma? His daughter? At least he thought

that was what Abby said. He must have mis-heard.

'Did I hear you correctly?' he said. He hoped to hell he hadn't.

'Yes. I didn't know at first. Sara wouldn't tell me who the father was, although, given the timing, I had my suspicions.'

'So she might not be mine?' He heard the relief in his voice.

'She didn't tell me it was you until she knew for certain she was going to die. Then she confirmed what I had suspected all along. You were the father.'

Mac felt as if he was in a nightmare. He couldn't have a daughter. It was impossible. God knew, he didn't want one. He would make a terrible father anyway. His mind was racing. Admittedly, Sara and he had spent almost the whole fortnight together and, yes, they'd had sex. Neither of them had ever pretended that what they'd shared had been anything more than a holiday romance. And he remembered he had asked about contraception. He hadn't been such an idiot as to have unprotected sex. Although Sara had insisted she was on the Pill, they had used condoms, too. In his twenty-one years he had hardly been a saint and he hadn't taken chances with anyone's sexual health. So how could she have fallen pregnant? But then it came back to him. There had been one evening after a beach party when they'd both had too much to drink and they hadn't used condoms. It had never crossed his mind that Sara could have become pregnant. He forced himself to focus on what Abby was saying.

'When Emma was three months old, I went back to Mykonos to try and find you, but it was no use. You were gone. All I knew was that you were called Mac. I asked around, but nobody could tell me anything that would help me trace you.'

'That summer was my last of teaching windsurfing. After that I was too busy doing my house jobs. I didn't need the money or, more to the point, have the time.' He still felt dazed. 'You can't be sure she's mine, whatever Sara told you.'

'Think about it, Mac. Sara had no reason to lie. If she had wanted to, she could have told you she was pregnant, but she didn't. It was only when she knew she was going to die that she told me. And that was only because she knew that one day Emma would want to know something about her father. Possibly find him.' She paused. 'But if you still have your doubts I'm sure we can arrange a DNA test.' Although that wasn't what she wanted. Emma would be hurt to find out that the father she so desperately wanted had needed proof that she was his daughter.

'I think that might be a good idea.' Mac stumbled to his feet. He had to get out of there. He needed time to think. He saw his life changing in front of his eyes. A father!

'Mac, I know this has been a shock to you. It was to me when I realised I would be working with you. At least, in my case, I've known about you for years.'

'Does Emma know? That I'm her father, I mean?'

'She knows that her father is out there somewhere. She doesn't know it's you. Not yet. I thought it was only fair to talk to you first.'

'Will you tell her?'

'Yes. She desperately wants to find her father.' Abby reached out and touched him on the hand. 'Mac, please sit down. I can't think with you standing over me like that.'

Reluctantly Mac did as she asked. He owed it to Abby to hear her out, however much he didn't want to believe what she was telling him.

'The reason I took the job here was because Emma was being bullied at her school in London. You know how cruel kids can be. When they found out that Em didn't know who her father was they started teasing her. They wouldn't even come to her eleventh birthday party. Things just got worse from there.'

Ouch. Mac remembered only too well how that felt. Growing up in a small community, as he had done, it had been exactly the same for him, but at least he'd had his windsurfing. Out on the waves he'd been able to forget everything. Besides, his skill on the board had made him a bit of a hero in the other children's eyes. But their teasing had still hurt. He felt a rush of sympathy towards Emma. And anger. How dared those children pick on a little girl about something that was out of her control? If he had them in front of them right now, he'd be tempted to bang their heads together.

'If it turns out I am Emma's father, I won't deny her,' he said. 'I'll do what's right. Provide financial support, whatever you need.'

Abby's eyes flashed with anger. 'Financial support isn't what is needed, Mac. Emma and I manage fine. What Emma needs is far more complicated than that. As soon as she knows about you she is going to want a relationship. Can you give her that?'

Right now, Mac had no idea.

Mac got to his feet again. 'I'm sorry, Abby, I just don't know if I can do what you're asking. I never wanted to be a father. I don't have the first clue about being one. There's a good chance I'll be rubbish at it. Emma is probably better off without me.' He jammed his hands into his pockets. 'I need time to think about this. Decide what to do.'

'Don't think too long, Mac. I have to tell Emma that I've found you.' She got to her feet, too. 'You said you'd take her windsurfing next Saturday. Whether you show up or not is up to you.'

He could see the determination in her calm nut-brown eyes.

'But let me warn you. If you do decide to get involved with her, it's not something you can back out of later. You're in it for keeps. Make no mistake, Mac, if you hurt my child, you'll have me to reckon with.'

CHAPTER SIX

MAC let himself into his flat and flung his car keys on the table. He had dropped Abby back home and they had sat in silence the whole of the journey. He was still reeling from what Abby had told him. There he'd been thinking he had been doing nothing more than taking a beautiful woman out to dinner. Now it seemed as if he was father to that woman's daughter!

He thought back to when he had seen Emma on the beach. She was tall—like him. And she had blue eyes—like him. But was that enough to go on?

He crossed over to his full-length windows and stared out to sea. How could his life have changed so dramatically in just a matter of hours? The last thing he wanted, or needed, was an eleven-year-old daughter. Why hadn't Sara told him she was pregnant? He felt a grudging respect for the woman who had given birth to his child. She had known how much his medical career had meant to him. She had also probably known, he admitted ruefully, that back then he had not been up to being a father. But was he up to it now?

The wind had risen, whipping the sea against the rocks. He wished he was out there, challenging himself against the elements. It was so much easier than dealing with the bomb Abby had thrown at him.

He poured himself a whisky and swirled the amber liquid around the glass. Memories of his own childhood came rushing back. The endless stream of men his mother had brought home, insisting that he call them Dad. He had refused. And just as well; none of them, except Dougie, had lasted more than a couple of months. Mac had got on with him. It had been Dougie who had given him his first second-hand board and Mac would have considered calling him Dad, but eventually Dougie had left, too, driven away by his mother's excessive demands. She had blamed Mac. Told him that he had ruined her chances of finding happiness. No wonder he had learned to windsurf. The time on the waves had been his only relief from his bitter, resentful mother. That, and school. As soon as he'd been able to, he had left home, supporting himself through medical school by taking out loans and teaching windsurfing. It had been hard. There had been too many times when he'd had to choose between buying a textbook and eating. But he'd survived, learning to depend on only himself. No wonder he'd never let anyone get close to him and so far it had worked out exactly the way he wanted. He was living the perfect life. A job he loved, this flat, mountain biking, free climbing and kite boarding whenever he could, and dating the kind of women who seemed happy to fit in around his other pleasures.

Until now.

He took a swig of his whisky, letting the liquid roll around his tongue. His life was going to be turned upside down. But what if Sara had been wrong? What if Emma wasn't his child? He had to know for certain one way or another. If she was his, he wouldn't abandon her. He couldn't do the same thing to a child, his child, as his father had done to him. At least Emma had Abby. An image of hazel eyes and a warm smile floated in front of his eyes. She was the opposite of the women he normally went after. She was serious, warm, caring and fiercely protective. He knew instinctively she would be like a tigress when it came to protecting her daughter. Abby, he was sure, would never have told him he was Emma's father if she hadn't been certain of it herself. She had taken a risk telling him and she knew it. Sighing, he placed his empty glass on the table and reached for the phone. He had to see Abby and arrange the DNA test after she had a chance to tell Emma. The sooner he knew for sure that Emma was his, the better for all concerned. But deep down he was getting used to the idea. Already he felt something strange, a sense of protectiveness towards the young girl who Abby claimed was his child.

Abby finished tidying the kitchen while listening to Emma's excited chatter. It was so good to see the little girl back to her usual self.

'Emma, I need to talk to you about something,' Abby said when Emma drew breath. 'Why don't I make us a cup of cocoa and we can take it in to the sitting room and chat there?'

When they were settled, Abby turned to Emma.

'You know how we spoke about your dad? Remember I told you I tried to find him when you were very little?'

Emma nodded and waited for Abby to continue.

'Well, I've found him.'

'Where? Who is he? How did you find him? Did he come looking for me?' The hope in Emma's eyes made Abby's heart stumble.

'He couldn't look for you, sweetie, because he didn't know about you. I kind of found him by accident.' Abby took a deep breath. There was no going back now.

'You know Dr MacNeil? The man we met on the beach? He's your father.'

Emma looked stunned. 'Dr MacNeil? I thought you said my dad was a windsurfer.'

'Well, he is. We saw that down on the beach, but he's also a doctor. He taught windsurfing as a way to put himself through medical school.'

A slow smile crept across Emma's face. 'That's so cool. Does he know? Did you tell him? What did he say?'

Abby smiled at Emma's excitement. 'Yes, he knows. I told him.' Abby leaned across and took Emma's hand in hers. 'It was a bit of a surprise to him. He had no idea that your mother had even been pregnant. I guess it'll take him a little time to get used to the idea he has a daughter.'

Emma's brow puckered. 'You mean he doesn't want me.'

Abby took the mug from Emma and placed it on the coffee table, before pulling her daughter into her arms. 'Of course he'll want you. He just needs time to get to know you better. You and I have always known that you had a dad out there somewhere, but this has all come as a big surprise to him.'

'Is he still going to take me windsurfing?'

'I'm not sure. Em, don't get your hopes up too much. Remember when we've spoken about this before, we always said that even if we found your father, he might not want to be as involved as you might hope.'

'I don't care,' Emma said fiercely. 'I know I've always got you.' She sat up, her brows furrowing. 'This won't make any difference to us, will it? I mean, you'll always be my mum, won't you? He can't take me away from you, even if he wants to, right?'

Abby had wondered the same thing herself. When Sara had died, Abby had thought about adopting Emma officially, but it hadn't seem to be necessary. The social services had been more than happy to leave Emma in her care. Surely, and Abby thought this was unlikely, even if Mac did want to have Emma with him full time, no one would give him custody?

'I don't think that's going to happen. You're my daughter and no one is ever going to take you away from me. Look, let's take this one day at a time. You and Mac can get to know each other and we'll take it from there.'

Emma nodded. 'At least the kids won't be able to tease me about not having a father any more.' She hugged Abby. 'I can't wait to meet him properly. What's he like? Tell me everything you know.'

Emma was too excited to go to bed and she and Abby talked into the night. Abby brought out all her old photos of Sara and repeated the stories of their childhood that Emma could never get enough of. Finally she was able to persuade an exhausted but happy Emma to go to bed. Looking down at her sleeping child, Abby made a vow: Dr William MacNeil would not be allowed to cause her daughter so much as a moment's pain.

Early the next morning, there was a knock on the door. Abby opened it to find Mac standing there, an uncertain smile on his face.

'Can I come in?'

Abby was glad Emma was still in bed, catching up on sleep after their late night.

She stood back to let him in.

He brushed past her and started pacing her small sitting room. He only managed a couple of strides in each direction before he had to turn round.

'Have you told her?' He hadn't even said hello.

'Yes. Last night.'

'How did she take the news?' He seemed nervous, uncharacteristically unsure of himself.

'She was thrilled. I warned her that I didn't know what you were going to do about it.'

'I'm not going to ask for a DNA test,' Mac said abruptly.

'Oh? Why not?' Had he made up his mind that regardless of whether it could be proven Emma was his child, he still didn't want to know? Abby's heart gave a sickening thud. It would be hard telling Emma, but perhaps it was for the best. In that case, either Mac or she and Emma would have to leave Cornwall. It would be too cruel for Emma to be reminded daily that she had a father who didn't want her.

'I don't want a DNA test because it's not fair to Emma. You say she's my child. The dates fit. She looks like me. If I insist on a DNA test, how will that make her feel? I know that if I were in her shoes, I would think that my father was trying to prove I wasn't his. No child deserves to be put through that.'

'So what are you saying, Mac? I'm afraid you're going to have to spell it out.'

'Look, I don't know what sort of father I'll make, but I'm going to give it my best shot. You and Emma will just have to be patient with me. Can you do that, Abby? Can you accept I can only do the best I can? That it might not be good enough?'

Abby was relieved he wasn't insisting on a DNA test. But as far as what kind of father he would be? Well, that was up to him. It wasn't as if she could go and pick him up a set of instructions from some kind of parent supermarket.

'Just promise me you'll do the best you can,' she said softly.

He sighed. 'You're going to have to help me here, Abby. As I said, I have no idea how to go about being a father. I mean, what do I do?'

He looked so different from his usual confident self that Abby's heart melted a little.

'I think taking her windsurfing is a good start,' she said. 'That way you and Emma can get to know each other without it seeming forced and unnatural.'

'I can do that. What else?'

'Let's just take it day by day, Mac. Learning to be a father takes time.'

'Tell Emma I'll see her on Saturday.' And with that he turned on his heel and was out the door as if the devil himself were after him.

CHAPTER SEVEN

MAC took a gulp of his beer as he waited for Josh to emerge from the changing room. It had been a good match, even if it had been closer than Mac would have liked. Shortly after Mac had started working on the air ambulance crew, Josh had invited him to join the five-a-side football team that many of the staff at the hospital played for. In the end, their team had just pulled the match out of the bag. Mac was pleased. He hated to lose.

'I got one in for you,' he told Josh when he appeared, gesturing towards the pint he had placed on the table.

After the match, the team would have a quick pint and usually talk about work. For various reasons tonight it was just him and Josh who'd stayed for a drink. Everyone else had had reasons to rush away, but although

Josh was married he never seemed in a hurry to leave after the game.

Mac knew little about Josh's personal life. He had met his wife, Rebecca, once or twice when she had dropped into A & E to see her husband. Mac had got the impression that Rebecca was a little lonely. The life as a wife of a consultant could be like that, especially if, like Rebecca, she didn't work. Another reason to stay footloose and fancy-free, Mac decided— except he wasn't, not any more.

'How's Rebecca?' Mac asked. 'Does she like living here?'

Josh studied his pint glass as he twirled it around in his hand. 'I think Rebecca is more of a city girl. She misses being able to pop into the shops any time she pleases.'

'Yet she agreed to move here?' Mac said.

'It was too good an opportunity for me to miss. Hopefully in time Rebecca will make friends. Although it's difficult when she doesn't work. Not having children doesn't help either. If we had kids, she'd probably meet some mothers down at the school gates.'

'If you're planning on having some, I wouldn't leave it too long. How old is Rebecca? Thirty-three? Thirty-four?'

Josh frowned. 'Thirty-four. But we always agreed they weren't part of the plan.'

The expression on Josh's face darkened for a moment. What's going on here? Mac thought. But whatever it was, it was none of his business. Josh and Rebecca's private life had nothing to do with him.

'Anyway, what about you? I guess you're not the father type either. Or haven't you met the right woman yet?'

Mac shifted in his seat. Served him right. He had started this conversation. Besides, people were bound to find out sooner or later.

'Er... Actually, it turns out I am a father,' he said. The words sounded strange, still unbelievable.

Josh's eyebrows shot up. 'You kept that quiet. A bit of a dark horse, aren't you?'

'I only just found out myself.' If it were possible, Josh looked even more astonished. But he said nothing, simply waited for Mac to continue.

'It's complicated,' Mac said. 'You know our new paramedic, Abby Stevens?'

'She's the mother of your child?' Josh's eyebrows couldn't go any higher.

'No. She's the aunt of my child. Emma, my

daughter, is the result of a relationship I had with Abby's twin—years ago.'

'I think you're going to have to be more explicit,' Josh said, leaning back in his chair. 'Go on, I'm all ears.'

Mac wasn't used to talking about himself, but he had to tell someone. Perhaps thinking out loud would help. So, hesitantly, between sips of beer, he told Josh the whole story.

'And you had no idea Sara was pregnant?' A shadow crossed Josh's face, making Mac wonder, but he kept his thoughts to himself.

'None. It never crossed my mind.'

'And you believe Abby?'

'If you knew Abby better, you'd know that's a daft question. She's not the kind of woman to lie about something like this. She's totally upfront. With Abby, what you see is what you get.'

Josh raised an eyebrow again. There was a hint of a smile at the corner of his mouth. Mac wanted to tell him that he was mistaken, that there was nothing between him and Abby, but he knew his protests would only increase that amused look in Josh's eyes.

'Besides, it is entirely possible. The timing works out. And I was young at the time. Not always as responsible as I should have been.'

Josh's frown deepened. Did he disapprove? Surely Josh must have behaved in ways he now regretted when he had been a medical student. But perhaps Josh had been sensible enough always to take precautions. As medics, they knew better. Or, at least in his case, should have known better. But, damn it, he wasn't asking Josh for his approval. 'Shortly before she died, Sara told Abby I was the father and I can see no reason why Sara would lie. Besides, Emma has my eyes. I don't think there's much doubt.'

'So what are you going to do about it?'

'No idea, Josh. It's not as if I planned to be a father. I'm pretty sure I'll make a rotten one. But I can't turn away from my responsibilities. I told Abby that I'll spend time with Emma. I'm going to teach her to windsurf. At least I can do that.'

Josh looked thoughtful. He put his glass down on the table and leaned forward. 'You know, Mac, sometimes life deals us a hand we never wanted, or expected. We get one chance at grabbing what's in front of us. If we don't take it while we can, it might be a mistake we end up regretting for the rest of our lives.'

Something in his voice made Mac wonder if he was speaking from personal experience, but before he could decide whether to probe further, Josh went on. 'If I were you, I would think very carefully before you turn away from something that might turn out to be the best thing that's ever happened to you.'

'It sounds as if you know what you're talking about,' Mac said.

'Let's just say, if I had a particular time over in my life, I might have made different choices.' Josh picked up his and Mac's empty glasses. He nodded in the direction of the bar. 'Fancy a refill?' he asked.

On the way home Mac thought about what Josh had said. There was a mystery there, he was sure of it, but he respected his colleague too much to speculate on what it could be. If he wanted him to know, he'd tell him. As far as his advice about Abby and Emma went— that was different. He had promised Abby that he would get to know Emma and he had never gone back on his promise. But the thought still scared him witless. What did he know about being a father? He hadn't exactly had a good example himself. Unless it had been how not to be a father. His father had walked out on him and his mother without a backward glance. Walking out of the marriage had been one thing, but abandoning your only child had been quite another.

He swallowed his anger. It was no use thinking like that. What he did have to think about was *his* child. Whatever the future brought, however much he hadn't planned on having a child and however much disruption that might bring to the life he had carved out for himself, there was really no choice. He was Emma's father and he wouldn't—couldn't—abandon her.

CHAPTER EIGHT

THE next couple of days were busy, and Mac and Abby were seldom alone together, for which Mac was grateful.

He was still getting used to the fact that he had a daughter and almost as strange was that Abby was the mother of his child. For the first time in his life he was confused by his feelings for a woman.

He liked working with Abby. He admired the way she was with the patients: calm, assured but gentle, as if they really mattered to her.

They had the usual callouts to walkers with broken ankles that turned out to be badly twisted, and a couple of car accidents that thankfully turned out to be less serious than initially thought. When there wasn't a callout, the team went over rescue procedures and updated each other with new medical developments. Mac was careful to treat Abby like simply another member of the team.

It wasn't easy. He'd come to recognise the habit she had of biting her lip whenever she was anxious, and more than once he had to stop himself from leaning across and brushing a lock of hair from her eyes. He could hardly keep his eyes off her. He loved the way her mouth curved and her eyes lit up when she was pleased about something and he resented the way he kept imagining what it would be like to feel her mouth on his. Okay, so she was beautiful and sexy and warm but now he knew about Emma, Abby was out of bounds. He already had one commitment he had never expected and he didn't need another.

It was just after lunch on Wednesday when they received a call to attend a woman who had been thrown off her horse and then trampled. The only information they had to go on was that the woman was unconscious and in a field with no road access. The call had been transferred to the RAF, which was sending out a Sea King so that the medics could be winched down to the casualty if necessary

Within minutes Abby and Mac were being flown towards the injured woman.

'This could be nasty,' Mac said into his

radio. 'If she's unconscious, it'll be difficult for us to be sure just how badly injured she is.'

'In that case, don't we treat her as if she has a spinal injury?' Abby asked.

'The most important thing is to keep her breathing,' Mac agreed. 'And not to make things worse.'

Ten short minutes later they were hovering over the accident site. A man was standing next to the woman, waving a brightly coloured jacket to get their attention.

'As we thought, there's nowhere to put down, I'm afraid,' the pilot said. 'It's too marshy. You're going to have to be winched out.'

Mac glanced at Abby and was surprised to see a flash of fear in her eyes.

'Are you okay?'

Abby nibbled her lip. 'It's the first time other than training that I've had to winch down. I'm just a little nervous.'

'Tell you what,' he said. 'Seeing there is someone on board that can lower us both, why don't we go down together? That way we can get down quicker.' It wouldn't really make much difference timewise, but going down in tandem would make Abby feel better. It was the first time she had revealed a less than certain side to her and it made him feel unusually protective. Whether it was because she was the mother of his child or because this woman engendered feelings he had never experienced before, he didn't want to think about. He much preferred to think it was the former.

Mac stood and attached the winch to the harness they always wore in the helicopter. Although she was determined not to show it, Abby was relieved he'd be going down with her. She was intensely aware of the touch of his hands on her legs and hips as he tested the buckles.

The last few days he had been polite but distant towards her. When she'd asked him whether he still intended to take Emma wind-surfing, he'd looked surprised. 'I don't go back on promises, Abby,' he'd said. 'Especially not to a child.'

They were lowered over the side, pressed together, one of Mac's arms holding her close. This was almost worse than going down alone. Her fear disappeared under her awareness of his hard, muscular body touching every inch of hers. She raised her head to look at him and he winked. She wasn't sure whether she was glad or disappointed when they touched the ground and Mac released them from the winch. All she knew was that her body felt as if it was on fire and that the blood was whooshing in her ears.

Mac raced to the fallen woman, leaving Abby to follow in his wake.

He crouched down beside her, feeling for a pulse. Then he used the small torch they all carried in the top pockets of their jumpsuits to shine a light in her eyes. Abby's heart sank when she saw that only one pupil reacted to the light.

'How long since it happened?' Mac asked the man who had stayed with her.

'I don't know, but not long before I found her. She cantered past me a few minutes earlier. I lost sight of her but then I saw her horse galloping away without a rider, so I knew something had happened. I telephoned for help immediately.' He looked at his watch. 'About twenty-five minutes ago. So I would estimate it's been approximately half an hour since she fell.'

'Has she been conscious at all? Have you moved her, Mr...?'

'Fox. No, I know you're not supposed to. I had some medical training when I was in the army. I just checked that she was breathing.'

Abby slipped a neck brace out of her bag.

Although the head injury was their primary concern, they had to assume until they knew otherwise that the victim had a spinal injury, too.

Mac nodded and working together they slipped the brace round the fallen woman's neck and an oxygen mask over her face.

Then they strapped the rider's legs together to make the transfer to the helicopter. With Mr Fox helping, they slipped the two halves of the stretcher underneath her.

Mac was winched into the helicopter with the stretcher and a short time later the line was dropped again. Her heart thudding, Abby attached herself and gave the thumbs-up signal to be lifted. She could hardly ask Mac to leave their patient and come back for her. But to her relief the upward lift was okay. Having done it on the way down with Mac had helped. Abby knew that from now on she would never again worry about that part of the rescue, and she had Mac's thoughtfulness to thank for that.

Back in the helicopter, Mac had already attached their patient to the onboard monitoring system and was gently feeling her abdomen. As he did so, Abby noted some swelling just below the woman's ribs. She glanced up at

Mac, who was shaking his head and looking worried.

'Damage to the spleen?' she asked.

He nodded. 'The sooner we get her to hospital the better. If she has ruptured her spleen she'll need surgery as soon as possible. I'll radio ahead and let them know so they can have the surgeons and a theatre standing by.'

The next ten minutes were tense as Abby continued to monitor the woman's vital signs and neuro observations. Her pulse was rapid, making the possibility of a ruptured spleen more likely. Mac helped Abby put up a drip. Giving the injured woman fluids would help keep her stabilised in the short term.

Abby sighed with relief when the helicopter landed gently on the landing pad at the hospital. As before, they were met by the A & E team. There was no time for introductions as they wheeled the woman straight into Resus and Abby stepped back, allowing the A & E team to take over. As they carried out their own assessment, Mac relayed what he and Abby had done so far.

'I think you're right about the ruptured spleen, Mac,' the dark-haired emergency consultant who had loaned them his car told them. 'Could I have a portable ultrasound over here, please?' While the A & E consultant prepared to scan the victim's abdomen, Mac was checking her reflexes. 'Right pupil still blown,' he said. 'I suspect a subdural haematoma, Josh. We should get the neurosurgeons down here to have a look.'

'I'm here.'

Abby whirled around to see a Latin-looking man enter the room. He crossed over to the trolley and Mac stepped aside to allow him to examine the rider. By this time the resus room was crowded. Apart from Dr Corezzi, the neurosurgeon, and Josh, there were several other people in the room, all occupied with the patient.

Mac passed an endotracheal tube down the woman's throat.

'Okay, let's get her to Theatre. The spleen *is* ruptured so she's going to need that fixed, too,' Josh said quietly. Despite his calm voice, Abby knew they were worried. A few moments later the woman was being wheeled out of the room to Theatre.

The emergency over, Josh and Mac peeled off their gloves.

'That was close,' Josh said. 'It was a good thing you were there, Mac. It makes a difference knowing in advance what we might be dealing with. This is exactly the type of case where having a doctor attached to the ambulance service makes a difference.'

'You're right. But whether a few successful cases will persuade the powers that be that having a full-time doctor attached to the service makes financial sense is a different story. She still might not make it,' Mac replied. 'But at least she has a chance.'

Mac glanced over at Abby, seeming surprised to see her still standing there. 'I couldn't have done it without Abby. Abby, this is Dr Josh O'Hara, one of the A & E consultants here. Josh, this is Abby, our new paramedic, who has joined us from the London service.'

Josh grinned. 'We're lucky to have you.'

Abby took in his dark hair and ready smile. He was very good-looking, but for some reason he did nothing to her pulse. Unlike Mac. Unfortunately.

'Have you had a chance to look around St Piran's, Abby?' Josh asked.

Abby smiled. 'Not yet. There hasn't really been time. But I'd really like to go to the special care nursery. I have a patient there I'd like to see.'

'I have to pop into ITU,' Mac said. 'Josh, if

you're not busy, perhaps you could take Abby up to Special Care? I'll meet you there in five.'

'Sure. No probs. I'll just let the nursing staff know where I am. I can introduce you to whoever is on duty at the same time, Abby.'

There were too many faces for Abby to take in, but everyone welcomed her warmly. She couldn't help but notice that Josh caused quite a stir in the department. There were several wistful looks in his direction of which he seemed oblivious. After they left the department, Josh took Abby upstairs to the SCBU. A nurse met them as they entered.

Josh introduced Abby. 'Abby was the paramedic who helped Mrs Hargreaves when she went into labour. She wanted to say hello and see how the baby's getting on.'

'Mum is with the baby now and they are both doing fine. It would have been a different story if you and Dr MacNeil hadn't got them here so quickly.' She peered over Abby's shoulder, as if expecting to find Mac standing behind her. She looked disappointed to find he wasn't. The nurse pointed to a cot near the middle of the room. 'They're over there if you want to go over.'

'Is Dr Phillips on duty?' Josh asked.

'Megan? Yes. Isn't she always? She's in the staffroom, catching up on paperwork.'

Josh looked at Abby. 'That's where I'll be if you need me. Mac should be along shortly.'

Abby found Jenny sitting by the cot, gazing down at her baby. As soon as she noticed Abby, her face broke into an enormous smile.

'How's he doing?' Abby whispered, peering into the cot. A tiny infant lay in it, his nappy almost taking up half of his small body. There were a few lines snaking from his tiny hands and feet, but he was breathing on his own. That was a good sign.

'He's doing okay. They think I'll be able to take him home in a week or two. And it's all thanks to you and Dr MacNeil. The staff say that if I'd been any later getting to hospital I might have lost him—or died, too. I don't know how to thank you enough.' Her voice cracked slightly. She had been through a very stressful experience and was bound to still be worried.

'You don't have to thank us. It's our job. I'm just thrilled that it all worked out okay.' Abby held out her arms and Jenny passed her sleeping child to her. Abby breathed in the particular blissful scent of baby.

Jenny was looking at something over Abby's

shoulder. Abby turned round to find Mac standing there, looking at them. Jenny smiled and waved him over.

Mac approached them slowly, looking as if he'd rather be anywhere else than there.

'Dr MacNeil, I'm so glad I caught you. I wanted to thank you personally for saving my baby. And for taking care of Tim. I know he had his brave face on, but he was truly terrified until you came along.'

Mac shuffled his feet, looking uncomfortable. 'As I'm sure Abby told you, it was nothing. All in a day's work. How is Tim anyway?'

'He's at school today. His dad will bring him up later. He's totally besotted with his little brother. He kind of feels that he almost helped deliver him. He was a bit embarrassed when he first heard I was pregnant—you know how young boys can be about that sort of stuff—but now he couldn't be prouder.'

Just then Josh approached them, accompanied by a woman with russet hair and fine, delicate features.

'Abby, this is Dr Megan Phillips—one of the paediatric registrars,' Josh introduced her.

'Hi, Abby. I've heard all about you from Mrs Hargreaves here. I understand that it's thanks to you our latest miracle baby is doing well,' Megan said.

'Would you like to hold him, Dr Phillips?' Jenny asked. 'And seeing as you're all here, I might take the opportunity to pop to the bathroom.'

But Abby was surprised when Megan blanched. Instead, Josh stepped forward and took the tiny infant in his arms, cradling him with practised ease.

'Hey, Josh,' Mac teased. 'Looks like you're a natural after all. Are you practising for when you and Rebecca have kids? The nurses in A & E tell me that's all she talks about when she visits the department. You'd better make the most of the next few months. One of these days you'll be up to your ears in nappies.'

'Not me, I'm afraid,' Josh said lightly.

Abby saw Josh and Megan exchange a look. It was brief, the merest glance, but the paediatric registrar's face went even whiter. If she hadn't known Josh was married to Rebecca, Abby would have sworn there was something between the two doctors. But perhaps her own situation was making her hypersensitive. That was all.

As soon as Jenny returned Megan made her excuses. 'I'll be back to check on this little one in a while,' she told the happy mother. 'But if you'll excuse me, right now I have other patients to look in on.' She smiled, but Abby could see it didn't quite reach her eyes. After a brief nod at the two men, she left the ward.

'I should be getting back to A & E,' Josh said, handing the baby back to his mother. 'So if you'll excuse me, too? Abby, it was good to meet you. I'm sure we'll meet again soon.'

'We should go, too, Abby,' Mac said.

'No problem. If someone could just point me in the direction of the bathroom first? It was lovely to see you again, Jenny. And your baby. We don't always get the chance to catch up with our patients, so when we do, it's a real pleasure.'

'Thank you both, again.' She gazed down at her sleeping child, who was just beginning to stir. 'Looks like he's ready for a feed.'

'The bathroom's just outside the swing doors, Abby,' Mac said. 'I'll meet you downstairs.'

Abby found the bathroom. To her surprise Megan was leaning against the basin, her face streaked with tears. Concerned, Abby moved towards her and touched her on the arm.

'Megan? What's wrong?'

Megan managed a wan smile and leaned

over the sink to splash her face with water. 'Don't mind me. I'm just having one of those days.'

'Are you sure there's nothing I can do?'

Megan reached for a paper towel to pat her face dry. 'No, really. But I'd appreciate it if you kept this to yourself. It doesn't seem too professional for the doctor to be found crying in the bathroom.'

'We all have our moments,' Abby said, 'when stuff gets on top of us.' She paused. 'Look, I'm new here and I haven't really met many people yet, and I'm always up for a bit of adult female company. Why don't you come over for supper one night?'

Megan smiled. She really is beautiful, Abby thought. But her eyes are so sad. Something was bothering her and it was more than just an off day, Abby would have staked her life on it.

'I would like that,' Megan said.

Abby wrote down her address and mobile number and passed it to Megan.

'Phone me?'

'Sure,' Megan said, pocketing the number. But somehow Abby didn't think she would.

CHAPTER NINE

ABBY woke early on Saturday morning to find that Emma was up before her. That in itself was unusual. She normally had to call Em at least twice before she could get her out of bed. Even more unusual was the smell of toast drifting from the kitchen. Moments later Emma appeared by her bed, carrying a tray with tea and buttered toast.

'Hey, what's this?' Abby said, sitting up and taking the tray.

'I woke up really early. I couldn't stay in bed so I thought I'd make you breakfast for a change.'

Emma's eyes were bright with excitement and it worried Abby. Perhaps she shouldn't have told her about Mac? Maybe she should have waited to see how the relationship developed? What if after today Mac backed away from having anything to do with his daughter?

Abby knew the rejection would break Emma's heart. But what was the alternative? Lying to Emma? One way or another her daughter would have found out about Mac. Maybe not straight away, but eventually. And then how would she have felt about Abby keeping the truth from her? That would have been worse. One of the things Abby had always promised Em was that she would never lie to her.

Emma was dressed, with her long blonde hair, so like Sara's, tied back in a ponytail. She crept into bed beside Abby. 'When do you think he'll be here?' she asked.

Abby glanced at her watch and groaned. It was only six-thirty.

'Not for a little while. I think he said eight.'

'What if he doesn't come?' Emma asked anxiously.

'He'll come,' Abby promised. Or he'll have me to answer to, she thought grimly. But somehow she knew that once Mac had made a decision he would stick to it.

'Are you coming, too?' Emma asked.

'Do you want me to?'

'I think so,' Emma said.

'Then I will.' Abby tossed the bedclothes aside and jumped out of bed. 'But there is no way I'm going to try windsurfing. The sea's far too cold for me.'

Emma grinned up at her. 'Don't be such a wuss. We'll be wearing wetsuits. Come on, Mum. You have to give it a go. It'll be fun.'

'We'll see,' Abby said evasively. 'Right now, I need a shower.'

Bang on eight o'clock there was a knock on the door. Abby opened it to find Mac standing there, looking almost as nervous as Emma. He had a bunch of flowers in his hand. 'I brought these for Emma,' he said. 'To be honest, I didn't know what the form was for meeting one's daughter officially for the first time.'

Abby smiled. 'She'll be delighted. I don't think anyone's given her flowers before.' She took the bouquet from him. 'Emma!' she called out. 'Mac's here.' As she stood aside to let Mac into the small hall she added, 'I think Mac is best at this stage, don't you?'

Mac nodded, craning his neck to look behind her.

'Hi, Mac,' Emma said from behind her.

'Mac brought these flowers for you. I'll put them in water before we go, shall I?'

Emma's smile lit up her face. 'Flowers. Wicked. Thank you, Mac.'

Mac bowed slightly in acknowledgement.

'It is my pleasure. Have you got your costume and something warm to put on after your lesson? We'll be warm enough while we're moving, but when we get out of the water, you might get cold.'

Emma nodded. 'Mum's already been through all that. She's coming, too. She said she might even try it herself.'

Mac raised an eyebrow. 'Good for her.' He paused. 'Did you know I taught Sara how to windsurf?'

Emma nodded again. 'Mum told me. She said that's how you and my real mum met. Was she good at it?'

Abby's heart cracked a little. Emma was so desperate for any titbits about Sara. Abby had told her as much as she could about her, leaving out the bits about Sara's wild side, concentrating on the warm, fun-loving side of Sara. The only reason Sara had taken windsurfing lessons had been to get to know Mac. As far as Abby knew, once Sara and Mac had become an item, Sara had given up windsurfing, preferring to sit on the beach and watch.

'She wasn't bad.' Mac grinned. 'But she didn't take the lessons for very long.' Abby was grateful to Mac for his tactful answer. 'I have a feeling you're going to take to it.'

* * *

Ten minutes later they were on the almost deserted beach, and only the real die-hard surfers were out on the waves. While Emma was getting changed, Mac popped into one of the surfing shops that hired out equipment and returned with a couple of wetsuits. 'I brought one for you,' he told Abby, 'in case you do give it a shot. 'I'm just going to get a beginner's board for Emma then we'll be set.'

Abby was getting the distinct impression she wasn't going to be allowed off the hook.

By the time Emma appeared, wrapped in her towel and shivering in the cool morning air, Mac had organised a board for her. He handed her a wetsuit and helped her into it.

'Okay, this first bit we do on land. Abby can join in without getting changed. All she needs to do is slip off her shoes.'

Just as she'd suspected, Abby thought ruefully. There was no getting out of it. She undid the laces of her trainers and removed her socks. The sand squirmed pleasantly between her toes.

'Okay, Emma. Pop onto the board. I'll show you how you lift the sail and how to balance yourself. Then we'll have a go on the water.'

Emma got the hang of the basics pretty quickly. 'It will be more difficult in the sea,'

Mac warned, 'but so far I'm impressed. Now, Abby, how about you having a go?'

Reluctantly, Abby stepped on the board and, following Mac's instructions, tugged on the sail to try and lift it. It was harder than she had expected. Determined to do it, she pulled with all her strength and almost toppled over when the sail whooshed up towards her. But Mac had anticipated her losing her balance and she felt strong hands circle her waist, steadying her. The feel of his hands cupping her waist sent all kinds of sensations shooting through her body and she prayed neither he nor Emma noticed the heat that rushed to her face. The last thing she wanted or needed was to have such a physical reaction to this man and, even worse, for either of them to notice.

Mac remained behind her, close enough for every cell in her body to be acutely aware of him. His breath tickled her neck as he placed his hands over hers, showing her how to hold the board. She was getting more and more flustered. Abruptly she let the sail fall back to the ground and stepped off the board. She knew she had to put some physical distance between her and this man.

'That's enough for me for the time being,'

she said, trying to keep her voice light. 'I think Emma's dying to get out on the water.'

Mac looked at her and the way his eyes danced told her he knew exactly why she had jumped off the board. His mouth twitched. 'Okay, then. Let's go, Emma.'

Abby found a rock and watched as Emma clambered onto the board and valiantly tried to pull the sail from the water. It took several attempts, but with Mac helping her she eventually got the sail up and started to move out towards the open sea. She must have surprised herself as she immediately let go of the sail and fell into the water. Even from a distance, Abby could see the flash of Mac's white teeth as he threw his head back and laughed. In response, Emma splashed him. Relief coursed through Abby. It really was the perfect way for Emma and Mac to get to know each other. From what she could see, the initial awkwardness of earlier had passed. It was early days, of course, but at least it was the right start.

After an hour, Abby was getting chilled despite having a cup of coffee from the flask she had packed. Emma had managed to get up on the board and move a little distance before falling off. Abby knew she must be getting tired and, sure enough, a few minutes later

Emma and Mac, both grinning widely, made their way to shore. Emma flopped down beside Abby, her cheeks flushed and her eyes sparkling. 'That was so good.' She looked up at Mac, who was detaching the sail from the board. 'Can we do it again? Soon? Please?'

'Sure thing. But I think you should get changed now. I don't want you to get cold.'

As Emma hurried away to get dressed, Abby looked up at Mac. He really was gorgeous. No wonder Sara had fallen for him hook, line and sinker. She found herself wondering about him. How come a man as cute and as eligible as he was hadn't been snapped up? But perhaps he had. For all she knew, he had been married at one time.

'I think she enjoyed that,' Abby said.

Mac looked after Emma's retreating back. 'She could be very good, you know. She has natural balance and, more importantly perhaps, seems hugely determined to succeed. Is she like that in everything?'

Abby didn't attempt to hide her pride. 'She's a wonderful girl, Mac. She gives everything she does her best shot. I know her drive and determination will take her far in life.'

'And a lot of that must be down to the way you brought her up.' Mac's eyes glittered and once again Abby felt her body tingle in response.

'I hope so. But she has a lot of her mother in her, too.'

When Mac raised an eyebrow, a shot of anger coursed through Abby. She would not have this man making judgements about Sara. Okay, so Sara had been pretty wild, but she'd also been kind and loyal.

'Sara was a good person, Mac,' Abby said quietly.

Mac opened his mouth as if to reply but Emma, dressed in jeans and a thick woollen jumper, arrived back.

'Can we have something to eat now? I'm starving!'

The tension disappeared as they all laughed. 'It's not even ten o'clock yet, Em,' Abby protested.

'But it's ages since I had breakfast.'

'I swear I don't know where she puts it all,' Abby told Mac. 'She eats like a horse but is as thin as a rake.'

'At least she eats,' Mac said mildly. 'And she's still growing.'

'Mum says I'm going to be tall.' Emma looked shyly at Mac. 'I must take after you. How tall are you anyway?'

'Six foot three, or something like that. I'm hungry, too. What do you say we grab a burger?'

Abby frowned. 'I don't really like Emma to have junk food,' she said primly.

'I don't think one will hurt,' Mac protested.

Abby felt her hackles rise. One day as a father and already he was interfering. But she swallowed the angry words that rose to her lips. She was being overly sensitive. Why spoil the day by falling out over something as ridiculous as a burger? Nevertheless, she would have to speak to him and make it clear that as far as Emma was concerned, it *was she* who made the decisions.

'On the other hand,' Mac went on smoothly, 'there is a café up the road a little that does great home-made soup and sandwiches. And they have the best hot chocolate, too. Why don't we go there?'

'Whatever,' Emma said. 'I don't mind.'

Inside the café, Mac and Emma tucked into their soup and sandwiches while Abby nursed a mug of coffee. She listened as Emma fired questions at Mac, and Mac replied with much the same answers he had given Abby. Nevertheless, there was a reticence, a carefulness about his replies that made her think he wasn't being totally candid. But why should he? No doubt he was, quite sensibly, feeling the way with his new-found daughter.

'Can I meet my grandmother?' Emma asked.

'Tiree is a long way from here,' Mac said evasively. 'But maybe one day.'

'Have you got brothers and sisters?'

'Only me, I'm afraid.'

Emma looked glum for a moment. Abby knew that part of her fantasy about finding her father was the hope that she'd discover a whole load of aunts, uncles and cousins at the same time.

But it wasn't long before her natural cheerfulness re-emerged.

'Did you always want to be a doctor?'

'For as long as I can remember,' Mac replied. 'What do you want to be when you grow up, or haven't you decided yet?'

'Not really decided. I might be a pilot or a vet.' She looked thoughtful. 'Or a doctor like you who rescues people. It looks fun.'

'Yeah, it can be fun, but it can also be a little scary at times.'

Emma's eyebrows shot up. 'I don't think you find anything scary.'

Oh, dear, Abby thought. One day in and already Emma had found a hero in Mac.

Mac flicked a glance at Abby and smiled. 'I find lots of things scary,' he said. Then he changed the subject. 'One of the other things I like doing is mountain biking. How do you fancy coming with me one day?'

'Oh, I'm not sure about that,' Abby interrupted before she could help herself. 'Can't that be pretty dangerous?'

Mac narrowed his eyes at her. 'It can be dangerous crossing the road, if you're not looking where you are going,' he said mildly. 'The important thing is to weigh up the risks, decide how you can best protect yourself then go for it.' Abby had the uneasy feeling he wasn't just talking about mountain biking. 'It's good for kids to test themselves. I believe it stops them from taking risks in other ways. Anyway, I'll only take Emma on gentle slopes and make sure she's wearing all the right gear to protect her.'

Once again he was challenging her authority as a mother and Abby didn't like it one bit. Keeping her voice level, she stood up. 'I'll think about it. Emma, it's time for us to get back. We need to go shopping for groceries.'

'Oh, do we have to?' Emma said. 'Can't I stay with Mac?'

Before Mac could say anything, Abby

shook her head. 'I'm sure Mac has something planned for the rest of the day, and I would really like your help with the shopping, Em.' It was a pretty poor excuse, but Abby wanted Emma to get to know Mac slowly. Give them both time to let the relationship develop.

Reluctantly Emma got to her feet. 'Thanks, Mac. It was great.'

'We'll do it again next weekend, if you like,' Mac promised. 'And I'll try and work on Abby about the mountain biking thing.'

Emma smiled happily and Abby knew she was too late. Emma had found exactly the kind of father she had always wanted.

CHAPTER TEN

THE next few weeks flew past. Abby looked at a couple of cottages that would have been perfect for her and Emma—if the price hadn't been out of her reach. Mac and Emma had developed a routine, seeing each other a couple of times a week—either to go windsurfing or mountain biking. Abby's heart still leaped every time she saw Mac, but she tried to make sure they were never alone. He didn't ask her out again either. She didn't know whether to be pleased or disappointed. All she did know was that it was better this way. Much, much safer.

As the weather became more unpredictable, Mac had agreed with Abby, much to Emma's disappointment, that the windsurfing had to stop—winter was on its way.

'I don't mind getting cold,' Emma had protested. 'And I'm just getting the hang of it.'

'You're doing more than getting the hang of

it.' Mac had grinned. 'I've rarely had a pupil that's taken to it as quickly as you have. But it's not just the cold. The waves are getting bigger now, and neither your mother nor I want to risk anything happening to you.' He ruffled Emma's hair as the child glowed with pleasure at his praise.

Abby was relieved. Although she trusted Mac not to let Emma do anything outside her capabilities, there was a recklessness in both father and daughter that frightened her. They were both risk-takers.

'But we can carry on mountain biking?' Emma asked. 'I like that, too.' Abby reluctantly capitulated and agreed to let Mac take Emma.

'As long as it doesn't get too wet, yes. And as soon as spring arrives, we can go wind-surfing again.'

Emma wasn't prepared to give up without a fight. 'Are *you* going to stop kite boarding?'

Mac laughed again. 'When you learned to windsurf in Tiree, as I did, a little cold and big waves don't put you off.'

Emma started to protest, but Mac cut her off. 'I promised Abby that I won't let you do anything dangerous and I'm sticking to that promise, okay?'

Seeing the easy way Mac dealt with Emma, Abby was pleased. Despite her concerns, Mac seemed to be developing a real bond with his daughter. Emma's confidence was growing by leaps and bounds. Abby had one concern, though. She knew how much Emma wanted to impress her newly found father and she wouldn't put it past her to do something outside her comfort zone to impress him. But there was little she could do about that. She would just have to trust Mac.

Over the last couple of weeks Abby had been on several callouts with Mac. He was always calm and very efficient. Every day she was learning to respect him more and more. But that wasn't all. Every day she was finding herself more and more attracted to him, and not just physically. She was learning that he had an easygoing nature and that nothing ever fazed him. She often found herself wondering why he had never married.

This morning Mac came in looking tired.

'Late night?' Kirsten teased. 'Some woman keeping you up?'

Abby caught her breath as an unfamiliar stab of jealousy hit her in the solar plexus.

Mac shook his head. 'I wish.' He smiled. 'No, I was called late yesterday afternoon.

There was a nasty accident on one of the main roads. Two fatalities, I'm afraid.'

'But you saved one,' said Mike, who had walked in in time to hear the last of the conversation. 'I heard it was a real touch and go.'

Mac pulled his hand through his hair. 'I had to intubate at the scene. It wasn't easy, even with the fire brigade giving me some light to work with—and some shelter. The rain was pretty torrential. But, yes, the driver of the second car is going to be okay. I just wish we could have done something for the occupants of the other car, but it looks like they died on impact.'

Everyone hated hearing about death, even if they knew it came with the job. Abby was a little surprised to hear the sadness in Mac's voice. He usually gave away very little of himself.

'I ended up staying at the hospital until the small hours. I wanted to make sure before I left that the man pulled from the car was stable.'

He caught Abby's eye and smiled. 'I think it's important we follow up on our patients. Don't you, Abby?'

Abby smiled back. It seemed that Mac was

breaking his no involvement rules in more ways than one.

Except with her, that was. He was always friendly when he collected and returned Emma.

'Anyway,' Mac said, 'back to work. Anything on the board?'

'Shouldn't you be at home, catching up on your sleep?' Abby asked.

Mac shrugged his shoulders. 'I'll be fine. We doctors learn very early on to do without sleep. A gallon of coffee and I'll be fine.' He must have noticed that Abby was far from convinced. 'Honest.' He held up two fingers. 'Scout's honour.'

While he'd been talking Abby had spooned some coffee into a mug and added water from the recently boiled kettle. 'Drink this,' she ordered.

As Mac sipped his coffee, the radio came to life and everyone stopped talking. They could only hear Kirsten's side of the conversation, but the look on her face told them it was a bad one.

'We have a pregnant woman who has gone off the road. The road ambulance and fire brigade are there, but they're requesting assistance from us. She's complaining of severe abdominal pain and they have no idea what they are dealing with. The fire brigade is cutting her out of her vehicle at the moment.'

Mac jumped to his feet, every trace of tiredness banished.

'Okay, Abby. Let's go.'

'Mac has called from the air ambulance. They are bringing in a pregnant woman from an RTA with severe abdominal pain,' Josh told the assembled A & E team. 'Would someone page the obstetric and paediatric registrar, please?'

'I'm on it,' the senior nurse said, turning away and picking up the phone.

Josh pulled a hand through his hair. He was tired. Spending so much time at the hospital, putting in extra hours, was taking its toll.

But you don't need to, an insistent voice whispered in the back of his mind. The department copes well when you're not there. He knew the real reason. It was more and more difficult to spend time at home with Rebecca, pretending. Some time soon he would have to face the reality of the situation, but for now it would have to wait.

Minutes later he was called to Resus to see his patient. Mac and Abby were by her side.

'Who have we got here?' he asked.

'Mrs Diane Clifford,' Mac replied calmly. 'Twenty-four weeks pregnant and has been having right-sided abdominal pain for the last six hours. She was driving herself to hospital when she blacked out and crashed. No obvious injury from the accident. We're going to have to leave you guys to it, I'm afraid. We have another call to go to.'

As Mac and Abby left, Josh smiled reassuringly as he palpated his anxious patient's abdomen. 'Don't worry, Diane. We'll get to the bottom of this.'

He glanced up as Megan swept into the room. As usual she looked every inch the calm professional, her dark hair neatly swept back from her face, her expressive eyes already taking in the scene.

'You called the paediatric registrar?' she said, acknowledging Josh with a faint smile before introducing herself to the woman on the bed. 'I'm Dr Phillips,' she said softly. 'We're going to get your baby attached to a monitor so we can monitor the heartbeat. Is that okay?'

Diane's frightened eyes darted from Josh to Megan.

'Do you think there's something wrong with

my baby?' She reached out and grabbed Megan's hand. 'Don't let me lose my baby.'

Pain flickered in Megan's eyes before she rearranged her expression into her usual professional mask. Anyone else would have missed it, but for Josh it was plain to see. Damn it. Why did it have to be Megan who was called to this particular case?

'Dr Phillips, could I have a word?' he said, indicating that Megan step outside the cubicle with him. 'Diane, the nurse is just going to get you attached to the monitor while I have a quick chat with Dr Phillips here. Is that okay?'

Diane nodded silently and Josh followed Megan outside the cubicle. They moved away so they weren't overheard by their patient.

'What are you thinking, Josh?' Megan's voice was calm and steady, but she couldn't quite hide the anxiety in her eyes. He knew her too well.

'It could be three or four things. Appendicitis, premature labour or an abruption. But I don't really believe it's appendicitis.'

Megan sucked in a breath.

'You could get someone else to take over,' Josh said gently.

Megan's eyes flashed. 'No, I couldn't. Josh,

you have to stop treating me as if I were made of china. I'm here now and Diane is my case.'

'She's twenty-four weeks,' Josh continued. 'I hope to God we don't have to deliver her.'

Megan bit her lip. 'We both know a twenty-four-weeker doesn't have much of a chance. We'll give her steroids just in case. But if you need to deliver, we'll do the best for the baby.'

Josh wanted to reach out and touch her. The need to comfort her was so strong he had to lock his hands behind his back.

'Okay. We'll do an ultrasound. See how the baby's doing when we get the CTG result. After that we'll make a decision. I'll give you a shout if we need you.'

But before he could turn away, Megan grabbed his arm.

'I'm staying,' she said. 'If she has an abruption you might have to deliver her without waiting for the obstetric team. But have a look at her ovaries. A cyst could present in much the same way.'

He nodded. He hoped she was right.

Everyone waited anxiously while Josh ran the ultrasound probe over the injured woman's abdomen. He looked up and smiled.

'There's a ten-centimetre cyst on the right

where the pain is.' He caught Megan's eye. 'Good call, Dr Phillips. We were right to wait.'

They both knew they were far from out of the woods but at least it wasn't premature labour and it wasn't an abruption. It was still serious and Diane had to be taken to Theatre immediately. But at least this was one woman who wasn't going to lose her baby. Josh explained to Diane that the cyst had probably become twisted on its stalk, cutting off the blood supply to the ovary and resulting in severe pain.

Megan blinked rapidly. 'I better go and get changed. They'll need a paediatrician standing by in Theatre, just in case.'

Then she smiled. God, he loved her smile. It seemed to start somewhere deep inside her until her whole face lit up. Once more he felt a pang of regret so deep it hurt. Why couldn't things have been different between them? How in God's name had he made such an almighty mess of his life?

CHAPTER ELEVEN

ABBY was surprised to find Mac waiting for her when she emerged from the building after changing into her civvies.

'Are you okay?' he asked, his eyes searching hers.

Abby nodded. 'I am now. It got a bit hairy there for a while. I always get really anxious when the victim is pregnant.'

Mac smiled slowly and his eyes creased at the corners. Abby's heart lurched. How could anyone look so cool and sexy after all they had just been through? She was sure she looked as if she'd done a couple of rounds in the boxing ring. It felt like it anyway.

For a moment Mac looked directly into her eyes and what she saw there made her heart start pounding again. The world started spinning around her.

'How about you and Emma coming out for dinner?' he asked.

Abby struggled to control her breathing. What she was feeling was nothing more than a delayed reaction to the rescue.

'Normally we'd love to, but Em is going around to a friend's after school. Maybe another time?' She was pleased to hear that her voice was steady, betraying nothing of her inner turmoil, and she thanked the years of practice she'd had of keeping her feelings hidden.

'We could go on our own.' He smiled at her. 'Go on, say yes. I don't know about you, but every time I go on a rescue, I get hungry.'

There wasn't any reason to refuse as far as she could see, except for her reluctance to be alone in his company a moment longer than she had to. Every time she was near him, her body kept behaving in the strangest way. On the other hand, what harm could it do? It wasn't as if she could avoid being alone with Mac for the rest of her life. Not when they worked together and not when they shared Emma. Emma would be having supper at her friend's and Abby had planned on warming up soup to have with a sandwich. She hardly saw her daughter these days. Emma was either going round to see friends, or staying on at school for hockey practice, or out with Mac. But although she missed spending time with her, she knew it meant her daughter was happy and settled. It was natural for Emma to want some independence, and it was a sign that she was continuing to develop her confidence, knowing that Mac and Abby were there if she needed them.

'Unless you'd like to have supper at my place?' she said. The moment the words were out of her mouth, she regretted them. Although the thought of an evening alone with Mac excited her, it unnerved her, too.

'Home cooking? How could I refuse?'

Too late. She could hardly retract the invitation now.

'It won't be very fancy, I'm afraid. You might regret it.'

'Let me tell you, Abby, for a man who lives on take-outs and microwave meals when I'm not eating out, the thought of home cooking is irresistible.'

'Okay, then, you're on. Why don't you come home with me now? It'll save you a trip to your flat and back.'

'Sure thing. I'll stop off on the way and pick us up some wine, shall I? Red or white?'

'White. Although I'm not much of a drinker, so you might be drinking most of it yourself.'

'Give me half an hour?'

By the time Mac knocked on the door, Abby had rummaged around in the fridge and found enough to make a stir-fry. As she'd told Mac, supper wouldn't be fancy, but with the soup it would be adequate. She hoped she had enough. A big man like Mac was bound to have a healthy appetite. Although there wasn't an inch of flab on his muscular frame, given all the exercise he did, he was bound to need calories.

'Wine—and some olives,' Mac said, proffering his purchases to Abby. 'I didn't know if you liked them, but I took a chance.'

'Love 'em. Why don't you pop the wine in the fridge? You don't fancy lighting the fire while I finish supper?' Abby gestured to the open fire with a nod of her head. 'You'll find everything you need there.'

By the time the meal was ready, the fire was burning cheerfully. There was no room in the tiny house for a kitchen table, so Abby set two places on the coffee table in front of the fire.

'Sorry,' she apologised. 'I guess it'll be

slightly awkward for you, but as you can see there isn't a lot of space.'

Mac looked around the small sitting room-cum-kitchen.

'I don't know,' he said. 'It's kind of cosy. But you know, if you and Emma need something bigger, I'll be happy to chip in.'

'We manage fine,' Abby said, more sharply than she'd intended to. 'I'm looking for something bigger to buy once we're sure where we want to live.' She didn't add that it was nigh on impossible on her salary, but she guessed she didn't need to.

'It must have been a struggle sometimes, bringing up a child on your own,' Mac said quietly. 'I wish Sara had told me. I would have done something to help.'

Abby shrugged. 'If you knew Sara, you'd know she had her pride. I guess when she found out she was pregnant the baby was the first thing she'd ever had that was truly hers. All through her pregnancy she refused to tell me who the father was. She said it wasn't important. She only told me about you right at the end.' Despite her best efforts her voice cracked. Mac put his fork down and laid a hand over hers.

'Tell me about her. Although we spent those

two weeks together, all I really knew about Sara was that she had a great sense of humour and a genuine love of life.'

Abby placed her knife and fork on her plate and leaned back on the sofa.

'To understand who Sara was you have to know something about our upbringing. Our mother—well, I guess you can say she wasn't the maternal type. When Sara and I were eighteen she told us it was time to leave home.'

'Go on,' Mac said quietly.

'I think my mother thought we got in the way of her life. Men weren't that interested in a woman with two children.'

She sneaked a look at Mac and was surprised to see anger in his eyes.

He smiled but his eyes remained bleak. 'My mother was the same.'

'Sara and I set up home together, if you could call it that. We didn't have much money, but we got by.'

'What about your father?'

'We never really knew him. He left when we were three and didn't come back.'

'Like mine,' Mac muttered. 'Except he didn't wait until I was three. He was off the minute he knew my mother was pregnant.'

Abby's heart ached for him.

'Anyway, Sara went a little off the rails when we left home. It's like she thought she was unlovable, and who could blame her? If your own mother doesn't want you, what does that say about you?'

'And you? How did you feel?'

'I was different from Sara. I decided that it was my mother's problem and I would find a way of proving to her that I could make it on my own. All through our childhood, I was the responsible one.'

Abby picked up a cushion and clutched it to her chest. Despite her words she had been hurt by her mother's rejection. It still hurt. 'I trained as a paramedic. I discovered I was good at it. Sara, though, couldn't find anything she really wanted to do.' Abby blinked the tears away. She had tried everything to get her sister to believe in her own self-worth, but Sara just wouldn't—couldn't—believe it.

'When we were twenty-one I had saved up enough money to pay for a holiday in Mykonos for both of us. I thought two weeks of sunshine, together, would bring us closer again. I had hoped that I could really talk to Sara. Convince her it was time she made something of her life.'

'And then she met me. I can't imagine you were best pleased.'

'Then she met you,' Abby said softly. 'I have never seen her so lit up. I think she fell in love with you the moment she set eyes on you.'

'She spent most of the holiday you had planned together with me,' Mac said.

'Yes. It wasn't exactly the way I had thought it was going to be. But I couldn't deny her her chance. It had been a long time since I had seen her so happy.'

Mac groaned. 'I had no idea. I was so wrapped up in myself then, all I knew was that there was this beautiful woman who wanted to be with me. And I guess meeting me then falling pregnant was the last thing Sara needed. But how come I never noticed you?' He touched Abby briefly on her cheek. 'You are just as beautiful.'

'I wasn't back then. I was so much shyer than Sara. Anyway, the holiday wasn't a total disaster. I left Sara to it and took a ferry to the Greek mainland. I visited the Temple of Poseidon, and the Acropolis in Athens. Even if Sara had not been…' she paused '…occupied, she wouldn't have come with me. So I guess she got the holiday she wanted and I did, too.

It was just a shame we didn't have the time I wanted to get closer to each other again.'

Abby smiled. 'I was happy for her. Those two weeks were the happiest I'd ever seen her. Instead of that vague sadness and emptiness that seemed to have followed her most of her life, it was as if she'd found something. Something that made her believe in herself.' Abby looked at Mac. 'I know I have you to thank for that.'

'When did she tell you she was pregnant?'

'About three months after we returned from Mykonos. After we came back she was quieter, almost serene. I don't know...as if she'd found peace. I asked her if something had changed, but she just smiled. Then for a bit she was different again. Anxious and withdrawn. After a while, when she started showing, she told me she was going to have a baby. She said she hadn't told me at first because she hadn't been sure she was going to keep it.

'As you can imagine, I was stunned. I guessed the father must be you, but when I asked her she wouldn't say. She said it wasn't important. I didn't know how the three of us were going to cope, but Sara was so happy.'

Mac was listening intently.

'I wanted her to tell the father, even if she

wouldn't tell me. I thought whoever it was had a right to know. But she refused point blank. She said the baby was hers and nobody was going to have any say about how she brought up her child. During her pregnancy she started a degree with the Open University. I could see she was determined to make a future for herself and the child and she knew I would always be there for her. Our own mother, of course, wasn't the slightest bit interested.'

'But she did tell you that I was the father— eventually.'

Abby squeezed her eyes closed.

'When she knew that she wasn't going to live to look after Emma, yes, she gave in and told me.'

The memory of those last few days were burnt into Abby's mind. At first everything had gone as planned and Sara's labour, although long, had resulted in a healthy baby girl. When Abby had seen her sister holding her child, it had been a moment of such joy Abby couldn't have felt prouder even if she had been the mother instead of Sara. Not even their mother's disinterest in the birth had blighted those first few days. After all, she and Sara had each other and however difficult and challenging the next few years would be, together they would be there for Emma, be their own little family. Then Sara had developed an infection and had been admitted to ITU. Even then, Abby had never suspected for one moment her sister might die. But Sara had got steadily worse. She hated thinking about it. Her sister, lying in ITU, pale and listless, and for once Abby had been totally unable to help her.

'Abby, I don't think I'm going to make it,' Sara had whispered, her face flushed with fever.

'Don't say that. Of course you're going to be okay.'

Sara smiled wanly. 'Somehow I knew deep inside that this was too good to last.'

Abby reached for her hand and squeezed it tight, trying to transfer all her strength to her failing sister.

'You can't die, Sara,' Abby cried. 'Emma needs you. I need you.'

'I'm not strong like you. You'll be okay.' For a moment strength returned. 'Look after Emma for me, promise. Don't let anything bad happen to her. I want her to know she's cherished and loved.'

'I promise, Sara. But you mustn't talk like that. You're going to be okay.'

'Hey, I thought I was the optimist.' Sara managed a smile. She struggled to speak. 'Remember Mac? Back on Mykonos? He's the father. I'll leave it to you to decide whether you want to tell him or not. Whatever you decide to do is okay with me.'

Shortly after, with Abby holding her hand, Sara had slipped into a coma. She never came round and died a few days later.

Tears fell as Abby repeated the story to Mac. She was barely conscious of his arm slipping around her shoulder and pulling her close.

'I'm so sorry,' he said. 'You must miss her. If I had known, I could have helped.'

'I tried to find you when Em was a few months old. But I knew nothing except that you were called Mac and taught windsurfing. I took Emma with me back to Mykonos to try and find you but the season was over and the resort closed down. I phoned their main office, but they refused to give me any details of the staff who worked there.' She shrugged. 'There was nothing more I could do, so we just came home.'

Suddenly conscious that she was in his arms, Abby pulled away. Her heart aching, she crossed to the fire and added a log. A sudden flurry of sparks crackled in the hearth.

'So you brought Emma up on your own. It couldn't have been easy. What about your mother?'

'She wasn't even there when Sara died. She had gone on holiday. Said she needed the break.' Abby couldn't keep the bitterness from her voice. 'To be fair, she couldn't have known Sara was going to die.'

'But you must have warned her? When Sara was admitted to ITU?' The anger in Mac's voice was almost palpable. How could anyone understand how a mother could stay away from her child when she needed her?

'She came back in time for the funeral,' Abby said. 'Then, unbelievably, when she held Emma for the first time, it was almost as if Mum changed before my eyes. She became besotted with her grandchild, in a way she never had been with her own daughters. Maybe it was different. There was no responsibility involved. She could have all the good times with Em without the bad. And maybe it was guilt. Guilt that she hadn't been there for Sara when she'd needed her most. Who knows? But she does love her granddaughter. She helped with child care when Emma was little so I could work. So people can change. And I'm glad. I've always felt it was important Emma knows who her family is. She's had little enough of them—until now, that is.' She forced a smile. 'But enough about that. What about your parents?'

This time it was Mac who shifted uneasily. 'My family isn't any better than yours, I'm afraid. If anything, they could be worse.'

Abby looked at him. He was studying his feet as if he could find answers there. She waited for him to continue.

'My mother sounds very much like yours. I also never knew my father. I sometimes wonder if my mother did. I was an only child and she made it clear from early on I was nothing but a nuisance.' He looked up and Abby saw the pain in his eyes. 'I spent as much time away from her as I could. She made it clear she didn't expect much from me, but I knew I wanted more from life. When I wasn't outside in the sea or on the hills, I was in my room studying. I was damned if I was going to give her the satisfaction of turning out the way she expected me to. I was lucky, I won a scholarship to medical school, and the rest is, as they say, history.'

'Do you see her?'

'I go back to Tiree once a year. She's not getting any younger. Whatever she is, she's still my mother.' He sent her a half-smile. 'You and I have a lot in common after all.'

'Does she know about Emma?'

'I phoned her. I thought she'd like to know. Perhaps she's mellowed or perhaps she's lonely, but she's asked to meet her.'

'Have you mentioned it to Emma?'

'I thought I should run it past you first.'

'Maybe we could all go?' Abby suggested. 'I'd like that.'

There was silence for a moment. 'I don't want Emma to grow up without a father. I told myself I would never have children, but now I have, I want her to know I'll always be there for her. Don't ever take her from me, Abby.'

Abby walked across the room and crouched by his side. She touched his face lightly.

'What makes you think I will? I want her to know her father, too.'

He touched her lips with a finger. 'Emma is lucky to have you as a mother.'

For a moment their faces were only inches apart. Abby could feel his breath on her skin, almost feel the warmth radiating from him. He smelled of wood smoke and earth. His eyes, drilling into hers, were as blue as the sea. Her heart was thudding so loudly she thought he must be able to hear it. Gently he slid his hand behind her neck. The feel of his fingers on her skin sent tiny shots of electricity fizzing through her.

She didn't know if he pulled her towards him or whether she was the one to make the move, but suddenly they were kissing. Softly at first, almost exploring each other's mouths, and then, as desire lit a flame in her belly, she was in his arms and he was kissing her as if his need for her was all-encompassing. No, no, no, a voice was shouting in her head. Don't do this. Nothing good can come of this. But her body wasn't listening. She could no more pull away from him than she could have walked across the desert.

Without knowing how it happened, they were lying on the sofa, their bodies pressed along the length of each other.

'Abby,' Mac whispered into her hair. 'Beautiful, sweet Abby.'

What was she doing? What were they doing? Apart from anything else, Emma would be back any moment. Reluctantly, Abby disentangled herself from Mac's arms and slid out of his grasp. Her heart was beating like a train and her breath was coming in short gasps. Mac reached for her again but she stepped away from his outstretched arm.

'This is so not a good idea,' she said.

'Why not? I think it's a very good idea.' His eyes darkened like the sea before a storm.

'Emma could come back any minute. I don't want her finding us in a clinch.'

'In a clinch?' The smile was back. 'Is that what you call it?' Laughter rippled under his words.

'Whatever.' Abby smoothed her hair with her hands. 'Nevertheless, if Emma walked in now...'

'Call it what you will, I think it's a very good idea.' He sat up and before she could move, his hand shot out lightning fast and caught her by the wrist, pulling her down on his lap. He buried his face in her neck, his lips touching her in places she hadn't even known, until now, had nerve endings.

She moaned softly. Being here with him felt so right. It had been so long since she'd been held. But she forced herself to push him away. There was no way she could think with him nibbling her neck.

'No, Mac. We can't. We have Emma to think about.'

Mac frowned at her. 'Emma?'

'Yes. Can't you see? If we start something, it'll give Emma all the wrong ideas. Besides, what if we fall out?' She held up her hand to stop the words he was about to say. 'It could happen, you know it could. How will it be for Emma then?'

Mac's frown deepened. 'I wasn't really thinking of a relationship. Hell, Abby, I wasn't really thinking at all. You must know I find you attractive. What's wrong with two adults…er…enjoying each other's company?'

Abby had to laugh. He was doing such a good impersonation of a well-known, ageing movie star. 'Seriously. Mac. Think about it. Don't we have enough to be getting on with? Trying to work out a way to co-parent Emma?'

Mac drew his hand across his face in a gesture Abby was beginning to know well. He looked so disappointed Abby almost changed her mind. Almost.

Mac stood up. 'Perhaps you're right,' he said, reaching for his jacket. He stopped and looked at her intently. 'Right now, Abby, you're holding all the cards.'

And before she could ask him what he meant, the door closed behind him with a gentle click.

CHAPTER TWELVE

BACK at his own house, Mac paced the floor. He still couldn't believe how much his life had changed in the last few weeks. It had been a shock finding out that he had a daughter, and the last thing he had expected was to feel the way he did about Emma. He found he was looking forward to spending time with her. She was so like him with her love of adventure.

And like Abby, too.

Over the last few weeks he had found himself drawn to Abby in a way that he had never been drawn to a woman before. It wasn't just that she was sexy, in that way that only a woman who had no idea of her own beauty could be, but it was her loyalty, her strength of character, her kindness that drew him. It couldn't have been easy bringing up a child—his child—on her own, but she had done it without a second thought. And she had made a good job of it.

But it was different now; he could help. Be there for Emma and Abby. Help financially. He thought about the little house they were renting. It was barely big enough for one, let alone two of them. And here he was in this spacious flat with more space than he knew what to do with. Perhaps he should ask them to move in with him?

Immediately he dismissed the idea. It was crazy. Abby would never agree. The thought of sharing his home with Abby made the blood rush to his head. Seeing her every day. Her sleeping just a short distance away would drive him crazy. He'd never be able to keep his hands off her. And that way lay madness. She was right. What if they started something and it didn't work out? Having a child was one thing, but having a permanent relationship with a woman quite another. He didn't do relationships. If he started something with Abby it would, like all his other relationships, end sooner or later. And when it did there would be hard feelings and recriminations. There always were. No matter how often he warned the women in his life that he wasn't in it for the long haul, they never really believed him.

They always thought they would be the one to change him. And if he gave in to his need to have Abby, what then? When it came to an end she might stop him from seeing Emma. He was surprised at how much the prospect alarmed him. Now he had got to know his daughter, he couldn't imagine a life without her.

And what if Abby met someone else? He didn't want that either. The thought of her in another man's arms made his blood boil. But if she did, what if she moved away and took Emma away from him? As it stood, he could do nothing to stop her. And what if that man treated Emma like his mother's boyfriends had treated him? As if she was a nuisance they could do without?

He pulled a hand through his hair. Now he had found Emma he was damned if he was going to let anyone take her away from him again.

The days sped by as winter approached. Abby kept her eyes open for a house for Emma and herself, but so far nothing remotely affordable had come onto the market. Abby knew the only realistic option for her and Emma would be to buy something in serious need of refurbishment, and she didn't have the time for that, or a small modern flat, and she didn't have the heart for that.

Emma and Mac continued to spend time together and had developed an easy teasing camaraderie. Often they would gang up on Abby, once forcing her to join them mountain biking. Although she had gone along with them, one experience of being soaked to the skin and terrified out of her mind had been enough. She had refused point blank to go again. Some evenings Mac would drop in and they would play Scrabble or play games on Emma's computer console, the latter usually causing Mac and Emma to share a laugh at Abby's expense. Abby didn't care. She treasured those evenings. It was the family life she had never known.

One Saturday, Mac turned up at the cottage with a big smile on his face. Although it was cold, the rain had stopped and the sun was doing its best to cast some sunshine their way.

'You're looking pleased with yourself,' Abby said as she stood aside to let him in. 'But if you're looking for Emma, I'm afraid she's gone into the town with some friends from school.'

'It's not Emma I'm looking for. I have something I want *you* to see.' His eyes were sparkling with barely suppressed excitement.

'Oh, and what could that be?'

'I'm not saying. You have to come with me. Go on, grab a jacket.'

Mystified, Abby did as she was told. Mac was waiting for her in his Jeep.

'Where are we going? Come on, give me a clue.'

'No way. You're going to have to wait and see.'

They followed the road out of Penhally, heading in the general direction of St Piran's. But then Mac turned off and headed inland. A little while later, still refusing to answer Abby's questions, he turned up a steep track and came to a halt.

'We're here,' he said.

'Here? And where's here?' From where they were standing, Abby could see the coastline in the distance. Otherwise they were on a small bit of land surrounded by trees on the sides facing away from the sea.

'This little piece of land I'm standing on is for sale. Remember the boy we rescued from the bottom of the cliff? Dave, his father, came to see me. He wanted to thank us all personally. Anyway, to cut a long story short, it turns out he owns an estate agency here in Cornwall. I told him that I was looking for a small piece of land to buy and he mentioned that he knew of one that hadn't gone on the market yet. This one. Well, what do you think?'

'Think of what, exactly?'

'Of this as a place to build a house. As a home for you and Emma. You can't continue living where you are right now. And I know you haven't found somewhere to buy. So what about here? It's the perfect place to build a house.'

Abby touched him on the shoulder. She almost couldn't bear to destroy his excitement, but she had no choice.

'Mac, I couldn't possibly afford to buy this land, let alone build a house. It's a lovely idea, but completely out of the question.'

'I would bear the costs. After all, Emma is my daughter. You've met the financial costs of bringing her up on her own for years. Now it's my turn.'

Abby shook her head regretfully. 'I'm sorry, Mac. I couldn't possibly agree to it.'

His mouth tightened. 'Why not?'

'Don't you see? It's a wonderful, generous gesture, but I couldn't let us be beholden to you like that. It wouldn't be right.'

Mac's frown deepened. 'Beholden? Not right? Why don't you just come out with whatever it is you're trying to say?'

'Please understand, Mac. I've been independent all my life. I don't want to have to rely on anybody else. What happens if you meet someone you want to be with? Move away? Have a new family? What happens to us then? I'd never be able to meet the repayments on my own.' She shook her head. 'I'm sorry. I can't risk it.'

If it were possible, Mac's eyes turned an even darker blue. 'I have the right to make sure my daughter has as good a life as possible. You have no right to deny her because of some misplaced sense of pride. And what's more, I promise you, regardless of what happens in the future, I'll never abandon my child the way my father abandoned me.' His eyes narrowed. 'It is far more likely to be the other way around. You can up and leave with Emma any time you like, and I won't be able to stop you. How do you think that feels?'

Abby took a step towards him and touched him lightly on the arm. 'I wouldn't do that to Emma, or to you, Mac,' she said softly. 'Remember, I also know what it's like to grow up without a father. I would never deprive Emma of hers.'

Mac turned away and stood looking out to the horizon. This was a different side to Mac and her heart ached for him. But neither was she going to budge. He could be involved, she wanted him to be involved, but Emma was her responsibility and he had to understand that.

Mac swung around to face Abby. 'I want a DNA test,' he said abruptly.

Abby reeled. 'Why? I thought you believed me when I said you were Emma's father? Good grief, Mac, do you think I'm playing some kind of game here?'

He rubbed his face. 'I know you say now that you'll never take Em away from me, and I believe you mean it. But things change in life, Abby. I know that to my cost. People might mean to stick around, but in the end they don't.'

Abby started to protest but he cut her off. 'Besides, God forbid, what if something happened to you? What rights would I have then? At the moment, legally, you are her only blood relative. I wouldn't have a leg to stand on. A DNA test would prove I was the father to any court.'

What he was saying made sense, Abby admitted grudgingly. If she were in his shoes, would she take a chance that one day she might lose Emma? Absolutely not. She nodded.

'Okay. If, and only if, Emma agrees. The last thing I want is for her to think that you want the test for the wrong reasons. If you can persuade her, and if she's happy to have the test, I'll agree.'

The furrows between Mac's brow disappeared and he smiled. 'Thank you, Abby. That means a lot to me.'

They stood looking at each other for a long time. Mac took a step towards Abby, but before he could touch her, she turned away.

'Let's go home,' she said.

On the way back to her house, Abby thought about what Mac had said. Although she wanted Emma to have a relationship with a father who would be a permanent feature in her life, it felt as though everything was moving too fast. Mac wanted to be part of Emma's life and that was good. It would have broken Emma's heart if Mac had rejected her, but this... Wanting to have legal rights, wanting to contribute financially, it was more than Abby had anticipated. When she had told Mac about Emma, she had imagined a more casual relationship between father and daughter.

But now? He wanted more. And she couldn't blame him. And then there was this *thing* between her and Mac. Back then, she'd thought he was going to kiss her. And she'd wanted him to. But that would only make everything more complicated than it already was.

'Do you want to suggest the DNA test or shall I?' Mac asked.

'I think we should talk to her about it together,' Abby said. 'As soon as we get home.' She glanced across at him. 'She needs to know we're united about this, Mac.'

'At least we're agreed on something.' His expression was unreadable.

When they got back to the house, Mac suggested that they take a walk along the beach. Emma, as usual, was delighted to have any opportunity to spend time with her father. She particularly liked it when the three of them spent time together.

They stopped near some rocks and Abby poured hot chocolate from a flask she had brought.

'Em,' she started hesitantly. 'Mac and I have been talking.'

Emma looked at her warily. 'What about?'

'I think it's great that I've found you,' Mac said. 'As you know, I had no idea you existed until Abby told me. But now I want to make things more official.' He paused. 'I've got to kind of like having you as my daughter.'

A smile spread over Emma's face. 'And I kind of like having you as my father.' She threw herself at him and, wrapping her arms around him, squeezed him tightly.

The look in Mac's eyes made Abby catch her breath. The love for his daughter was there for anyone to see.

After a few minutes Emma released him and screwed up her eyes. 'How are things going to be more official? What do you mean?' She looked at Abby then at Mac. Her eyes lit up. 'Do you mean you two—?'

'No, Emma. You're way off there,' Abby interrupted quickly. Where on earth had Emma got that idea?

'I know it's not at all likely,' Mac said cautiously, 'but say anything happened to Abby, I'd want to have a legal claim on you. You know, make sure no one could take you away from me.'

Alarm flashed in Emma's eyes. 'There's nothing wrong with you, Mum, is there?' she said. 'You're not going to die or anything?'

Abby laughed. 'I have no intention of dying. At least, not for years and years. But, Emma, accidents do happen. What Mac is saying is that he's become very fond of you, and he wants everyone, particularly the courts, to recognise you as his daughter. Or rather him as your father. To do that you would both have to do a DNA test. Then if, and this is a big if, something happens to me, both Mac and I want to make sure you would get to stay with someone who loves you.'

Emma still looked anxious. Abby slid a glance at Mac. This was the last thing she wanted, Emma thinking they were hiding something from her.

Abby took Emma's hand in hers. 'I promise you, there is nothing wrong with me. If you don't want to have the test, that's fine. We'll find another way.'

'This test, is it like those they do in *CSI*?' Emma asked.

'Yes.'

'Will it hurt?'

'Not in the slightest. They'll take a swab from the inside of your mouth and do the same for Mac.'

Emma sat in silence for a little while.

'I don't mind, then. If you both think it's

for the best.' She got to her feet and, finding a flat stone, turned to Mac. 'Can you make this skip on the water?' she asked. 'I can make it skip three times. Mum's record is four. Can you beat us?'

Abby and Mac shared a look of relief. Emma seemed reassured and what was even better, she was totally unconcerned about the test.

Mac took the stone from her hands. 'Four times, huh?' he said, grinning. 'I think I can do better than that.'

CHAPTER THIRTEEN

A FEW days later, Abby opened the door of her cottage to find Mac standing there. Her pulse stuttered disconcertingly. He was so damn good looking it just wasn't fair. But for once his easy confidence was absent. Instead, he looked ill at ease, almost embarrassed.

'Emma's out, I'm afraid,' she said. Anxiety rippled through her. He looked so serious. 'Is something wrong?'

'No,' Mac rushed to reassure her. 'It's just that I had an idea I wanted to run past you.'

Mac wanting to run something past her? That was a turn-up for the books.

'You'd better come in,' she said, standing aside to let him enter.

She signalled to him that he should sit, but Mac shook his head.

'Look, whatever it is, you'd better tell me.' Was this where he told her that the novelty of having a daughter was wearing off? Her heart rate upped another notch. If he let Emma down now, she'd throttle him.

'Remember you told me that Emma's birthday party had to be cancelled when nobody would come?'

Abby nodded. It had been almost the worst day of her life. It had been so cruel and so unbearable watching Emma pretend it didn't matter. But Emma hadn't been able to hide the sobs coming from her bedroom later that evening. Abby had crept into bed with her daughter, holding her until the tears had subsided. That was when she had decided to leave London. She would never let her child be hurt like that again. Not as long as she had breath in her body.

'Well, I thought we should give her another party. Here. She's made friends now and perhaps it will take away some of the bad memories of London.'

Abby was so surprised she felt her jaw drop. It was the last thing she'd expected Mac to say. But she was touched and delighted and not a little ashamed. Once again, she had underestimated this man. As she looked at him her heart melted. He was a better man than he gave himself credit for.

'We could organise something really cool, like paintball or…I don't know…something else. We could arrange it all as a surprise.' Now that the words were out, there was no hiding his enthusiasm. 'I never had a party as a kid.' He smiled but he couldn't disguise the hurt in his eyes. 'I always wanted one, but my mother always refused. She said there was no way she was going to let a bunch of kids run riot in her house.'

'Me too,' Abby whispered. 'I would have given anything to be able to dress up in a party dress, just once. But my mum said parties weren't for the likes of us.'

They looked at each other and the world spun on its axis. Abby could hardly breathe. For a moment she thought he was going to pull her into his arms, but then he stepped back and let his arms to drop to his side.

What just happened there? Abby wondered. Her heart was racing as if she'd run up the highest hill in England. Every nerve cell in her body was zinging. Lord help her, she wanted him to have taken her in his arms. She wanted to lay her head against his chest, have his arms wrap around her, feel the pressure of his mouth against her. What was she thinking? Thinking that way spelled danger. He was so not the man for her. Why, then, did she feel this crushing sense of disappointment? Because she was in love with him. The realisation hit her like a ten-ton truck. She loved him and would do until the day she died.

'I think it's a great idea, Mac,' she said, turning away lest he read her discovery in her face. 'I can speak to the mums at the school, swear them to secrecy and get the invites out. We could organise it for the weekend. If we leave it any longer, someone's bound to give in to temptation and tell her. And I think the paintballing is a great idea. Emma's always wanted to have a go and the boys should enjoy it, too.' Hoping that she'd removed every trace of latent lust from her eyes, she turned back to him. 'I'm warning you, though, we'll both have to take part. You do know that, don't you?'

Mac grinned broadly. 'Why do you think I suggested it?' he said.

Emma was surprised but thrilled to find out about her party. Mac arrived before the party-goers and Emma flung herself at him, forgetting in her excitement to adopt the cool façade she had been trying to perfect lately.

'Isn't this the best idea?' she said. 'I can't

wait for everyone to arrive so we can get started. Mum says she's going to join in, too.'

Mac looked at Abby over the top of Emma's head and grinned. 'I'm looking forward to seeing her moves,' he said.

Abby wagged a playful finger at him. 'Don't you underestimate me. I can run pretty fast when I have to.'

Emma's friends started to arrive, their laughter and shrieks of excitement filling the reception area. Mac had to shout above the clamour to make himself heard.

'Okay, guys. Before we get changed, we need to pick teams. Emma is captain of Team Arrows and, Simon, I believe you want to be captain of Team Blades. Since it's your party, Em, you get to pick first.'

Abby knew her daughter's every expression and she could see her hesitation as her eyes flicked between Abby and Mac. Abby's heart twisted painfully, sensing her torn loyalties. She wanted to choose Abby but also wanted to impress Mac. Was this how it was going to be from now on? She'd had her daughter all to herself for the past eleven years but now it was time to share her with someone else. Her father. Mac. The knot of jealousy felt alien to her but she had to remember this wasn't about her—it was about Emma.

Catching Emma's eye, she nodded her head slightly towards Mac. She caught the almost imperceptible flash of gratitude in her daughter's eyes as she selected Mac. Simon then chose Abby and the rest of the teams were quickly divided up.

Despite what she'd told Mac, Abby had no real idea what to expect. Obviously it had to do with firing balls of paint at each other and using various items around the course to hide behind to avoid being hit yourself. And taking the other team's flag.

When she emerged wearing her lurid green overall, she blushed under Mac's amused grin. She felt slightly ridiculous, holding her 'gun'. On the other hand, he looked the part in his blue overalls, like a dashing secret agent on a dangerous mission. The way he was looking at her warned her she was going to be his prime target. Abby felt a flutter of excitement—there was nothing she'd love better than to out-fox Mac. He was underestimating her if he thought she was Team Blade's weakest link! It was game on.

Fifteen minutes later Abby had to keep reminding herself it was only a game. The darkness, lit only sporadically by flashing lights and filled with atmospheric dry ice, heightened the tension and fun. Crouching behind a pillar, Abby paused to catch her breath. So far she'd managed to evade being shot, but so had Mac. Another flash of light and in that second she saw the top of his head behind a barrier. Abby crept forward, raising her gun slowly. Her finger tightened on the trigger and she stifled a giggle.

She didn't know how it happened but the next moment she was sprawled on her back with Mac's face inches from hers.

'Trying to sneak up on me, were you?' he growled into her ear. Abby could hear the triumph in his voice. She was distracted by the heat of his body on hers, his warm breath on her neck.

His eyes bored into hers. Her heart thumped against her ribs and she knew in that moment he was going to kiss her. Her lips parted involuntarily. At the very last moment, just before his mouth came down on hers, she wriggled out from underneath him. Despite being caught off guard, he moved much more quickly than she'd anticipated. Paint splattered from their respective guns until they were both covered from head to toe in myriad colours and laughing uncontrollably.

Grinning, Mac held out his hand. 'Truce?'

Abby took his proffered hand, only to let out a yelp of surprise when he yanked her towards him. 'I believe you still owe me a kiss. And I intend to collect it…soon.'

It wasn't long before Emma's team triumphed, and after they had all cleaned up and changed they congregated in the café.

The children chattered happily about the game, arguing over their respective tactics.

Abby smiled at Mac, sitting opposite her at the table. 'Thanks for organising today. It's wonderful to see Emma looking so happy.'

'She's a fantastic kid. You have to take some of the credit for that.'

Abby glanced over at her daughter, her heart swelling with pride. 'Don't hurt her, Mac. I'll never forgive you if you do,' she said quietly. *And don't hurt me, she wanted to add.*

Mac shook his head. 'I've no intention of doing that.'

After they had cleaned up and the other children had left stuffed full of pizza and cake, Mac turned to Emma.

'The party isn't over yet,' he said. 'I've one more treat.'

Emma grinned at him. 'Tell me,' she implored.

'You have to come out to the car.' He led the way, a bemused Abby and Emma following in his footsteps.

'Close your eyes,' Mac told Emma. 'And no peeking.'

Emma did as she was told. Mac opened the boot of his Jeep and pulled out a board and something that looked like a kite. He placed them on the ground. 'Okay, you can open your eyes now, Emma.'

Emma's eyes grew wide. 'Is that what I think it is?'

'It's your very own kite-boarding stuff. In the spring, as soon as the weather is good enough, I'm going to teach you how to do it. You picked up windsurfing so quickly I'm sure we'll have you doing tricks with the kite board by the end of the summer.'

Emma turned to Mac and flung her arms around him. He picked her up and twirled her in the air. Abby's throat tightened. She knew this was Mac's way of telling them both he planned to stick around. When he deposited her back on the ground, Emma looked at him before hooking her arms into one of his and one of Abby's. 'This is the best day of my life,' she said.

Mac looked at Abby over the top of Emma's head.

'And mine,' he said quietly.

CHAPTER FOURTEEN

As DECEMBER approached, winter began to tighten its grip. The wind was sharper and the days shorter. Emma and Mac still went mountain biking and Abby rejoiced to see her child grow ever more confident, although she still fretted until Emma had returned home in one piece. The DNA results hadn't come back yet, but Abby wasn't surprised. They had been told that it could take months.

Mac and Emma arrived back just before darkness fell. They were both spattered with mud and their cheeks were flushed from the cold.

'I'm going to beat you one of these days,' Emma teased Mac.

'I hope you're not letting her go too fast,' Abby warned Mac. 'The last thing I want is to be involved in the rescue of you two.'

'Oh, Mum, you worry too much,' Emma

complained. 'Dad would never let anything happen to me.'

A chill ran up Abby's spine and as she caught Mac's eye she knew he, too, realised the import of Emma's words. She was calling him Dad. If there was any doubt in either of their minds, she knew there was none in Emma's.

'Run upstairs and shower and change out of your wet clothes,' Abby told Emma. 'I'll get supper on.'

Mac still looked in shock as Emma left the room.

'Dad!' he said. 'She called me Dad.'

'So she did. How does it feel?'

'It feels strange. Very strange. But good. Yes. Very good.'

'Would you like to stay for supper, too?' Abby asked.

Mac grinned. 'I don't even want to sit down. In case you haven't noticed, I'm filthy.'

Abby had to laugh. Mac's face was almost black with thick dust. Only his eyes, where he had been wearing his goggles, were mud free. Impulsively she leaned forward and wiped his cheek with her finger.

His hand caught hers and he looked down at

her with a glint in his eye. Her breath caught in her throat.

'Careful, Abby,' he warned. 'Don't start something you can't finish.'

She pulled her hand away as if she'd been stung. They stood staring at each other.

'Tell you what,' Mac said. 'Why don't I go home, get cleaned up, and I'll organise supper for the three of us?'

'I thought you didn't cook.'

'Didn't you notice I said *organise*? I didn't say anything about cooking. There is a great Chinese a few minutes' walk away from me. That's what I had in mind.'

'Emma is going to the cinema with a friend,' Abby said, looking at her watch. 'The mother is coming to collect her in an hour.'

'In that case, why don't you come? You could feed Emma and then come over. By that time I'll have cleaned myself up. You've never seen my place.'

'I don't know, Mac. Is it wise?' They both knew what she was talking about.

Mac took a lock of her hair between his fingers. 'I promise you, you'll be safe,' he said. 'It's just two work colleagues, friends, spending time together.'

Safe? What did he mean, safe? The flash of

disappointment was unexpected. Was he implying that she wasn't his type? Perhaps she had misread him? Flirting came as naturally as breathing to men like Mac. He probably wasn't even aware he was doing it. She really needed to remember that.

'Or did you have something less innocent in mind?' he said.

She flushed. Damn the man. It was as if he could read her thoughts.

'Of course not,' she said coolly. 'You and I both know that.'

'So that's sorted, then. I'll see you around eight. Don't worry, I'll let you get back in plenty of time to be here for Em.'

'Okay,' she agreed finally, knowing she was risking her heart. 'I'll be there at eight.'

Mac smiled to himself as he drove home. Abby was much more transparent than she realised. He could read every thought and emotion that flitted across her face. She just couldn't pretend. That was what he loved about her.

Good God. Where had that come from? No way was he in love with Abby. Okay, he found her attractive, well, more than attractive, sexy as hell, and she was brave and funny and good and loyal and, damn it—he was in love with her. The shock almost made him collide with a car coming in the opposite direction. He pulled over to his own side of the road and the car passed him with a blare of its horn.

No! This was crazy. It was simply that he lusted after her. She was a challenge. The first woman he had ever wanted that hadn't fallen into his arms. But he knew he was lying to himself. He was in love. For the first time. And with Abby Stevens, the woman who was the mother of his child. So to speak. This wasn't at all what he had planned. He didn't do love. He didn't do for ever.

Mac was in all kinds of trouble.

Abby knocked on the door, thinking for the umpteenth time that she should have phoned and made her excuses. Was she stark, raving mad? Every bone in her body was telling her that it was a mistake to be alone with Mac.

Just as she was thinking of turning tail, he opened the door. Her breath caught in her throat. What a difference from the mud-splattered man of earlier. He had showered and changed into a dazzlingly white short-sleeved shirt and black jeans. Her heart rate went into overdrive. He looked divine. So confident and self-assured.

'Abby!' He smiled at her as if he had been waiting just for this moment and her legs turned to jelly.

'Hello, Mac.' Damn it. She sounded breathless. She cleared her throat. 'I'm not late, am I?'

'Bang on time,' he said. 'Our food should be here shortly. Come on in.'

He stood aside to let her pass and she squeezed past him, terrified lest she brush up against him. She could almost feel the waves of magnetism emanating from him.

'Let me take your coat.'

She almost yelped as she felt his warm hands brushing the back of her neck as he helped her shrug out of her coat. Little goosebumps sprang up all over her body.

He tossed her coat onto the sofa. 'Can I get you something to drink?'

'Some sparkling water would be nice.'

His flat was the opposite from her little house in every way possible. Where her home had cramped, if cosy rooms, his was modern and open plan, with floor-to-ceiling windows looking out over the sea. Where her home was cluttered with the everyday minutiae that living with a teenager brought, his was sparsely but expensively furnished with enormous white sofas and bleached floorboards. On one side of the room there was a small kitchen with white units and a black granite worktop. It was fitted with every conceivable appliance down to an in-built coffee maker, she noted enviously. Not that it looked used.

In front of the sofas, which were arranged to form an L-shape, was a modern gas fire that looked almost real.

As Mac was pouring her drink, she wandered over to the ceiling-height book shelves opposite the windows. She found herself intensely curious to see what he read. Apart from several well-thumbed copies of the classics, there were thrillers and medical textbooks. She found herself smiling. There were few clues here about Mac. Was that intentional?

'One sparkling water,' Mac said, holding out a glass.

As she took it from him their fingers brushed and once again she felt a zap of electricity run down her spine.

'What do you think?' Mac waved his glass at the room.

'I like it.' Taking a sip of her water, she walked to the window and took in the view. Beneath her the lights twinkled and the moon, as bright and full as she could remember seeing, lit up the sea, so that she could see the waves rolling onto the shore. The windows where she was standing were actually a set of double doors leading out onto a small balcony.

'You can hear the surf from outside on a quiet night,' Mac said, coming to stand behind her. He was close enough for her to catch a faint smell of soap. 'It's one of the reasons I bought it.'

'I've always fancied a place with a view,' Abby said. 'Who wouldn't? But at the same time just having my own place with Em is good enough for me.'

'You really love her, don't you?'

'It would kill me if anything happened to her.'

'Why have you never married, Abby?'

The question startled her. She whirled round, taken aback to find herself within inches of his broad chest. She lifted her eyes to his, trying to ignore the blood rushing in her ears. 'I never met anyone who wanted me enough to take on a child, I guess,' she said softly. Then she grinned. 'Actually, that's not the whole truth. I've never met anyone that I thought I could live with, let alone marry. And the older I get, the more used to having my independence I get. What about you?' she challenged. 'Have you never met anyone you wanted to marry?'

'Me?' Mac laughed. 'I'm not into marriage, I'm afraid. I can't see the point. Why get married only to tear each other apart? It also implies that there is only one person for each of us and I don't believe that either. Unlike swans, I don't think humans are meant to mate for life.'

'What about children?'

Mac looked thoughtful. 'Having children was something I thought I would never do. What was the point? I liked my life exactly the way it was. But now...'

'But now...?' Abby prompted.

'But now I find I like being a father.' He turned away. 'Emma's amazing. I'm proud to be her dad.' He turned back to Abby and grinned. 'I never thought I'd say that, let alone mean it. And I have you to thank.' He crossed over to where Abby was standing. 'Thank you for letting me share her.' He touched her gently on the cheek and tipped her face so that she was forced to look him in the eye. 'I've had some of the best days of my life since I got to know her...and you.'

Abby's breath caught in her throat. Her heart was hammering against her chest. Slowly he lowered his head and, tipping her chin, brought his mouth down on hers. Abby had never felt sensations like the ones that were rocketing around her body. His lips were warm and hard, demanding a response from her. His tongue flicked against her and spurts of heat ricocheted from the tips of her toes to the top of her head. Her body felt as if it were on fire.

She couldn't resist him if her life depended on it. She could do nothing except give in to the feelings that were zipping around her. Her body melted into his as if it belonged there.

He groaned and, dropping his hands to her hips, pulled her against him. She fitted there in the circle of his arms as if once they had been one, and she let her hands go around his neck as she gave in to her need.

Still kissing her, he lifted her into his arms as if she weighed nothing and carried her out of the sitting room and into his bedroom. He laid her gently on the bed and she looked at him, knowing what was going to happen yet powerless to stop it.

His eyes were dark, almost hazy, as he looked at her. Without taking his eyes from her, he slid his hands up her hips and, hooking the top of her tights with his thumbs, he began to unroll them slowly. She lifted her hips to help him. Inside she was a mass of confusion. What little part of her brain that could still think was shouting, No! Don't do this! But the far greater part was taken over by urgent need of her body. She knew she was helpless to deny him…or herself.

The only light in the room came from the lounge and the moon outside. It was dark enough to hide her shyness but light enough for her to read every nuance of his expression.

Once her tights were off he turned his attention to her blouse. He leaned over and dropped kisses in the hollow of her throat, across her collarbone, his hands all the while deftly undoing her buttons. He stopped kissing her as he drew the blouse apart. He was breathing hard as he looked down at her. Now she felt no embarrassment, no shyness, only wonder at the expression in his eyes.

Then she lifted her hips as he unbuttoned her skirt and let it drop to the floor.

'You are beautiful,' he said, his voice thick with desire.

She hated him being away from her even for a second and she pulled him back towards her. As he kissed her, she let her hands slide under his T-shirt, revelling in the feel of hard muscle under her fingertips. How could a man who was so toned be soft at the same time? she wondered as she lifted his T-shirt over his head. She pressed against him, feeling the hard warmth of his bare skin pressing against her. She wanted him so much, she didn't know if she could wait a minute longer to feel him, all of him against her, inside her.

A small moan escaped her lips as she searched for the button of his jeans, her fingers brushing the hair that travelled from his belly downwards.

This time it was him who was helping her as his jeans came off.

Then he stretched on the bed beside her. She blushed when she saw the extent of his desire for her.

He slipped a thumb inside the cup of her bra, teasing one nipple and then the other, until she didn't know how she could bear it.

Then his hand reached behind her, deftly unhooked her bra and her breasts sprang free.

He kissed her skin, running his tongue across each nipple. Her body was on fire. She couldn't wait any longer. She was going to explode.

'Please,' she whispered. 'I can't hold on...'

'Just a little longer,' he promised. 'But this time, our first time, I want to watch you.'

She shook her head from side to side. She wanted him inside her now. Moving with her. Filling this empty, aching void that she hadn't known, until now, existed.

'Shh,' he said. 'I promise you there will be time later.'

Giving in, she lay back, digging her fingers into his hair, curling her fingers tightly in an attempt to stop herself crying out as he inched his mouth downwards.

Dropping kisses on her belly, on the insides of her thighs, brushing his fingers gently between her legs. Then he removed her panties and just when she thought she couldn't bear the exquisite pain of her need any longer, he slipped his finger inside her. He raised his head and looked deeply into her eyes as she arched her body up to him. She couldn't help the cry that ripped from her throat as sensation after sensation rocked through her body. He was taking her somewhere she'd never been before, higher and higher, until at the top her body couldn't hold on any longer and she lost all sense of who she was.

Her head was still reeling as she clutched him to her. She needed him inside her, and greedily she pulled him on top of her, opening herself to him and using her hands to guide him inside her. They rocked together, more and more urgently, until triumphantly she heard him reach his climax, just seconds before she followed him.

They lay, breathing deeply, their bodies hot and entangled. She felt as if every cell in her body had merged with his. She had never known sex could be like this, a heady mix of the physical and emotional. His hands were brushing over her hair. Lightly touching her shoulder.

'My God, you're not nearly as prim and proper as you appear on the outside, are you?'

She blushed, but hearing the laughter in his voice she couldn't take offence.

'I haven't had many lovers,' she murmured.

He propped his head on his elbow as he looked down at her. 'I'm glad,' he said simply.

His hand trailed lazily over her neck and then onto her breasts and her breath began to quicken. 'I don't want to think of you being with anyone else,' he said possessively. 'I want you to be mine. Just mine.'

Her heart started its hammering again. She was surprised he couldn't feel it pounding against his hand as he continued to touch her body, searching for the spots that drove her wild. Didn't he realise that wherever he touched her drove her wild? Her last coherent thought as she succumbed once more to the relentless demands of his touch was that she loved him. Loved him, completely, irrevocably and for ever. Before she could help herself the words slipped out. 'I love you,' she whispered as he once more took possession of her, body and soul.

Mac lay listening to the gentle sound of Abby's breathing. Her hair was fanned out across his chest and he swore he could smell strawberries. It felt so right to have her curled up against him—right and peaceful.

As he began to drift off towards sleep, an image of Abby, Emma and himself came into his head. They were laughing together as they shared a meal around the table in Abby's kitchen. Abby and Emma were looking at him with such love and admiration it made him feel good. Better than he had felt in his life. But then he started. What had Abby said? She loved him. He knew women often said that in the throes of making love. They didn't necessarily mean it. He groaned quietly. But Abby wasn't any woman. She was strong and proud and honest. She wouldn't have said the words if she didn't mean them.

There was no chance of him falling asleep now. His mind was racing too fast for that. Gently he disentangled himself from Abby and eased himself out of bed. He wrapped a towel around his hips and crept out of the bedroom and into the sitting room. He opened the door to his small balcony and stepped outside into the cold air. Maybe it would knock some sense into him. He had been a crazy, selfish fool to let it get this far. He should have known better than to play with Abby. But he hadn't been able to help himself. Ever since she'd appeared back in his life, his need to take her to bed had been like an itch he'd needed to scratch. But he hadn't been thinking of her. What could he offer her? It was one thing to accept the responsibility of a child—there was nothing he could do about that, he had a duty towards Emma—but a relationship with Abby was out of the question. He hadn't changed his mind about not wanting commitment. Commitments brought trouble and pain. Commitments were not for him. Even if he loved her.

He heard the pad of feet behind him and two soft hands crept around his waist.

'What are you doing out here in the freezing cold?' Abby asked, laying her cheek against his back. Her silky hair was like a caress against his skin, and despite everything he had just been telling himself he wanted her there, always.

Suddenly she moved away from him and he felt it like a stab to his heart. He had to tell her what he felt before either of them got in any deeper.

'It can't be ten o'clock. Grief, Emma's due back at half past. I have to get home.' She had wrapped a sheet around her before coming onto the balcony and almost tripped over it in her haste to get back to her clothes in the bedroom. He smiled at her ungainly, faltering steps and had to force himself to stay where he was. If he touched her again, he'd be undone.

'My shoes—where are my shoes?' Abby's panicked voice came from the bedroom. She had slipped on her skirt and blouse and rammed her tights haphazardly into her bag.

'Hey, slow down. It'll only take you fifteen minutes to get home. Plenty of time.' He retrieved one of her high heels from under the sofa and the other from the floor halfway to the bedroom. 'Your shoes, milady,' he said.

She practically snatched them from his hands. 'It's no laughing matter,' she said crossly. 'I've never not been there for Emma when she comes home. She'll be anxious. And anything could happen. There might be a fire. She could get trapped. Hurt herself and need me. What was I thinking, falling asleep?'

She put her shoes on and looked around feverishly. Mac picked up her coat from the arm of the sofa and held it out so she could slip her arms into it.

'C'mon, Abby. You know nothing's going to happen to her in the few minutes she'll be alone. It's just that you've been on too many rescues. That's why you're imagining the worst.'

She glared at him. 'Being a parent brings responsibility, too, Mac. And one of those responsibilities is protecting your child from any danger.'

Mac knew it was useless to argue. Besides, which would he rather? The woman who was mother to his child caring too much or caring too little? He groaned inwardly. Wasn't that the problem? Abby was the kind of woman who would always care too much. And he didn't want or deserve that.

He was aware of her lips brushing his, and then she was gone.

Happily, Emma hadn't got back by the time Abby brought her car to a screeching halt outside her little house. Everything was still in darkness. Mac was right. She had overreacted. But if anything should ever happen to Emma, she would simply die.

As she let herself in, she thought back over the evening. It had been the most exciting night of her life. A delicious thrill ran up her spine as she recalled how it had felt to be in his arms. She had never imagined that making love could be like that. Although she'd had lovers in her life before, neither of them had made her feel like that. Was it because she loved Mac? The thought frightened and excited her at the same time and she grew hot as she remembered how she hadn't been able to stop herself murmuring the truth to him.

She ran upstairs and switched on the shower. It would give her time to regain her composure before facing Emma. As she let the hot water stream over her body, she pushed aside the memory of Mac's hands. She could have sworn he wasn't immune to her. But then again, what did she really know about men?

He didn't say he loved you. The voice wouldn't go away. But that was okay. For the first time in her life she was going to throw caution to the wind and let life take her where it would. If there was one thing being with

Mac had taught her, it was that life was nothing at all if you didn't take risks.

Nevertheless, she was still hurt and dismayed when over the next few days Mac was friendly but distant towards her. Although she hadn't expected protestations of undying love, neither had she expected to be treated like a one-night stand. Had she flung herself at him? Now that he had slept with her, was he no longer interested? He still spent time with Emma on a regular basis, but his invites no longer included her. It was becoming evident she had made a dreadful mistake. But one she could not regret. Making love with Mac, loving Mac, had made her feel alive. And if part of that was the dreadful pain of rejection she knew deep down that she accepted that, too. At least Emma had a father who loved and cherished her. That would have to do.

CHAPTER FIFTEEN

IT WAS another Saturday when Rebecca was on her own. Josh had gone to work, telling her that he had loads of paperwork to catch up on. Although he had promised to be back soon after lunch, it was almost three and he still hadn't returned. It was typical of Josh. In the four years they had been married she had grown to accept that his work would always take priority over her.

A few days earlier she had brought up the subject of children again. Josh had refused to even discuss it and they had argued. Since then they had been barely speaking. Josh was spending more and more time at the hospital and Rebecca had the distinct feeling that he was avoiding her.

She packed a sandwich and a flask of coffee. Josh hated hospital food. They could take their picnic and despite the cold, maybe they could find a bench and sit outside and talk. She blinked away the tears. When had they last talked properly? She couldn't remember.

As she drove towards the hospital she suddenly felt nervous. She could hardly blame Josh totally for the gulf in their marriage. She could make more of an effort, take an interest in his work, even if it did bore her senseless. She would suggest they go into London for dinner, meet up with old friends. It would be like it had been in the beginning. Her spirits lifted. Perhaps they could still find their way back to each other and then if they did, Josh might agree to have children. She would make him see that a baby would make them happy again.

She turned into the hospital car park and searched for a parking place. Then she rooted around in the back seat of her car until she found the paper bag with the picnic. Once again she checked her make-up and her hair. Was that a frown line between her eyes? She shivered. Every day she was seeing signs that she was getting older.

She hopped out of the car and took a few steps towards the door of A & E. But then, to her left, sitting on a bench under a tree, she saw them. Josh and another woman. Like Josh, the other woman was wearing scrubs, and although her hair was pulled back in a ponytail and her face was devoid of make-up, she was still startlingly beautiful in the way only certain women could be. Rebecca felt a flash of envy. She knew she was beautiful, too, but she needed the help of make-up. She didn't have the natural beauty of the woman sitting next to Josh.

She was about to call out when she froze in her tracks. Josh threw back his head and laughed at something the woman had said. His arm was draped over the back of the bench, almost touching her shoulder. There was a familiarity about the gesture that spoke volumes. Rebecca couldn't tear her eyes away. When had she last heard Josh laugh? When had she last seen him looking so relaxed, as if he didn't have a care in the world? When had she last seen him look *happy*?

The woman raised her face to Josh's and smiled into his eyes. Rebecca's throat ached and she raised her hand to brush away the tears that stung her eyes. Slowly she backed away, terrified now lest they see her. Although she couldn't bear it, she knew. Knew with a certainty that rocked her soul. Josh was in love with this woman. Rebecca could see it in every line of his body, in the way it seemed as if she were something precious he had to protect.

Tears were blinding her as she groped her way back to the car. Whatever she'd had planned, whatever hopes she'd had for her and Josh making a go of their marriage, it was too late. If Josh loved this woman, he would be with her. He was too honest to continue with a marriage when he was in love with someone else. Anger was beginning to erode some of the pain. How could she have been so stupid not to have seen what was in front of her eyes? It wasn't work that was making Josh spend all these extra hours at the hospital, it was another woman.

Rebecca gripped the steering-wheel with numb hands. He would leave her. Maybe not today, or tomorrow, but soon. He would look after her financially, she knew that, but leave her he would. And all these years she had stayed with him—giving up her dream, her longing to have a baby, giving up her happy life in London to follow him here, to a place she knew she could never be happy—had been futile.

She turned the key in the ignition. She was damned if she was going to walk away with nothing. At the very least she would have a baby to love.

* * *

The telephone was ringing as Mac stepped in to his flat after playing squash. At first he didn't recognise the voice.

'Mac? Robert here.' Mac stood still. He had almost forgotten about the doctor in charge of doing the DNA test.

'Hello, Robert. How's it going? Have you news for me?' Too impatient for small talk, he cut to the chase. He knew it was ridiculous but suddenly he was nervous.

Robert cleared his throat. 'I do. You'll get a letter confirming the results tomorrow, as will the other party, but I thought as a professional courtesy I would ring you.'

Get on with it, Mac wanted to shout down the phone, but he held himself in check. Robert could have left him to find out by letter.

'And?'

'I'm not sure if it's good news or bad, but…'

If he could have reached down the telephone line and shaken Robert he would have done so. Why didn't the man just get on with confirming that Emma was his child? As soon as he had the proof, he would ring the lawyer and start the proceedings that would allow him to be named officially as Emma's father.

'The test is negative,' Robert said flatly. 'There is no way at all she could be your child.'

The breath came out of him like an explosion. He hadn't been even aware he had stopped breathing.

'What?' he managed. He couldn't have heard right.

'Emma Stevens is not your biological daughter. As I said, I have no idea whether this is good or bad news, but that is the result. A letter is on its way to her guardian.'

Mac felt the world tip. Emma was not his daughter. He couldn't believe it. Everything in him said she was. He couldn't love her the way he did if she wasn't his flesh and blood.

He was hardly aware of thanking Robert and replacing the receiver. If it hadn't been mid-afternoon, he would have poured himself a stiff whisky.

Emma wasn't his child. Sara had either been lying or, he suspected, simply mistaken.

He was surprised at how devastated he felt at the news. What now? Would Abby stop him from seeing Emma? The thought made his stomach churn. Now he was about to lose her, he realised how much he had begun to enjoy the role of father.

And what about Emma? His heart ached for the little girl. She cared deeply about him. He knew that. How would she feel when she found out that he wasn't her father after all? He raked a hand through his hair. God, it was such a mess. Why hadn't he seen this coming? Why hadn't he reminded himself that there was always a possibility that the test would be negative?

But he knew the answer. Bit by bit he had fallen in love with the idea of being a father. He had enjoyed being around for Emma. Encouraging her to come out of her shell. All the things his father should have done for him, but hadn't. In some ways, he had been able to give Emma some of the childhood pleasures he'd never had, and it had healed something inside him.

Making up his mind, he picked up his jacket from where he'd flung it and was out of the door. He had to speak to Abby. She would know what to do.

Abby paced her small sitting room. Where was Emma? She'd promised she'd be back for lunch and it was now after one.

She picked up a magazine and attempted to read it, but there was no way she could concentrate. Emma knew Abby worried. She would have texted her had she been held up.

She had wheeled Abby into agreeing that

she could go down to the beach with a friend from school. Simon was a local boy and knew the area well, so why was she worrying? They were going to go down to the beach and stop off for a burger. But Emma had promised she'd come home after that. Abby checked her watch for the hundredth time. Only five more minutes had passed, although it felt like a lot longer.

She almost jumped out of her skin when her mobile rang. She leaped on top of it. It was bound to be Emma, probably apologising for not being home, for forgetting the time.

And it was Emma. At least, she thought it was. The signal kept fading and all she could hear were muffled snatches of words.

'Em? Is that you? I can't hear you. Can you go somewhere where you can get a better signal?'

'No...stuck...help...'

Abby's blood ran cold. She could hardly make out the words but there was no mistaking the fear in Emma's voice.

'Em? Where are you?'

More static. Then three words that made her physically ill. 'Trapped...cave...tide...' Then all of a sudden Emma's voice came over clearly. 'Help us, Mum.'

Her daughter, her beloved Emma, was in trouble. Abby forced back the waves of terror that threatened to overwhelm her.

'Stay calm, Emma, and tell me where you are.'

'Cave…beach…hurt…'

'Are you hurt? God, Emma!'

But there was only more static on the end of the phone. 'Look, Emma, I don't know if you can hear me, but leave your phone on. I'll find you. I promise. Keep calm, I'm coming.'

'No time… Hurry—' And then the phone cut out.

Abby was almost sobbing with terror. She had to find Emma. But where to start?

For a second she couldn't think what to do, and then suddenly the door opened and he was there. Mac! Relief made her knees go weak.

'I knocked,' Mac started to apologise, but the expression on her face must have told him something terrible had happened. He was by her side in seconds, pulling her close. 'Breathe, Abby. That's it. Slow, deep breaths, and tell me what's happened.'

This was wasting time! She pushed him away.

'It's Em. She phoned. Just now. I couldn't

hear properly. Just enough... Oh, my God. I have to go to her.'

Mac reached out for her and pulled her round to face him. His face had lost all colour and his eyes were as dark as ink.

'Tell me,' he said.

'She's trapped. And hurt. She needs us, Mac,' Abby moaned. 'Help me, find my baby. Our child. Please, Mac. You have to help me.'

'Listen to me.' He grabbed her by the shoulders. 'Look at me, Abby.'

She looked into his eyes. She saw fear and something else. Conviction.

'We're going to find our girl. Do you hear me? And she's going to be all right. But I need you to tell me everything.'

'She went to the beach with a boy from her class. Simon. That was almost three hours ago. She said she'd be back by one. She promised.' She took a gulp of air. Mac was right. Panicking now wouldn't help Emma. 'She phoned. The signal was bad. I could hardly hear her. All I could make out was that she was trapped. In a cave. And hurt.' She took a shuddering breath as terror returned. Her baby. Out there somewhere. Alone and scared.

Mac was already on his phone. 'I'm going to alert the rescue services. We need to get the coastguard and the other services out looking.' Abby paced as he spoke into the phone for a few minutes. All she could hear was Mac's side of the conversation, repeating what she had told him. When he finished the call, he looked grimmer than ever.

'What is it?' Abby asked. 'What did they say?'

'They said they'd mobilise a sea and air rescue,' Mac said. But Abby could tell there was something more. Something he wasn't telling her.

'Tell me everything they said.' She kept her voice level. 'I have a right to know.'

He hesitated.

'Please, Mac, tell me.'

'The tide is coming in,' he said. 'And it's higher than usual today. If they are trapped somewhere, it's only going to get worse.'

Abby cried out and sank to her knees. In a flash Mac was by her side. He lifted her into his arms and held her tight before placing her on the sofa.

'You stay here, Abby. In case Emma phones. Keep trying her mobile. I've got to go.'

Abby struggled to her feet. 'I'm coming, too.'

'It'll be best if you don't.'

'Don't even think of trying to stop me,' she said. She took a deep shuddering breath. 'I'll be okay. I promise. I won't panic and I won't get in the way. But I'm coming.'

Five minutes later they were prowling the cliffs above the beach front. Mac had managed to get hold of Simon's parents. They were also panic-stricken but had told them of a cave that Simon liked to explore. They told Mac that they had forbidden their son from going into the cave, but suspected that he, trying to impress his new friend, might have ignored their warnings. The cave was easily accessible when the tide was out but, depending on the size of the tide, could become filled with water, preventing escape. Instinctively Abby knew that this was where Emma was. At the very least they had nowhere else to try. When it arrived, the Royal Navy helicopter would keep searching from the air and the coastguard would search the shoreline.

As soon as Abby and Mac got the information about the cave, they ran towards the part of the beach where it was. Although Abby knew the tide was rising, she couldn't help a small cry when she saw that the beach had completely disappeared under the sea.

How would they get to the stranded children, and even if they did find them, how would they get them out?

'We need divers,' Mac was speaking into his mobile. 'The navy will have them. Get them down here immediately.'

Divers! If they needed divers to get to the children, they were in deep trouble. It would take time to get them here. And time was what they didn't have. With every minute, the tide was rising higher.

Mac ran into a shop selling gear for watersports. He returned a few minutes later with flippers. The kind divers used. 'I can move much faster with these. Try and get Emma again,' Mac said. 'Even if you can't hear her, she might be able to hear you. Tell her help is on the way. Try texting her, too. Sometimes a text will get through even if a call won't.' Uncaring of who might be watching, Mac stripped off his clothes until he was down to his boxers and T-shirt. Tossing his clothes to one side, he pulled on the flippers.

While he was doing that, Abby tried Emma's mobile again, despairing. She had tried every minute or two since she had got Emma's call, but it was hopeless. Her fingers fumbling with the tiny buttons, she sent a text.

Coming for you. Dad is here. Hold on. We love you.

As she pressed 'Send', Mac declared he was ready.

'We don't have time to wait for the rescue services. I'm going to go down there now. As soon as the Sea King gets here, make sure they know exactly which cave I'm searching. The coastguard, too. They'll have a pretty good idea of where the cave mouth is. The air ambulance is on its way with Lucy and Mike.'

He looked down at her and gently raised her chin, forcing her to look at him. 'I'm going to get her, Abby. I promise you. She'll be home safe with you soon.'

'Isn't it better to leave it to the Navy divers?' she had to ask.

Mac shook his head. 'She might be hurt. Or him. Or both. They may need medical attention. It has to be me.'

Abby nodded. Despite her terror, she knew Mac would do everything in his power to save their child, even if it meant sacrificing his own life. The thought of losing him, too, rocked her soul.

Just as he had done those weeks before, Mac disappeared over the side of the cliff. But this time the stakes were higher.

* * *

The water was freezing and murky. Mac forced himself to wait a minute or two to let the water settle. He had to be methodical and not let his impatience to get to Emma and her friend cloud his judgement. As he had hoped, after a few agonising seconds the water cleared and he was able to see the entrance to the cave. There was still a gap between the mouth of the cave and the sea, but Mac knew it wouldn't be long before that small opening disappeared.

He used his fins to propel himself towards the cave. The tide was so high. Would he be rescuing two corpses? No! Thinking like that did no one any good. He had to believe that Emma and her friend had found a high ledge to wait on.

He swam underwater towards the cave opening. After a few metres he stopped and raised his head to get his bearings. He was in a cave that stretched a metre above his head. It was almost completely dark inside and Mac had to strain to see anything. Damn it!

'Emma!' he shouted, his voice echoing in the semi-darkness. His heart plummeted when there was no reply. Had they got it completely wrong and were searching in the wrong spot? Or, even worse, was it too late?

He heard a noise coming from his right. He

whirled round, trying frantically to make out in the gloom where the noise had come from. Then he saw them. Two small figures huddled together on a ledge. Relief coursed through him, to be replaced almost instantly by anxiety. They were still in desperate danger. The rising tide was lapping at their feet.

'I'm coming,' he yelled, frantically searching for another ledge. A higher one, where the tide couldn't reach. But there wasn't one. He had to get the children out. But how?

Quickly he swam towards the children.

'Hey, there,' he said softly. 'How're you doing?' He knew the children would be very frightened.

'Dad!' It was Emma's voice, Mac noted. Whatever injuries she might have, at least she was conscious. 'You found us. See, Simon? I told you my dad would find us. He rescues people all the time.'

The irony wasn't lost on Mac. The first time she really needed him was the day he'd found out that he wasn't her father. But that didn't change the way he felt. Not one iota. He couldn't love Emma any more if she were his biological child.

'Dad. Simon's hurt his leg. We think it's broken. That's why we couldn't get out. When the tide started coming in we managed to get up here, but we couldn't go any further.'

And you didn't think of leaving your friend and saving yourself? My brave, darling child. She was so much his and Abby's child, whatever the DNA test said.

Mac heaved himself out of the water and onto the ledge beside the children. There wasn't much space. A quick examination of Simon's leg told him Emma was right. It was broken. And not just broken—the boy had a compound fracture and was bleeding badly. The loss of blood, combined with the cold and fright, was having a bad effect on the young lad. He was shivering uncontrollably. They had to get him to hospital, and soon.

'I'm going to strap your leg as best I can,' he told the boy, 'and then I'm going to get you out of here, okay?' As he spoke he struggled out of his soaking wet T-shirt. It wasn't a great bandage, but it was all he had.

'I'm sorry, but this will hurt a little,' he told Simon. He straightened the leg as best he could before strapping it with his T-shirt.

'Emma, I'm going to have to take you out of here one at a time, do you understand? And I'm going to have to take Simon first. He's the one in need of help most urgently.'

It broke his heart to see the fear then resolve on Emma's face. She lifted her chin. 'That's okay,' she said. 'I can wait.'

He was so proud of her. Any other child would be crying, but not his Emma.

'Abby is waiting for you outside.'

He explained to Simon what he wanted him to do. 'Lie on your back and don't, whatever you do, try and fight me. I'm going to put my hands on either side of your head, and pull you out. As long as you don't panic, you'll be fine.' There was just a big enough gap between the top of the entrance to the cave and the water for him to make it out with the boy. But would there still be a gap by the time he returned?

Mac was facing the worst dilemma of his life. How could he leave Emma? What if he didn't make it back in time? How would he live without Emma? How would Abby live without the child she loved?

But if he had any chance of saving Emma, he had to act now.

'I'll be back as quick as I can,' he said. 'Hold on.'

He grasped Simon around the head and pulled him out of the cave, taking care not to let water splash in the boy's mouth. If the boy panicked now, it could be fatal for both of them. As he swam, his heart and soul was back in the cave.

He found the rock where Abby was still waiting. She had been joined by the crew of the air ambulance. Lucy and Mike were standing by, waiting to help him. From the corner of his eye he could see the lifeboat circling nearby. He knew they couldn't risk getting any closer. There was no sign of the Sea King. It must still be waiting for the divers.

'Where's Em?' Abby's face was white.

'She's still in the cave. I'm going back for her. I couldn't take her as well as Simon.'

Mac was helping Lucy and Mike carefully lift Simon out of the water and onto a stretcher. Before he could stop her, Abby jumped into the water and was swimming towards the entrance of the cave.

'No, Abby, wait!' he shouted, but either she couldn't hear him or she was ignoring him. She carried on swimming towards the cave.

Muttering a curse, Mac gave one final heave and his arms lightened as the injured boy was taken out of his arms. He plunged back into the water after Abby. Didn't she know that she, too, could drown? He could lose both the people he loved most in the world. The realisation cut through his fear. He loved Abby.

He loved her more than his life itself. He had been running away from it but now, when he could lose her, he knew a life without her and Emma was no life at all.

The realisation added strength and soon he was back in the cave. By now there was no longer a gap between the top of the cave entrance and the cave and Mac had to take a deep gulp of air and swim underwater. His lungs were bursting as he once more emerged into the cave. To his horror he saw that the water was now up to Emma's waist, even though she was standing on the ledge. Abby was treading water nearby.

'Emma, we have to go now. You, too, Abby,' Mac said, trying to keep his voice even.

Emma was staring, her eyes wide with fear. 'I can't,' she said. 'I've hurt my arm.'

'Yes, you can, my love. Mac and I will each take one side of you. And we'll help you through. We won't let anything happen to you, I promise,' Abby said.

Mac marvelled at Abby. The fear was gone from her voice. It was steady and calm, as if she was suggesting a walk in the park.

'We'll be underwater for thirty seconds. But your mum and I will be on either side of you.

All you have to do is keep as still as you can and let us pull you along. Can you do that?' he said.

'Yes,' Emma replied.

'Good girl. But we have to go now.' Mac slid back into the water. Abby held onto Emma's good arm as she slipped into the water and then she jumped in beside them. Mac's heart lurched. Getting through the channel, swimming against the incoming current, would be a challenge. But what choice did they have?

'Okay. On my count of three, we're all going to take a deep breath and then go under. Okay?'

Abby and Emma nodded.

'One, two, three,' Mac said, and then between them he and Abby had Emma. He gripped Emma around the waist, careful to avoid her injured arm. To his relief, the rising tide meant that the current wasn't as strong as it had been. But still he felt every second of the time they spent underwater. True to her word, Emma relaxed, letting them pull her along.

At last, when he thought Emma wouldn't be able to hold her breath any longer, they broke through into the fresh air. The three of them trod water, breathing in deep lungfuls of fresh, clean air, and then the lifeboat was beside them and men were dropping into the water, helping them lift Emma gently onto the boat.

As soon as they were all safely on board, the boat sped off towards the shore. Over the top of Emma's head Mac and Abby shared a look. In Abby's eyes there was relief and gratitude and something else—love. Soon, when all this was over, he would tell her about the DNA test, but all that mattered right now was that he had his small precious family safe and well beside him.

CHAPTER SIXTEEN

'I was scared,' Emma said, 'but I remembered what Dad told me once and that helped me stay calm.' She was sitting on the hospital trolley. Her arm had been X-rayed and, as they'd expected, found to be broken. It had been put in a cast but the staff wanted to keep in her in overnight for observation. The bruise that was blossoming on her forehead suggested she had knocked her head, too.

'And what was that, darling?' Abby asked.

'He told me that panic kills more people than anything else. He said if you use your head, there is always a way out of most problems. So that's what I did.'

Abby slid a glance at Mac. Emma was more her father's daughter than she had realised. 'When Simon fell, I knew he had hurt his leg quite badly and I knew we couldn't walk out of the cave together. Not through the tide. So

I climbed down to stay with him. But I had to get help. My mobile wasn't working. I could hear you, Mum. Some of the words, at least, but not everything. I didn't know for sure if you could hear me.

'I waded out, the tide wasn't so high then, and I waved my arms until I got someone's attention. Then I went back to stay with Simon.' Her voice trembled slightly. 'But on the way I fell over a rock that I couldn't see in the water and bumped my head. I think that's when I hurt my arm.'

'You were very brave. It must have been difficult to climb back up to Simon with only one arm.'

Why didn't you stay out of the cave once you got out? Abby wanted to ask. But she knew the answer. Her heart swelled with pride. Abby hadn't wanted to leave her friend alone and hurt by himself. As Mac had pointed out, she couldn't change her daughter's nature. And despite everything she had been through in the last hour or two, she wouldn't change her daughter for the world.

Eventually, Emma closed her eyes, the exhaustion and the excitement of the last few hours catching up with her.

Abby reached for Mac's hand as they

watched her breathing deeply. To her surprise he didn't pull away. Instead, he brought her hand to his mouth and kissed each finger tenderly.

'My God, Abby. For a moment I thought I was going to lose you and Emma. Don't ever do anything like that to me again.' His voice was ragged.

'Don't want to have to train a new teammate?' she said lightly.

'I don't want to lose the woman I love,' Mac replied quietly.

Abby's heart kicked against her ribs. He'd said he loved her. Did he mean as a friend or a lover? She had to know. Silently she waited for him to go on.

'Two months ago I thought I was happy. I had a job I loved, a decent place to live where I could do the sports I enjoy whenever I wanted. It was a good life, a perfect life, until you walked into it.'

Abby couldn't stop her smile. He sounded almost annoyed. But she knew his life had been empty of all that was important, even if he didn't.

'And then I found out I had a child. This child.' He bent over and kissed Emma gently on the cheek. 'At first I could hardly take it in. I didn't want it to be true. Emma would be nothing except a duty and while I knew I couldn't ignore my responsibilities, I never thought that she would become such an important part of my life. And as for you...' He sighed. 'You drove me insane almost from the moment I set eyes on you. Not just those cat eyes, or that mouth that just cries out to be kissed, or your body, which would make most women weep—those are the things that counted in my other life, but as I got to know you, I realised I was falling hard for you. And it frightened me.' He half smiled. 'That was a new one for me. I didn't think I was scared of anything but I was. I was scared of being in love.'

A warm glow was spreading upwards from her toes and surrounding her heart like a blanket. But she still couldn't be certain he was saying what she so desperately wanted to hear.

'I thought if I took you to bed, that would break the spell. But I was wrong. If anything, I wanted more. I wanted nights and nights with you. I couldn't imagine a time when I would no longer want you. Then you told me you loved me and that frightened me even more. What if I couldn't live up to your expectations of me? What if I let you—and Emma—down?

What if I turned out to be like my father? I'd be dragging you and Em down with me. I couldn't do that. I tried to stay away from you, Abby. I wanted you to find someone else, even if the thought ripped me apart. And if it meant losing Emma, too, I knew the man you chose would be a good man. Someone who would love Emma the way she deserved.'

'Do you still believe that?' Abby clasped her hands together to stop herself from reaching out and pushing a wayward lock of hair out of his eyes. Didn't he know that she would never love another man as long as she lived?

'No. I don't. I came close to losing you and Emma today. I knew then that I couldn't let you go. I'm not strong enough to do that.'

Abby came and crouched by his side. Taking his hands in hers, she looked up into his eyes. 'You are the strongest man I know, Mac. In the truest sense of the word. You are not your father. And even if you were I would still take my chances with you. I would rather have a tempestuous life with you than one without you.'

He stood up abruptly, forcing her to drop her hands. 'But that's not all. The lab that took our DNA for testing called today. That's why I was on my way to see you.'

A tendril of fear curled around her heart. The look in Mac's eyes told her something was far from right.

He lowered his voice. 'Abby, Emma is not my child.'

'What?'

'Whatever Sara told you, Abby is not mine.'

Abby's head was reeling. 'But why did she say you were?' As soon as she said the words she guessed the truth. Sara probably hadn't been sure who the father was and that was why she hadn't wanted to give Abby a name at first. But when she'd known she was going to die, she'd given Abby the name of the man she would have liked most to be the father of her child, Mac. Perhaps in her heart she had harboured a dream that once her child was born, she would go to Mac and persuade him Emma was his. They would never know.

'Whoever the biological father of Emma is, it isn't me.'

The pain and disappointment in his eyes shook her.

What now? What would he do? There was no reason for him to continue with the relationship. He would walk out of Emma's life and what would that do to Emma?

'Emma's going to be devastated. She adores you. She's so proud to call you her father.'

Mac's jaw tightened. 'No prouder than I was to think she was my daughter. And I love her.' A small smile curled his lips. 'I never thought the day would come when I'd say that.' The smile faded from his eyes. 'I don't care what the test says. I don't care who the biological father is. Damn it, Abby, Emma is my daughter. I don't want to lose her.' He looked away. Emma was still sleeping peacefully.

He reached out and took Abby's hand and pulled her to her feet.

'Come with me. There's something I want to show you.'

'But, Emma… I don't want to leave her.'

'She'll be out for the count for an hour or two. We won't be that long. I'll ask them to bleep me the minute she wakes up.'

Abby hesitated.

'Please, Abby.'

She couldn't resist the appeal in his blue eyes. He was hurting.

She followed him out to the car park. He opened the door to his Jeep and helped her in.

'I don't suppose you're going to tell me where you're taking me?' she said.

He smiled at her and her heart cracked. She

loved him so much it hurt. She would have given anything for Emma to be his child.

They drove in silence, turning onto the track where Mac had taken her a few weeks earlier. Abby was baffled. As they drove they passed diggers and lorries. There was obviously work going on.

Mac helped Abby out of the car.

'You and Emma are everything I wanted. I just didn't know it. I love you both.' He turned to Abby, pinning her with the intensity in his blue eyes. 'I'm in love with you, Abby. I'm not good at finding the words, but I know I couldn't bear to live without you. I want to wake up every morning with you beside me and I want yours to be the last face I see when I go to sleep. I want to live my life with you and Emma by my side. I want to have breakfast and dinner with you and Em, take you to Tiree to show you the place I grew up. The works.'

Abby's heart started to pound.

'I thought I could run from you. But I couldn't. I wouldn't let myself accept that I was falling for you.' He smiled sadly. 'Thinking I was a father was shock enough and even though it turned out to be the best thing that ever happened to me, I didn't know if I could commit myself to a wife. All I knew was that I didn't want to let you go.'

He gestured to the building site. 'When you refused to let me build this house for you, I thought I would build it anyway. I began to realise that I was putting down roots. Then, when I was discussing the plans with the architect, I saw the little sitting room with you in it, looking out to sea, a book in your hand. The garden where you would grow your roses. The kitchen where we would eat, the bedroom where I would fall asleep with you in my arms and the starlight shining in the window. Everywhere I looked, there you were. You and Emma. My family. My heart. My reason for living.'

He reached out and tipped her chin so she was looking into his eyes. 'Abby, I love you. I want you to marry me. I want you and Emma to be my family. I know she's not my biological child and that one day she might want to find her real father, but until then, could you love me enough to spend the rest of your life with me?'

A frisson of joy was spreading through Abby's body. Happiness swelled inside her. He loved her. But she had to be sure that this wasn't his way of hanging onto Emma.

'I'll never stop you seeing Em, whatever the results of the test say, and as long as she wants you in her life, which, knowing Em, is going to be for ever. You do know that, Mac?'

He glared at her. 'You don't think I'm saying all this simply because of Em, do you?' He smiled grimly. 'I love you. Heart and soul. For ever. I want babies with you, to grow old with you. To laugh with you. Argue, too, if it comes to that.' He pulled her into his arms. 'I love you, Abby Stevens. Will you get that into your stubborn head?'

The blood was singing through her veins. The way he was looking at her left no doubt in her mind. She brought her face up to his. 'For heaven's sake, how long do I have to wait for my fiancé to kiss me, then?'

And then he was kissing her as if he would never let her go, and she knew at last they had both found the place they were meant to be.

Emma was just waking up when they tiptoed back into her cubicle. One look at their faces must have told her something was up.

'Hey, what's going on with you two?' she asked.

Mac and Abby sat on the bed on either side of Emma, careful not to bump her injured arm.

'We have two things to tell you. Both are surprises. The first you're going to have to prepare yourself for, the second we think you'll like.'

Emma eyed them warily. Then she broke into a wide smile. 'I know what one of the surprises is,' she said. 'You two are getting married. Am I right?'

'You are. But how did you guess?' Abby said.

'Grown-ups can be so silly,' Emma said scornfully. 'I knew you were in love ages ago. Anybody, even a kid like me…' she slid Abby a mocking glance '…could see it a mile away. Even if you are old.'

Abby and Mac laughed. 'Hey, we're not that old,' Mac protested. 'There's still a few years before we get really ancient.'

'So you're okay with us getting married?' Abby asked.

There was no need for a reply. The smile that lit up Emma's face was all the answer Abby needed. 'I wished you would get married. Does that mean we'll all live together? For ever? Like a real family? I'll have my mum and my dad just like all the other children?'

Despite her happiness, Abby felt a chill. It

was going to be a blow to Emma finding out Mac wasn't her biological father.

'Emma,' Mac said, taking her hand. 'I have something to tell you. But first I want you to know that I couldn't love you more than I do now.'

The smile left Emma's face. 'What's going on?' she whispered. She clutched Abby's hand again.

'Remember that test we had? To prove I was your dad?'

'When you and me went to the hospital?'

'Yes, that one.' He took a deep breath and Abby knew he was having difficulty finding the right words. 'It turns out that I'm not your father. At least, I never made you.'

'You mean it wasn't your sperm with my real mummy's eggs?'

Mac looked so shocked that Abby had to laugh. 'I've always told Emma the truth. And it seemed silly to wait until some other child gave her the wrong information. Emma knows how babies are made. At least,' she rushed on, in case Mac misunderstood, 'the biological basis.'

Emma frowned. 'I thought you said people made babies when they loved each other. But my real mum didn't even know who my father was.'

Oh, dear. Abby thought. This was going to take some explaining…

Luckily Mac stepped in. 'Your mum, Sara, was a kind, lovely person. But she was a little lonely. Sometimes people make babies because they want someone to love and look after. I think that's why Sara made you. Whoever your real father is, your mother made you out of love.'

'And you always have to remember that,' Abby said softly. 'She loved you more than anything in the world. So much she didn't want to share you.'

'But if Mac's not my real dad…' Emma's lip trembled and tears spilled down her cheek '…then we're not really a family.'

'Emma, look at me,' Mac said firmly. He waited until Emma turned her blue eyes to his. Abby's throat tightened when she saw the trust there. 'You and Abby are my family. I love you both more than anything in the world. I want to be your dad for as long as you'll let me. I want to be the one who chases the boyfriends away, who picks you up from parties.' His voice softened. 'Who walks you up the aisle. We can carry on looking for your real dad, but if you let me, us...' he turned to Abby '...we want to adopt you, so you really belong to us. What do you say?'

Emma cuddled into Mac, snuggling deep into his arms. He stroked her hair, comforting her.

'I say yes,' Emma said. Then she pulled away and took hold of Abby's hand, too. 'So does that mean I can go to night-time parties now?'

EPILOGUE

ABBY stood by the window of her new home. In the sitting room, her mother and Mac's were chatting ninety to the dozen, each trying to outdo the other. Mac's mother had come down for the wedding and although she had grumbled about being away from Tiree almost constantly since she had got to Cornwall, Abby suspected she was pleased and touched that Mac had asked her to come to their wedding. Two more days then she'd be walking down the aisle with Mac, and she still couldn't believe it.

She felt his arm slip around her waist and she leaned against him, savouring the warmth and security of his embrace.

'Happy?' he whispered into her ear.

She nodded. Two more days and he'd be coming to live with her and Emma. He had refused to move in before, saying he wanted to wait until after they married. The house was everything he had told her it would be. Although enormous windows captured the view from every side, it was still cosy.

'You must come to Tiree to visit me,' Mac's mother was saying. 'I don't live in a grand house like this,' she sniffed, but Abby was beginning to realise that she didn't mean half of what she said, 'or in London, where all the fancy people live, but my house is good enough for me.'

'Your house is so sweet, Gran MacNeil,' Emma protested. 'I love it. Especially the chickens. And so is yours, Grandma Stevens,' she added hastily.

Abby smiled. Emma was ever the diplomat. Whatever differences the two older women had with their own children, there was no doubt they doted on their grandchild. Indeed, they spent all their time trying to compete for her affection.

Behind her, she heard Mac stifle a laugh. He had learned to be tolerant of both parents. 'At the very least,' he had told Abby, 'we both know how not to do it.'

Emma left the two old women to their bickering and came to stand next to Abby. She was to be bridesmaid at their wedding and was barely able to control her excitement about having a brother or sister to boss around in a few months' time. Mac reached across to pull her into the circle of his embrace.

'My two best girls,' he said. 'My daughter and my wife-to-be.' Mac and Abby had formally adopted Emma. His voice turned serious. 'Have I told you both that I consider myself to be the luckiest man alive?'

Emma giggled. 'Only all the time. You're so sad, Dad.'

He placed a proprietorial hand on Abby's stomach, where her body was just beginning to swell with her pregnancy.

'No, not that. Not any more.'

Abby raised her face to his. She never got over seeing her love reflected in his eyes.

'I have the best life,' Emma sighed happily.

'The best life. That's what we have. No one could be luckier.'

Together they watched as the sun melted into the sea.

* * * * *

DEVOTIONS®

Peace I leave with you; my peace I give you.

—John 14:27

JANUARY

Photo © Eyewire

Gary Allen, Editor

WYSIWYG

This was John's testimony when the Jews of Jerusalem sent priests and Levites to ask him who he was. He . . . confessed freely, "I am not the Christ" (John 1:19, 20).

Scripture: **John 1:19-28**
Song: **"Just As I Am"**

The youngest of four children, I struggled with my identity and desperately wanted to be like my older sister. I would dress up in her clothing, right down to her high heels, and pretend to be her. But I'd usually get caught in the act and hear the inevitable question, "Just who do you think you *are*, young lady?"

I wonder how I'd answer that question today. Can I be as forthright as John when questioned by the priests and Levites about who he was?

I suppose we're all guilty of some sort of role-playing occasionally. Whatever may compel us at times to put on appearances, perhaps it's best to follow the computer-age WYSIWYG principle: What you see is what you get. John was sure of his purpose and his position with regard to the Christ. The priests were looking at a humble, courageous preacher of Christ's coming. There was no hiding it.

Dear Heavenly Father, You love me just as I am—while calling me to grow in holiness day by day. Thank You so much for not basing salvation on my potential but on my need! In the name of the Father, the Son, and the Holy Spirit, I pray. Amen.

January 1–7. **Michelle Starkey,** brain aneurysm survivor, thanks God for a second chance at life. She lives life to the fullest with her husband, Keith, in New York.

Final Rinse Cycle

The next day John saw Jesus coming toward him and said, "Look, the Lamb of God, who takes away the sin of the world!" (John 1:29).

Scripture: **John 1:29-34**
Song: **"Behold, the Lamb of God"**

A late-night infomercial blared from the TV set. I'd fallen asleep on the couch and woke up just in time to catch the announcer's concluding sales pitch: "Just add a capful to your final rinse cycle, and it will miraculously wash the garment clean. Whatever you've spilled on it, dripped on it, or dragged it through . . . will be wiped clean."

This is exactly what the Lamb of God has done for our hearts. The sin stains within us are miraculously washed away (see Titus 3:5, 6). The Son of God was sent to earth to rinse away our sins through the washing of rebirth and baptism. I like the way King David put it in Psalm 51:1—"Have mercy on me, O God, according to your unfailing love; according to your great compassion blot out my transgressions. Wash away all my iniquity and cleanse me from my sin."

Here we have the greatest truth about the gospel and also the most formidable obstacle for its critics: that we are saved by pure grace alone. This wonderful washing is a gracious gift.

*Thank You, **Father,** that Your Son, who led a blameless life, took the burden of the world upon His shoulders and bore the entire load of my sins. Praise to Him for washing me clean! Through Christ I pray. Amen.*

Softening a Hardened Heart

This people's heart has become calloused; they hardly hear with their ears, and they have closed their eyes (Matthew 13:15).

Scripture: **Matthew 13:10-17**
Song: **"Hearken to the Solemn Voice"**

The Holy Spirit works in us to soften the calluses on our hardened hearts. No doubt it was He who opened my heart to the distressed woman I encountered downtown last week.

The shoppers rushed past her as she stopped by the curb. She had paused to fasten the only button on the tattered coat hanging loosely on her thin frame. No one paid attention to the old woman. Even I watched her from a safe distance as she nervously glanced at the busyness surrounding her. It was a bitter cold morning, and her only gloved hand held tight to her shopping cart full of worldly possessions. We don't seem to notice such folks until they "get in our way." But this time I smiled and offered her some help.

Matthew tells us that our hearts can be closed not only to people but to God's message of salvation as well. It was true in his day, and we must beware of it in our own lives. Can you tell when your heart is soft to God's Word? Or are certain calluses, even now, making the message seem less than crucial to your spiritual life?

*Open my heart to Your Word, **Lord,** and keep me ever willing to practice what I learn. In Jesus' name I pray. Amen.*

It Is Well

Peace I leave with you; my peace I give you. I do not give to you as the world gives. Do not let your hearts be troubled and do not be afraid (John 14:27).

Scripture: **John 14:23-31**
Song: **"Peace, Troubled Soul"**

My husband seems to exude the essence of peace, even under the most stressful situations. He is the most peaceful person I know, especially when it comes to raising our teenage daughters.

Have you noticed that teenagers can easily stretch the limits of parental endurance? On one occasion this involved our eldest daughter slamming a door after she left the dinner table abruptly. My husband calmly approached her closed bedroom door, opened it, and offered this observation in his most peaceful tones, "This should come off these hinges easily." I heard her gasp, even though I was a room away. "No, Daddy, please don't take my door away!"

He calmly replied, "If you slam it, you lose it." No one (even me) ever slammed a door in this home again.

It is well with my husband's soul. I know he has the peace only Jesus can offer us in this world of slamming doors. When I asked him, "How did you manage to maintain your composure?" he replied, "I prayed for calm, strength, and peace. I wouldn't let my heart be troubled."

Lord, I accept Your gift of peace. Help me package up my fears and anxieties today and lean on You. In Christ's name, amen.

Show Your ID, Please!

Are you the one who was to come, or should we expect someone else? (Matthew 11:3).

Scripture: **Matthew 11:2-6**
Song: **"Messiah, Prince of Peace"**

Anticipation. We all experience it. We happily anticipate the holidays. We anxiously await the birth of a child. We nervously predict the verdict in a courtroom. Our anticipation applies to both good and bad events.

John the Baptist spent his life anticipating the arrival of the Son of God, for this would surely be a time for happy celebration. Yet John harbored some doubts about the identity of Jesus. He needed some assurance that Jesus was truly the prophesied Messiah.

So, locked in his prison cell, awaiting an uncertain fate, John sent his disciples to question this Jesus. Did He have a heavenly ID? We can imagine John's anxious moments.

The reply Jesus delivered was more of a status report than an actual identity check: just observe the miracles abounding in my ministry!

Who else could this young man be? Or, as Jesus later put it: "Even though you do not believe me, believe the miracles, that you may know and understand that the Father is in me, and I in the Father" (John 10:38). The person and his works go hand in hand as perfect IDs.

Lord, amid my anxious moments of doubt and uncertainty, fill me with Your blessed assurance. In all that You have revealed of Your Son, it's clear He is worthy of all my worship. In His holy name I pray. Amen.

Pathway to Freedom

You will know the truth, and the truth will set you free (John 8:32).

Scripture: **John 8:31-38**
Song: **"Victory All the Time"**

A bumper sticker proclaims, "Freedom isn't free." In other words, someone is always paying the cost of freedom whether it's warriors who battle for democracy or missionaries who fight against injustice. Jesus taught us "the truth will set you free," and He himself *is* the truth (John 14:6). Thankfully, He has paid the price for our freedom from sin.

As a little girl, I heard my own father often saying, "If you just tell me the truth. . . ." I learned early on that it was better to tell the truth than to try lying my way out of things. And we've passed along this principle to our own children. Admitting wrongdoing is the right way; if we choose to lie, we become a slave to our sin.

When the children of Abraham asked Jesus how He could tell them that they'd be set free, He replied that "if the Son sets you free, you will be free indeed" (John 8:36). In other words, we have found a pathway to freedom by following Jesus.

Almighty Father, I am "free at last"—but not without cost. Thank You for sending Jesus to pay the price for redemption that I could never pay on my own. Please let Your mercy and grace fill me with Your joy today. And keep Your truth ever in my heart and upon my lips. In the holy name of Jesus, my Lord and Savior, I pray. Amen.

Eternal Existence

"I tell you the truth," Jesus answered, "before Abraham was born, I am!" (John 8:58).

Scripture: **John 8:48-59**
Song: **"Eternal Son, Eternal Love"**

One evening I went outside and marveled at the infinite number of stars in the sky. Millions upon millions of tiny lights sparkled above my head. Yet infinity is a difficult concept for the human mind to grasp. Even mathematicians struggle to conceive it and represent it. And, of course, the actual number of stars is finite.

Jesus spent much time justifying His eternal nature to others—an existence that extends into infinity, beyond time, looking in all directions. Naturally, His statements baffled the religious critics. "You are not yet fifty years old," the Jews said to Him, "and you have seen Abraham!" (John 8:57). These folks just couldn't fathom the idea that Jesus knew their ancient forefathers.

Today I'm reminded that "Jesus Christ is the same yesterday and today and forever" (Hebrews 13:8). And it is a blessed thing to know. Anyone who has ever stood below the expanse of an evening sky glistening with stars knows the awesomeness of the created cosmos. Just how awesome, then, is the eternal, uncreated being who is as close to me as my next breath?

Eternal One, I stand in awe of Your presence. You are everywhere—in the farthest reaches of the universe and in the deepest recesses of my soul. In this quiet moment, I lift my heart in grateful praise. Through Christ, amen.

Excess Baggage

Get up! Pick up your mat and walk (John 5:8).

Scripture: **John 5:1-9**
Song: **"Walking in the King's Highway"**

In India I slept on a straw mat, which just doesn't compare in comfort to the Western sleeping bag. I know the discomfort of that thin layer next to hard ground. So the very idea of a person with a disability sleeping on a mat makes me cringe in empathy.

The words of Jesus presented a challenge to this man who hadn't been able to walk for 38 years. It was a three-part command: get up, pick up that mat, and walk. A marvelous healing then took place.

The story causes me to consider: What is the "mat" in my life? It's not necessarily a place of discomfort, but it could represent a situation in which I am stuck, seemingly unable to help myself. For instance, when am I paralyzed with fear? When do past failures discourage me? And what questionable thought patterns are immobilizing me at the moment?

Yes, the man picked up his mat. But I'm quite sure that, once he began walking, he let go of that shabby excess baggage forever.

Father, Your hand lifts me out of my unworthy preoccupations and into Your plans for me. Help me rise above past mistakes and present difficulties to affirm Your sovereignty over all things. In Jesus' name, amen.

January 8–14. **Penny Smith**, of Harrisburg, Pennsylvania, wrote *Gateways to Growth,* based upon the book of Esther. Penny has five grandchildren.

Cloudy Vision?

He who comes from above is above all, he who is of the earth is from the earth and speaks of the earth. He who comes from heaven is above all (John 3:31, *New American Standard Bible*).

Scripture: **John 3:31-36**
Song: **"Hail to the Lord Who Comes"**

Flying is my favorite mode of travel. How exhilarating to break through the clouds and cruise above them, where blue skies seem brighter and even bluer! The songwriters who penned the words and music to "Above All" have captured the truth that John the Baptist proclaimed before he was imprisoned. John, the forerunner, spoke of the heavenly bridegroom as being above all.

The apostle Paul witnessed to this same truth in Ephesians 4:10, "He who descended is Himself also He who ascended far above all the heavens, that He might fill all things" *(NASB)*. And in Philippians 2:9 we read, "God highly exalted Him, and bestowed on Him the name which is above every name"*(NASB)*.

No wonder Paul admonished the Colossian believers to set their thoughts on the things of Heaven rather than keeping their eyes glued to the earth (see Colossians 3:2). Ironic, isn't it, that if we're thoroughly entangled in things down here, our spiritual vision will be . . . clouded?

*Thank You, **God,** for enabling me, through the power of Your Spirit and the finished work of Christ, to break through the clouds of despondency and live above the many pressures of life. In the name of the Father, the Son, and the Holy Spirit, I pray. Amen.*

Identity Crisis Solution

Jesus declared, "I who speak to you am he" (John 4:26).

Scripture: **John 4:19-26**
Song: **"Speak, O Lord, Thy Servant Heareth"**

When my younger son would call me on the telephone, he had the habit of saying, "Mom, this is Blain." I thought it was cute. I have only two sons, and I sure do know their voices.

But Blain doesn't do that anymore. Perhaps he thinks he has identified himself on the phone often enough through the years that my ears are now thoroughly trained to his unique tones. Or is it because he has children of his own and realizes how *individual* each one is? I am certain he recognizes their voices, even when they're out of his sight.

As we develop the pattern of daily prayer, Bible reading, and worship, we learn to recognize the voice of our brother Jesus. I am more sensitive to His nudging today than I was when my Christian pilgrimage began years ago, and I expect that sensitivity to increase with time. Furthermore, the greater my spiritual capacity, the greater is my desire to worship Him. For though He is "family," He is also my Lord—the *royal* brother, Savior, and God.

The woman at the well was waiting for Messiah to "call" someday. Jesus told her clearly: just listen; recognize this voice. I'm already here.

Dear Lord, keep me attentive to Your voice this day, especially when You speak in the times of stillness. In Jesus' name I pray. Amen.

Listen . . . Listen . . . Listen

The result was that when Jesus had finished these words, the multitudes were amazed at His teaching (Matthew 7:28, *New American Standard Bible*).

Scripture: **Matthew 7:24-29**
Song: **"Alleluia! Sing to Jesus!"**

In the stillness of the early dawn, I sat with my Bible in my lap. The only sound was the crackling of the fire in the potbellied stove. As I meditated upon the words of Scripture, I became aware of another sound, gradually increasing in volume as I focused upon it. It was the sound of water, like a rushing river. As it became louder, I looked to see what could be causing it.

I found nothing. Then I glanced at the Bible text again. I had been reading the words of Jesus, "He who believes in Me, as the Scripture said, 'From his innermost being shall flow rivers of living water'" (John 7:38, *NASB*). Had I heard the sound of this river of God?

Just as the crowds were amazed with Jesus' teaching centuries ago, so I am often amazed in His presence today. Whether we experience some glorious revelation or the simple humdrum of daily life, the living waters are flowing within. When the only sound seems to be the drip of a faucet or the crackling of a fireplace, we can listen . . . listen . . . listen a bit more closely.

O God, let me hide Your amazing Word in my heart, and give me boldness to share it with others who need the revelation of Your eternal life. In the name of Jesus, my Savior, I pray. Amen.

Seasoned Prayers

Preach the Word; be prepared in season and out of season; correct, rebuke and encourage—with great patience and careful instruction (2 Timothy 4:2).

Scripture: **2 Timothy 4:1-5**
Song: **"How Good Is the God We Adore"**

After teaching our adult Bible class, I greeted one of the ladies—only to face a cold stare and: "Why did you say that to me last week?" I didn't have a clue as to what she meant. She explained that when she'd shared a problem with me, I'd walked away saying, "Pity, pity, pity."

But this seemed so foreign to my nature! I asked whether she might have misheard my response. But when she insisted she'd gotten it right, I asked her to forgive me. Her response was less than satisfying though: "I forgive you, but I *know* what I heard." Sadly, this scenario was replayed for weeks, after every Bible class that I taught.

In this instance, I believe I learned what Paul meant by those words, "with great patience and careful instruction." The problem would not go away, and it was difficult to teach with this lady staring me down.

Sometimes the "out of season" seems longer than the "in season," doesn't it? However, I not only learned to prepare a lesson but also to prepare myself to meet whatever offense might come. Thanks be to God!

Lord, *I forgive in advance any who might offend me today, and I ask You to bless them. In Jesus' name, amen.*

Trinitarian Honor

In order that all may honor the Son, even as they honor the Father. He who does not honor the Son does not honor the Father who sent Him (John 5:23, *New American Standard Bible*).

Scripture: John 5:19-23
Song: "Blessing and Honor and Glory and Power"

My Uncle Ike celebrated his 95th birthday without any fanfare. Referring to his longevity, he says with a chuckle, "Had I known I was going to live this long, I'd have taken better care of myself!" As far as his health is concerned, he doesn't have any life-threatening illnesses, but sometimes he feels quite weak. After he naps for a while, his physical strength returns along with his sense of humor. He does realize that God is the source of his strength.

Let us all honor our three-in-one strengthener. The Holy Spirit is a life-giving Spirit. His quickening affects not only our spirits but our physical beings also. And Jesus—who healed the sick, opened blind eyes, unstopped deaf ears, and raised the dead—testified that He only did that which He saw His Father do.

With each renewal, whether physical or spiritual, we can remind ourselves that our Father is initiating a quickening force within us that we may bring honor to Him. It delights the Father's heart when His children, in the power of the Spirit, praise and glorify His Son.

Father, even as Your Son has glorified You, work by Your Spirit within me that I may faithfully give glory to Your Son for His sacrifice on Calvary's cross. In His precious name I pray. Amen.

Love Drew a Circle

Truly, truly, I say to you, he who hears My word, and believes Him who sent Me, has eternal life, and does not come into judgment, but has passed out of death into life (John 5:24, *New American Standard Bible*).

Scripture: **John 5:24-30**
Song: **"Bring Them In"**

The Kenyan minister escorted us through his village, which was largely comprised of his extended family members. His parents lived in their own hut, then the siblings with their families in mud huts that formed a circle around the village floor.

As we approached one of the huts, a small elderly lady ran down the path to welcome us into her "house." Although there was a language barrier, her pleasure was obvious to us. Two days later, she showed up at the church building—for the first time—and after hearing my message, she responded to the invitation to trust in Christ and be baptized. She told the minister that she had come because my friend and I were the only white people from America ever to enter her home.

We never know what it will take for a particular person to listen—to truly *hear*—the message of Christ. In this case, "Mama" had her own criteria, and our gracious Savior met it. It is His desire to bring us all to himself.

*Your ways are so much higher than ours, **Lord.** Help me to see through Your eyes so that I won't miss any opportunity to declare Your life-giving Word to open ears. In the name of Christ I pray. Amen.*

Exaggerated Report

I pray that out of his glorious riches he may strengthen you with power through his Spirit in your inner being (Ephesians 3:16).

Scripture: **Ephesians 3:14-21**
Song: **"Prayer Is the Soul's Sincere Desire"**

"It was 1983. I came home from college to find a street full of emergency vehicles," said our minister, Jeff. "I pushed through and saw Mom stretched out on the floor. On the way to the hospital, I prayed the only verse I knew, 'God so loved the world . . . that none should perish' (see John 3:16). Please, God, don't let her die."

Jeff rushed into the hospital to find his mother unattended. He ran into the hall for help and was informed she'd been reported DOA (dead on arrival).

"Mom, are you dead?" Jeff called out.

"I don't think so, Jeff," answered his mom.

Medical personnel rushed into the room. One heart ventricle wasn't pumping blood. They didn't expect her to survive, but Jeff kept praying. Until then, Jeff's faith had been in medical science. Since then, his faith is in God's Word. For, I'm happy to say, Jeff's mother visited our church recently. Her heart is still going strong.

Lord God, *thank You for answering my prayers and doing immeasurably more than I could ask or imagine through Your power at work within me. Through Christ I pray. Amen.*

January 15–21. **SanDee Hardwig** writes material for her church and does prison ministry near Milwaukee. Her cats are Mr. Miagi, Paddywhacker, and Angel.

In Any Weather

They saw Jesus approaching the boat, walking on the water; and they were terrified. But he said to them, "It is I; don't be afraid" (John 6:19, 20).

Scripture: **John 6:16-21**
Song: **"The Storm Is Passing Over"**

Three storms collided off the coast of Nova Scotia on October 28, 1991. "She's comin' on, boys, and she's comin' on strong," radioed Captain Billy Tyne. Minutes later, the *Andrea Gail*, a swordfishing boat from Gloucester, Massachusetts, and her six-man crew disappeared. Waves rising 30 to 99 feet were reported. Imagine the terror in those men.

Jesus' disciples were experienced fishermen, so they'd encountered plenty of other storms, though this one was apparently also comin' on strong. But no doubt the most frightening thing for them was to see a man actually *walking* on those rough waters. Jesus calmed their fears, though, and when they took Him into the boat, they immediately reached shore. Two marvelous miracles!

We might wonder how to apply this unusual event to our own daily lives. One thing that strikes me is this: Christ is always present with me, but how often during the day do I stop to look, to simply *recognize* Him? What a blessing to do so in any kind of weather!

Father God, when I look, let me see. Help me recognize Your presence with me amid every difficulty and stormy trial. And in moments of peace, too, keep my focus on You. Through Christ I pray. Amen.

Who's Holy?

Jesus answered, "The work of God is this: to believe in the one he has sent" (John 6:29).

Scripture: **John 6:25-34**
Song: **"Believe Not Those Who Say"**

Three-year-old Uriah and I sang, "Open the eyes of my heart, Lord. I want to see You. Pour out Your power and love. . . ." We repeated the last verse, "Holy, holy, holy" three times before it was time for him to go to sleep.

"Who's holy?" asked Uriah. "God is holy," I said.

"*Why* is God holy?"

"Because God is perfect."

"*Why* is God perfect?"

I had to think for a moment. Then I said, "God never has to sleep. Everyone else has to sleep—even your mom and dad. But they trust God to watch over you while you're sleeping because He *never sleeps*." The next day, Uriah told his mother, "You know what? God is perfect and God is holy."

A crowd questioned Jesus the day after He fed 5,000 of them with a little boy's lunch. They wanted to know what works God required of them. So Jesus told them the perfect work they could perform: simply believe in Him. In this case—regarding our own "perfection"—it can be nothing less than to rely on the truly perfect one from Heaven. Every other work falls short of salvation.

Heavenly Father, I desire to be holy. Help me to do good works motivated by Your Spirit through heart-deep belief. In the holy name of Jesus, amen.

Have a Taste!

I am the bread of life. He who comes to me will never go hungry (John 6:35).

Scripture: **John 6:35-40**
Song: **"My Life, Dear Lord, I Give to Thee"**

I just love the smell of freshly baked bread. The first time I helped Grandma bake bread, we rolled dough into fat strips and laid them on cookie sheets. Then we waited patiently for them to bake. I still remember how great that finger bread tasted. I ate until I couldn't eat anymore. . . . But in a few hours, I was hungry again.

The people knew their ancestors were fed manna, a kind of bread that dropped from Heaven, for 40 years. That's why they weren't overly impressed with just one meal. Yet Jesus said they were seeking bread that wouldn't last—though one "meal" of faith in Him would satisfy them forever. No wonder He is the bread of life!

The Greek word *artos* ("bread") appears 13 times in the book of John, and six times Jesus says He comes from Heaven (see John 6:33-58) and that God sent Him so all might have eternal life (v. 40).

You see, before Adam and Eve sinned, God created humans to live forever with Him in complete fulfillment and peace. But the sin caused hunger—a burning desire for more, more, more. Only the living bread can satisfy that spiritual yearning. Taste and see!

Father, You gave me the bread of life in Jesus. Make me willing to share this soul-nourishment with others who need Him. In Christ's name, amen.

He Wants . . . Me

No one can come to me unless the Father who sent me draws him, and I will raise him up at the last day (John 6:44).

Scripture: **John 6:41-51**
Song: **"Come Believing!"**

A cat meowed forlornly outside my building. I walked into the dark and kneeled on the damp earth. I held out my arms and called, "Come, kitty, kitty." A skinny, black cat ran straight into my arms. She wrapped her paws around my neck and licked my face enthusiastically. No one answered my ads seeking her owner, so I named her Tatsinda and raised her as my own.

I loved, fed, and cared for Tatsinda. But nothing I did prevented her from contracting feline leukemia. I had her put to sleep when she was 6.

Jesus holds out His arms. He loves and cares for us. But He offers us much more than I could offer Tatsinda. He offers more than food for our physical bodies and love for our souls. He offers eternal life with Him in Heaven.

The most wonderful thing about all of this is that we can come to Him because the Father draws us. The Lord of the universe *wants* us—wants us to be with Him, to know His love and care, to fellowship with Him now and throughout eternity.

Lord God of Heaven, *thank You for loving me completely and unconditionally. Thank You for never giving up on me. And thank You for guiding and protecting me during my days on earth. I pray that I never will be found resisting Your call. In Jesus' name, amen.*

Be Free

Say to the captives, "Come out," and to those in darkness, "Be free!" (Isaiah 49:9).

Scripture: **Isaiah 49:7-13**
Song: **"Where He Leads Me"**

Captain Stottlemeyer consults Monk when investigating a difficult crime. The annoying yet endearing Monk (played on TV by actor Tony Shaloub) isn't allowed to carry a weapon because of his many phobias and obsessive compulsions. But with the help of his nurse-assistant, this significantly flawed human being fights through his irrational fears and solves criminal cases.

Messiah, who was completely without flaws, did what was impossible for any other person. He reconciled flawed humans with God.

The prophet Isaiah describes the majesty of this awesome work of God through His servant, a work of freeing the captives. This was especially crucial for the captive nation of Israel, but it applies to each of us today as well. You see, we all struggle as captives to some form of flaw. We may not be OCD like Monk, but many of us do have neuroses, physical ailments, destructive habits, addictions, and besetting sins.

The good news is that a better day looms ahead. We await our complete freedom, a full redemption that will surely come to pass (see Romans 8:17-25).

*How I long for that day of complete freedom, **Dear Father!** Come, Lord Jesus, in whom I pray. Amen.*

A Real Advantage

Others said, "He is the Christ." Still others asked, "How can the Christ come from Galilee?" (John 7:41)

Scripture: John 7:37-41
Song: "The Comforter Has Come"

When I was young I use to think how wonderful it would have been to live on earth when Jesus Christ, the Son of God, was born in a manger in Bethlehem. Yet we have an advantage over those who lived in Jesus' day. They knew His family was from Galilee, but Messiah was prophesied to be born in Bethlehem of David. So many doubted that Jesus was who He said He was. But we today have the New Testament, which clearly tells us that Jesus was born in Bethlehem, though His family later moved to Galilee, where Jesus began His earthly ministry.

We have another advantage over those folks. After Jesus ascended back to Heaven, He sent the Holy Spirit to be our comforter and to guide us into truth. No longer is God's holy presence out of reach: He's chosen to live within us. Lori Wilke sings, "But nothing can exceed the view of seeing Jesus born in you." So we know where He was born, but we also know *why* He was born—that we might be born again. What a privilege to know this Christ!

O God, how awesome that You have chosen to live in me through Your indwelling Spirit, the Spirit of Christ! Holy Trinity, please reveal anything in my heart that may displease You today. In the name of the Father, Son, and Holy Spirit, amen.

Joy to Come

Then will the lame leap like a deer, and the mute tongue shout for joy (Isaiah 35:6).

Scripture: **Isaiah 35:3-10**
Song: **"Joy Unspeakable"**

I hate to admit this, but on some days my body feels the wear and tear of the decades and of the four children, some of whom are now adults. Nothing too serious, just the normal aging process we're promised this side of Heaven. It may take me just a bit longer to rise from a low couch, or I may find an unexpected stiffness after sitting for a while. Gone are the days when I leaped up gracefully without a moment's thought.

I accept this process—and am resoundingly thankful to be getting up at all. But this reality also makes the promise of our verse today all the sweeter to anticipate. What joy we will experience when we leave behind the frailties of our human bodies! I envision unrestrained joy and wholeness, with crutches tossed to the side in excitement.

The hand of God has planted this future within our hearts, whether we're young or old. Brothers and sisters, let faith rise up as you dream of the glorious days to come.

*Thank You so much, **Lord,** for promising and preparing such a magnificent future for Your children. And thank You for the joy you've placed within my heart already, my delight in knowing You and being Yours. May my life reflect that gratitude and delight daily. I pray in Jesus' name. Amen.*

January 22–28. **Kevan Breitinger** lives with her family of six in Ocean City, New Jersey, where she writes and pursues other adventures with the Lord.

Worship the Son!

The people living in darkness have seen a great light; on those living in the land of the shadow of death a light has dawned (Matthew 4:16).

Scripture: **Matthew 4:12-17**
Song: **"Dark Is the Night"**

Living in a seaside resort, I watch thousands of out-of-towners pour into town each Friday night during the summers. They endure long, hot drives on congested highways to reach the beach, to follow the sun. Sun worshipers, they're called. The light they love is physical, but I see their connection with today's verse, especially when I observe their enthusiastic chasing after the sun's rays.

God has sent us another light, far greater than the brilliant one in the sky so adored by these eventually well-tanned travelers. He sent it to a people who lived in great darkness, whether they recognized the gloom or not. He sent it to fulfill His eternal promises and to express His great love. Truly a light worth worshiping.

My sun-starved tourists bear myriad inconveniences and discomforts to attain their skin-deep goal. The Son we worship—who has saved us to the depths of our being by His radiant grace—deserves a similar desire and commitment, and so much more. Yes, may our lives display even greater passion as we long for the light of the world to light up our pathway each day.

Father, Your love lights my world with the intensity of a thousand suns. All thanks for leading me out of the darkness of sin. Through the Son, amen.

Forever Changed

He himself insisted, "I am the man" (John 9:9).

Scripture: **John 9:1-11**
Song: **"I'm Happy in Jesus Today"**

What a drastic change in the man born blind! After Jesus healed him, his neighbors wondered, "Is this the same guy we know?" With no driver's license or social security card to offer as proof of identity, he could only keep insisting: "Yes, it really is *me!*"

The Gospel writer shows us Jesus, light of the world, often invading the dark existences of human beings in wonderful, surprising ways—but always for the purpose of glorifying God. Yes, Jesus works distinctly and uniquely in each heart. How has He worked in you so far? For this blind man, He mixed mud with saliva before applying it to the man's eyes, an unusual approach to healing.

The light may have entered your life in a very unique and emotional encounter. Or maybe your initial experience with Christ was somewhat low-key by comparison. Either way, the entrance of the light was perfectly personal and transformational. We who were blind see now with new eyes, and we will never be the same. May our lives reflect this wondrous healing in a way that pleases and honors the one who is our light.

Father, I echo my brother's words today: "I am one touched by Him." I will never get over it, nor do I want to. Lord, have Your way in me today. May I glorify You with this gift of light within. I am Yours forever. I pray this prayer in the name of Jesus, my great physician. Amen.

The Rest Is Just Details

The man said, "Lord, I believe," and he worshiped him (John 9:38).

Scripture: John 9:35-41
Song: "Don't Lose the Vision"

Have you ever wakened from sleep in the pitch dark and found yourself trying to figure out the room's conditions? Maybe your spouse added an extra blanket while you were asleep, and you can't understand why you're sweating. Or you feel a draft that wasn't there before. You only know you're chilly, until you turn the light on and realize somebody opened a window. So *that's* it!

The man healed of blindness had no theological explanation, and certainly no scientific facts, with which he might enlighten his critics. All he knew was that he was once blind but now he could see. He didn't understand his own miracle . . . until Christ revealed who had produced that miracle. So *that's* it—the Son of God did it! Then everything made sense, and the man offered the most appropriate response: He worshiped Jesus.

There is much we still don't understand about light and darkness, about life and death. But we do know that the light has come to our planet and led us out of the darkness of sin by His death and resurrection; everything else is details.

Dear God, You are my light on the days when I understand and on the more confusing days as well. I thank You for rescuing me from the darkness and for leading me into Your marvelous light. Through Christ, amen.

Joy of Worship

Sing and make music in your heart to the Lord (Ephesians 5:19).

Scripture: **Ephesians 5:15-21**
Song: **"Sing Aloud with Gladness"**

The babysitter was gentle as she put the two sisters in bed for the night, but for the younger girl the combination of the dark room and her parents' absence was too much. Her quiet sobs filled the room shortly after the door closed. It was only when she took a deep breath that she heard her older sister's soft voice singing from the top bunk. The familiar hymn soothed her fears, and she found herself humming along with the old songs of devotion she knew so well.

Yes, the days are evil, and the darkness can appear overwhelming at times. But we are not left without comfort or hope, for Paul's wise instructions come to us as encouragement on our spiritual journey. Speaking and singing of the things of God can only strengthen us for the vital tasks ahead. In fact, singing to Him of our devotion is its own reward.

Will you join me today in pushing back the darkness by intentionally lifting His glorious name in worship? See if your spirits don't rise in thanksgiving. Simply put: make His praise glorious!

O God, I'm happy to sing of Your goodness and offer my praise to You today, for You are more than worthy! Thank You for overcoming every evil day with the power of Your love. All praise to You, in Christ's name. Amen.

Uniquely One

I stand with the Father, who sent me (John 8:16).

Scripture: **John 8:12-20**
Song: **"With One Consent Let All the Earth"**

Those who are married can testify to the extraordinary oneness found in a God-centered marriage. We don't necessarily get along perfectly with our mates at all times, but generally we do feel one another's sorrows, joys, and mistakes. If my husband is struggling in a particular area, I usually feel as if something is just a bit "off" in me, even if I don't know the specifics. We are one flesh before the Lord, whether our lives always reflect that or not.

The oneness between the Father and the Son is much the same, except for the fact that it is perfect, unmarred by the human frailties we carry. The Pharisees' own law honored the testimony of two witnesses. But the complete harmony, the total unity of these two witnesses was like no other. If they knew Jesus, they would know the Father; that's how cohesive they were.

The Father sent the light into the world to draw men and women to himself. But even as Christ traveled the rough earth, He stood with the Father, for this was a oneness that could not be diminished by distance or broken by even the sinfulness of humankind.

*I stand amazed at Your power, **Mighty God,** and the intricacies of Your ways. My finite mind cannot comprehend all the fullness of Your experience, but I know enough to bow before You in awe, in complete surrender. For You, O Lord, are wholly perfect. In Jesus' name, amen.*

God's Circle of Life

I have come into the world as a light, so that no one who believes in me should stay in darkness (John 12:46).

Scripture: **John 12:44-50**
Song: **"And Can It Be That I Should Gain?"**

One of the things I love about God's creation is the way things work together perfectly to fulfill a purpose. The sun heats the earth and the plants on it, the plants grow, purifying the air and feeding the animals, who breathe the air and provide us with food and service, under the sun. All of the creations in this circle of life, in serving their purpose, glorify God.

Jesus the Son was equally committed to fulfilling His purpose. Sent to rescue fallen sinners from the darkness of their own creation, He never wavered from His appointed mission. The Father sent His love and mercy in the person of Jesus, recognizing our great need and providing the precise sacrifice needed to accomplish His goal—the salvation of our souls. The light illuminated the darkness and enabled us to see, finally, our perilous condition. In seeing Jesus, we saw the Father and His love incarnate, and our hearts opened to believe.

No mission was ever more perfectly completed, no errand more breathtaking in its generosity. My heart melts at the lavish love in God's purposes for us.

O Lord, I can scarcely grasp the depths of Your amazing love. My understanding is so small, and Your mercies are so great. May my life show forth my gratitude for Your glory today. Through Jesus Christ I pray. Amen.

A Real Perfectionist

Whom did the LORD consult to enlighten him, and who taught him the right way? (Isaiah 40:14).

Scripture: **Isaiah 40:10-14**
Song: **"An Awe-Full Mystery Is Here"**

I remember vividly the day my husband told our 8-year-old son, Chad, to take some rotten grapes "out to the street." What he really meant was for Chad to take the grapes out and put them in the garbage cans sitting *near* the street for the garbage truck to come along. Eight-year-olds are still quite literal in their thinking, so you can probably imagine what happened next. He took those rotten globs and put them next to the curb, in the neatest little pile you've ever seen.

We have chuckled over that story for years. And for us, the moral of the story is: we all need clear instruction; we all need to be taught how to do things the right way. But this doesn't come naturally! Often we tend to do things only as we see fit.

In contrast, our creator God didn't need any help. Our Scripture verse tells us that He didn't need anyone to enlighten Him. He is the original perfectionist, perfection being a quality that fits Him. Perfectly.

Lord, You are perfectly amazing. I can't fathom how You measure the oceans or weigh the mountains. And so I trust You, Almighty God, creator of the universe, to care for me today. In Jesus' name, amen.

January 29–31. **Maralee Parker** is a wife, mother, and marketing manager of an accelerated adult degree program at a Christian college in the Chicago suburbs.

The Devoted Shepherd

Should not shepherds take care of the flock? (Ezekiel 34:2).

Scripture: **Ezekiel 34:1-6**
Song: **"Shepherd of Souls, Refresh and Bless"**

My cousin is a sheep-whisperer. Yes, she talks to sheep. She raises sheep. She loves sheep. I personally don't see the allure of hanging around with sheep, but she doesn't think it's baaaaaad at all (forgive the pun).

Actually, nothing could make her happier. She talks as if these gentle creatures are her babies, finds great joy in their every move, and paces the floor like a worried mother if any of them are sick. When the time comes for them to have babies each spring, she's out there in the barn all night long, if need be, waiting for her grandsheep to arrive.

I must say that when we were kids, I don't remember her telling me she wanted to be a shepherd someday. But that's what she is, and she lovingly tends to her beloved flock.

And aren't shepherds supposed to be like that? Her life excellently represents for me the loving relationship between a trusted shepherd and a helpless sheep as the prophet Ezekiel envisioned it. In that relationship, each lamb must rely on the shepherd for dear life. I am that lamb, and Christ is my shepherd. How I long to follow Him, moment by moment, and remain in His loving care!

*My life is in Your gentle hands, **Father.** I thank You for upholding me always in loving arms. In the name of the good shepherd, I pray. Amen.*

Stormy Day Savior

I will rescue them from all the places where they were scattered on a day of clouds and darkness (Ezekiel 34:12).

Scripture: **Ezekiel 34:11-16**
Song: **"A Shelter in the Time of Storm"**

You may have heard the old saying, "God never gives you more than you can handle." However, some of us may respond: "He has too much confidence in me!"

I do sometimes feel that way. My early life was idyllic—I grew up on a farm, graduated with honors from a small high school, then went on to graduate from college. I married, and we welcomed Child Number One at just the "right time." To our surprise, Baby Number Two didn't come three years later, as indicated in our master plan. Nor four years later, nor five. We then decided to adopt.

That was 16 years ago. We love our daughter immensely, but her "surprise" diagnoses of autism, social anxiety, and bipolar disorder make daily living challenging, to say the least. Then four years ago, I was diagnosed with kidney cancer. Those days were extremely scary, as I waited for surgery to determine the extent of the growth (stage III, but they got it all).

Though the fairy-tale life has left, I have learned, through life's challenges, to trust my Savior, as He has always provided for me. Before the storm begins, during the crisis, and after . . . He is ever faithful.

God, no matter what a day may bring, I know You will be with me. Keep me clinging to You, even in clouds and darkness. In Jesus' name, amen.

DEVOTIONS

*N*ow then . . . listen to me; blessed are those who keep my ways.

—(Proverbs 8:32)

FEBRUARY

Photo © Eyewire

Gary Allen, Editor

More than Maslow

They will live in safety, and no one will make them afraid (Ezekiel 34:28).

Scripture: **Ezekiel 34:25-31**
Song: **"Safely Through Another Week"**

If you've ever studied psychology, you've probably heard of Maslow's Hierarchy of Needs. According to Abraham Maslow, physiological needs are our most basic requirements—air, water, food, and so on. Only after those needs are met can we move our attention to the second level: our safety needs. We need to feel safe and secure in order to function as human beings. Then come the needs for belonging, esteem, and self-actualization.

As I look around me, I realize that many people in our society just don't feel safe. Some children grow up in abusive homes, for example, and never feel secure—even years after they've endured horrific experiences. Even as adults, some have trouble developing trusting relationships; they've never felt safe within another person's love.

Through Ezekiel, God assures His people of protection. Wrapped in His love, they need not fear. So it is today. Will you thank God with me that He offers us a peace that passes all understanding? In fact, He *is* our peace.

Lord of all creation, I trust You for the very breath I breathe. You are my safe haven, Lord God, and I thank You for meeting my physical, emotional, and spiritual needs. In Jesus' name, amen.

February 1–4. **Maralee Parker** is a wife, mother, and marketing manager of an adult degree program at a Christian college in the Chicago suburbs.

Listen Up!

His sheep follow him because they know his voice (John 10:4).

Scripture: **John 10:1-5**
Song: **"Softly and Tenderly"**

I am a cat person. Cats allow me to keep my busy lifestyle and still have warm, fuzzy, loving critters around. My husband and I can go away for a long weekend, put out plenty of food, water, and clean litter boxes—and the pets will stay happy.

It's interesting though: no matter how nicely my husband treats our lovable felines, they prefer me. They can be hiding, as kitties sometimes do, and when I sit down on the couch, they come out and want to cuddle up in my lap. My husband often asks them, "Why don't you do that when *I* sit down?" (He's still waiting for a response.)

Even when I'm sitting and watching old family videos, if the cats hear my voice on a tape, they come out from hiding. I guess just the sound of my voice makes them happy.

So it is with the sheep in today's Scripture passage. The sheep implicitly trust their shepherd, so much that merely the sound of his voice beckons them. They will not come when a stranger calls, but when their beloved shepherd calls, there is no hesitation.

May it be so with us and our great shepherd!

Father, in my busy world, help me to be still and listen for Your voice. I thank You for speaking through my intuition and more clearly through the written Word—and the living Word, Your Son, in whom I pray. Amen.

Muddy Abundance

I came that they might have life, and might have it abundantly (John 10:10, *New American Standard Bible*).

Scripture: **John 10:7-11**
Song: **"Afflictions, Though They Seem Severe"**

One day a friend of mine drove her elderly mother to the doctor's office. When they arrived, her mother quickly stepped out of the car and began sinking into some soft mud next to the sidewalk. Being a fastidious lady, she exclaimed, "Oh no, oh no, *oh no!*"

By this time my friend was running to rescue her, apologizing all the way, when she also inadvertently stepped into the mud. She stood there, wondering what she should do next, when she noticed her mom starting to totter a little. She reached out to support her, taking a step, but her shoe was stuck firmly in the mud. Her foot came out, and she ended up planting her foot, sock and all, into more mud. To make matters worse, shortly after that, her mom ended up . . . accidentally . . . *sitting* in the mud.

At that point, all sanity was lost. My friend and her mom looked at each other and started to giggle. They snickered and chortled and laughed. They didn't fall down laughing; they stood up laughing! It was a piece of life—*abundant* life—that they will treasure always.

O God, You are the source of abundant life. I couldn't make it through this crazy, stressful world with my sanity intact if I didn't know that You love me so deeply, so much that You laid down Your life for me. Thank You, in Jesus' name. Amen.

God, Your Supervisor

The man runs away because he is a hired hand and cares nothing for the sheep (John 10:13).

Scripture: **John 10:12-18**
Song: **"Safe in the Shepherd's Care"**

I aspired to my current management position, but on some days I wonder . . . *why?* Supervising people can be extremely challenging. I can't manufacture a desire for success in my employees; ultimately, they must find an inner motivation.

I've learned that when I assign a project and tell my folks *exactly how it must be done*—allowing little input—they are often less than enthusiastic. However, if I tell them the goal, let them have at it in their own way (and stop hovering over them), they develop ownership and a legitimate pride in their work. Simply put, they care more because it's theirs. And we all enjoy a better result.

In today's Scripture, the hired hand ran away when danger approached. He wanted to protect himself more than the sheep. After all, the sheep weren't his.

Lately I'm realizing that if I want to be like Jesus, the good shepherd, I need to put my whole heart into whatever I'm doing. My work reflects who I am, as well as my commitment to the one who created me. As the apostle Paul put it: "Whatever you do, work at it with all your heart, as working for the Lord" (Colossians 3:23).

Father, *help me to model Your model of commitment, whether it be with family, friends, or colleagues at work. In Jesus' name I pray. Amen.*

Real Christians: Please Stand Up!

There will be scoffers who will follow their own ungodly desires . . . and do not have the Spirit (Jude 18, 19).

Scripture: **Jude 17-25**
Song: "Stand Up, Stand Up for Jesus"

Years ago, Mom enjoyed watching *To Tell the Truth*, boasting of her ability to discern the real McCoy from the impostors. You may recall that this TV show hosted three candidates, all claiming to be the same interesting person. Each looked the part and answered pointed questions with suitable ease. However, only one of them was telling the truth. Eventually that person would stand up.

In ancient days and today, our churches may harbor impostors. Jude tells us that these folks—although they will look like Christians and talk like Christians—have never received the indwelling Holy Spirit.

But what a blessing to have this Spirit, given us through baptism! His ministry is to guide us into all truth, even helping us discern those who are true brothers and sisters in the Lord. Perhaps more importantly, He gives us the ability to assess ourselves. Yes, the Spirit enables us to know who we are in Christ. Isn't it comforting to know that He abides with us forever and is the down payment on our heavenly home (see Ephesians 1:14)?

Father God, thank You for Your Spirit who gives me the power to seek Your will today. In Jesus' name I pray. Amen.

February 5–11. **Vivian Stiles** is a writer, speaker, and evangelism counselor. She lives with her husband, Larry, in Palmyra, New Jersey.

Highway Hearkening

Now therefore hearken unto me, O ye children: for blessed are they that keep my ways (Proverbs 8:32, *King James Version*).

Scripture: **Proverbs 8:22-32**
Song: **"Ye Sons of Men, Oh, Hearken"**

It was a gorgeous day, just right for traveling. Traffic was at a minimum. In fact, at times we were all alone on the road. But suddenly I felt we ought to take a different route.

I couldn't explain why. Nevertheless, my husband reluctantly honored my request and made a quick turn that took us onto a road that was under construction and heavily congested. Under my breath I prayed, "Did I really hear You right, Lord?"

When we stopped and entered a convenience store for something to drink, a truck driver came up to us and said, "I really like what's on your T-shirts: *Lift the Savior Up!* It reminds me of when I was close to the Lord." Then he confided that he'd been getting ready to do something he knew was wrong. He continued, "You know, I think maybe the Lord is warning me to change my direction."

I believe this was an instance of "hearkening" to the Lord. What do you think? In any case, I'm certainly thankful that our truck driver did, indeed, hear our T-shirt message. Will you spend this moment with me in prayer for him?

Father God, let me hear Your voice in this stillness. As I hear of Your ways, give me the will and the strength to keep them. In Jesus' name, amen.

Delayed, But . . .

When he heard that Lazarus was sick, he stayed where he was two more days (John 11:6).

Scripture: **John 11:1-6**
Song: **"Jesus! The Name High over All"**

They'd ordered several tests; I'd gotten second and third opinions. Final diagnosis: a tumor on my right kidney. I prayed night and day that God would shrink it out of existence. I studied every healing Scripture I could find.

Then, at three o'clock one morning, I lay on the floor praying and crying until I was physically weak. In my spirit I felt that God may have healed me. I thanked and praised Him for His faithfulness; however, several days later the pain returned with more intensity. The next step was surgery. And I was devastated.

As I was being prepared for the operation, the anesthesiologist told me to count backwards from 100. The next thing I knew, the doctor was waking me up. He said, "I didn't have to operate. I can't explain it, but the tumor has disappeared." This thought leaped to mind: delayed, not denied.

I know God doesn't heal all our diseases. He calls us to live by faith amid all the painful circumstances of earthly life. We won't be perfectly healthy until we're with the Lord in Heaven. But from now on, when He says "Wait," I will do it with hopeful expectation.

Lord, *You let Lazarus wait in the grave, and You still let me wait amid trying times. Strengthen my patience this day! In Jesus' name, amen.*

Will You Believe the Truth?

I am glad for your sakes that I was not there, to the intent ye may believe (John 11:15, *King James Version*).

Scripture: **John 11:7-16**
Song: **"Only Believe"**

The eagle is one of the largest and most powerful birds in the world, typically building its nest on high cliffs or in tall trees. When a baby eagle is about 12 weeks old, it is gently pushed out of its high, cozy shelter. Imagine the eaglet's trauma suddenly realizing it is all alone, falling through the air! But how else could it learn to fly?

Sometimes an eaglet will struggle to flap its wings, but the force of the wind is too strong; it starts to fall. As it rapidly descends to the ground, the mother swoops in—in the nick of time—and comes to the baby bird's rescue.

At times we face desperate situations, when no one is able to help us, and our only hope is God. However, His presence feels hidden from us. Yet it seems our Father allows these fiery trials, in His apparent absence, in order to increase our faith. We're forced to distinguish feeling from fact. We're gently pushed into a walk of faith.

No, we don't always *feel* the presence of the Lord, but the *truth* is, He never leaves us. For the disciples who arrived with Jesus at Lazarus's grave—what a blessing to have the ultimate test of faith, to think the dead could rise!

Dear God, I can relate to Lazarus. I was dead in my trespasses and sins, yet You refused to forsake me. By Your grace You raised me to new life. I praise You in the name of Jesus, my merciful Savior and Lord. Amen.

Believe and Receive

He who believes in me will live, even though he dies; and whoever lives and believes in me will never die. Do you believe this? (John 11:25, 26).

Scripture: **John 11:17-27**
Song: **"And Am I Only Born to Die?"**

It was a special Women's Day in our church assembly, and a young woman squeezed herself into the pew next to me. There was plenty of room elsewhere, but she ignored the usher. She stepped over several people, absolutely determined to sit next to me. I wondered if I'd met her previously. I usually don't forget a face.

Soon the congregation was lifting praises to God, but the young woman next to me hung her head and cried hysterically. I put my arm around her to comfort her, and before I could ask what was wrong, she ran out of the building.

I followed her. She said, "I recently lost my mother. I want to see her again, but I've done so many horrible things." I showed her from the Scriptures that it was for us—the *sinners*—that Christ died. And whoever believes in Him will never die an eternal death. Then I asked her the profound question that Christ still asks all of us: "Do you believe this?"

Heavenly Father, *like all human beings, I dread the thought of having to die someday. However, I am so thankful that Your Son Jesus broke through the chains of death and prepared the way to Heaven for all who cling to Him in faith. I believe it! In His name, amen.*

Tranquil Washing Away

Jesus wept. Then said the Jews, Behold how he loved him!
(John 11:35, 36, *King James Version*).

Scripture: **John 11:28-37**
Song: **"Beautiful Vale of Rest"**

The water glistened in the burning hot rays of the sun, but a breeze was blowing in across the shore. It was a perfect day to be at the beach. Watching the ocean waves gave me a feeling of tranquility. I started taking inventory of my life. I thought about the tragedies I'd been through—the bitter divorce and loss of children. My mind seemed to focus on all the mistakes.

We've all made them! We've blundered and tripped, so often looking for the loopholes to justify doing our own thing. Some of us have been in painful, desolate places merely because of our obstinate wills. And yet Jesus weeps for the human condition, our existence filled with sin and death.

The great thing is that when the king of the universe weeps for you, you've got a mighty ally indeed. He goes beyond tears, though, and offers new life. What love!

I wonder how it felt to be wrapped in grave clothes, struggling to walk out of a tomb? Of course, I must say it's a wonderful feeling to walk away from a past that is buried and forgiven. I think I'll sit here a little longer by these rippling waves as they wash . . . wash . . . wash.

God, nothing I've done, or could do, will make You love me any more or less than You already do. How good You are! Through Christ, amen.

Experience the Glory!

Jesus said, "Did I not tell you that if you believed, you would see the glory of God?" (John 11:40).

Scripture: **John 11:38-44**
Song: **"In the Cross of Christ I Glory"**

When we stopped to visit some friends who were celebrating their seventh wedding anniversary, we expected to see two people still madly in love. Instead, Karen greeted us with tears running down her face.

I asked, "What's wrong—is there anything we can do to help?" She said, "We're not celebrating tonight because Greg is working late again. I know we need the money, but this is our anniversary. It's so inconsiderate!" As she continued talking, I realized this was just the tip of the iceberg. I asked if we could pray.

Karen opened up even more. She said Greg had been gone for a few days, and she feared he was thinking about making it permanent. She admitted they both had made some mistakes, but she wanted a chance to work things out. So we held hands and prayed again—that the Lord would bring Greg home with a desire to resolve their problems.

An hour later, Greg walked in. He asked Karen to forgive him. He said, "I've been praying. I know that if we believe, we'll see the glory of God in our marriage."

God, even when it seems the life has gone out of us—or out of a relationship—You can restore it all through Your mighty power. Give me the faith to trust Your perfect will in all things, for Your glory. In Jesus' name, amen.

My Passport

Brothers, . . . we have confidence to enter the Most Holy Place by the blood of Jesus (Hebrews 10:19).

Scripture: **Hebrews 10:19-23**
Song: **"I Come, O Savior, to Thy Table"**

My passport identifies me as an American citizen, but with it I've entered Ireland, Italy, and Canada. With that little document I can go just about anywhere.

Jesus' blood is somewhat like a passport, isn't it? By it, God has identified His people. Whereas a government-issued passport gives the place and year of birth, our God-issued passport details our cleansed, new hearts. With Jesus' blood we can go with confidence to the only place that really matters: the most holy place; that is, near to God" (v. 22). We will be admitted with open arms.

Italy is nice, Canada is too, and I do long to see more of the world with my U.S. passport. However, each day I can use my other passport and find rest or invigoration in the presence of my holy Lord. Through prayer and worship—in the car or at the kitchen table—I'm so thankful I can enter in with boldness.

Holy God, thank You that I can enter into Your presence with confidence because of the sacrifice of the perfect Lamb on my behalf. As I enjoy Your company, let my faith be bolstered and my trust in You be multiplied, so I can bring You glory through my life. In the name of Jesus, Lord and Savior of all, I pray. Amen.

February 12–18. **Elizabeth Fabiani,** of New Jersey, loves to write, quilt, and collect rocks. She and her best friend run an online magazine for women.

Why Were You Born?

"You are a king, then!" said Pilate. Jesus answered, "You are right in saying I am a king. In fact, for this reason I was born, and for this I came into the world, to testify to the truth. Everyone on the side of truth listens to me" (John 18:37).

Scripture: John 18:33-40
Song: "Who Are These Like Stars Appearing?"

My little brother Louis was born with birth defects. He would never walk, do simple math, or carry on the family name, yet God had a purpose for his life. God used my brother's life to lead our parents to Jesus.

Jesus knew His own purpose was to save the world from sin and death. This didn't make sense to the people of His day, because they were more concerned with Roman occupation than freedom for the soul. Though His path was painful, Jesus was never derailed in His mission.

It's not our job to save the world from death, but we can be teachers or mothers or businessmen who financially support missionaries. In myriad ways we, too, can testify to the truth.

We are all born for a purpose, just as my brother was. Day by day our mission is to submit to the filling and guidance of the Holy Spirit. Then, as we follow His lead in our witnessing, we will surely encounter openhearted listeners.

Lord, help me to live out my purpose with passion as You did. Keep in the forefront of my mind what You've planned for me each day, whether it's big or small. Help me be the person I was born to be. In Jesus' name, amen.

Grace for Each Day

Join with me in suffering for the gospel, by the power of God, who has saved us and called us to a holy life—not because of anything we have done but because of his own purpose and grace (2 Timothy 1:8, 9).

Scripture: **2 Timothy 1:8-14**
Song: **"Grace, Enough for Me"**

Do you ever find God to be somewhat ironic? I haven't had a valentine in years, and here I am writing a devotional that falls on Valentine's Day. (It was hard to write, too, believe it or not.) Yet God knew in advance I would be assigned to write for this day. He also knew that eventually I would look to His grace to help me finish it, without a hint of bitterness or disappointment that may sometimes simmer in the soul of a single woman.

Paul asks us to join him in suffering for the gospel. I know I would rather run the other way! Just as I would rather wear black and avoid restaurants on Valentine's Day. Yet with grace we can handle each new day whether it holds suffering or joy.

Thankfully, we can face each new trial and trust that the grace to endure it has already been provided. Today, if you find yourself suffering from singleness, arthritic hands, or a coworker's persecutions, remember that before the beginning of time, God planned just the right amount of grace to get you through this day.

God, *what a thrill to know the saving power of Your grace! It gets me through the best and worst of days. Praise to You, in Christ's name. Amen.*

Dress with Holiness

Put on the new self, created to be like God in true righteousness and holiness (Ephesians 4:24).

Scripture: **Ephesians 4:17-24**
Song: **"Washed in the Blood"**

While working for our township one summer, I learned about wood chippers, the sewage plant, and the trash truck. One day I watched Sam, a longtime township worker, put on his grubby, greasy coveralls and climb inside the trash truck to grease the hydraulic system. This kept the truck crushing trash smoothly. When finished, he stepped out and hung up the coveralls for next time. I, on the other hand, would have used latex gloves to undress after the grease job. Then I would have boiled and bleached the clothes. But that's just me.

Grubby and greasy could describe a lot of people, but all who have chosen to follow Christ have had their "selves" laundered, no matter the state of their wardrobes. The believer's inner life now resembles a new Easter outfit more than dirty coveralls.

But even Easter clothes get soiled. Though forgiven, we're not perfect. Every day, I must consciously refuse "deceitful desires" (v. 22) and let this new life in me—the indwelling Spirit of God—guide me in the paths of righteousness. What a miracle: to be able to dress as God does!

O Lord, You cleaned me up and made me new. I pray that others may see Your gracious work and long to put on a new self as well. I praise and adore You, Father, in the name of Your Son, Jesus. Amen.

Tell It from the Lawn Chair

It gave me great joy to have some brothers come and tell about your faithfulness to the truth and how you continue to walk in the truth. I have no greater joy than to hear that my children are walking in the truth (3 John 3, 4).

Scripture: **3 John 2-8**
Song: **"Go, Tell It on the Mountain"**

By the side of a lonely country road, she sat on her lawn chair with mobile phone in hand. She was talking and laughing with great animation. Surprised by her random location for a friendly conversation, I laughed out loud in my car as I passed her by. I figured that, with our area's poor cellular reception, she probably had to leave her house—lawn chair in hand—and walk to a spot on the road that allowed a good connection. She reminded me of how important it is to keep in touch with people, despite our busy lives.

Similarly, according to our Scripture today, it's important to keep communicating encouraging things about one another in the church. When we see good things happening in our lives, we ought to tell about them and give thanks to God. That is what gave the apostle John such great joy, and it can launch us into rejoicing as well. Our listening ear, encouraging word, or uplifting story may be just what's needed to help someone to keep walking in the truth.

Dear Heavenly Father, *remind me to remind others that we need to keep believing the truth, even when it's difficult to do. In Jesus' name, amen.*

Decor Debate?

Do not let your hearts be troubled. Trust in God; trust also in me. In my Father's house are many rooms; if it were not so, I would have told you. I am going there to prepare a place for you (John 14:1, 2).

Scripture: **John 14:1-7**
Song: **"I've Got a Mansion Just Over the Hilltop"**

"I'm just not sure You'd know how to decorate my heavenly mansion the way I would like it. What if You give me a Mediterranean-style dining room when I would prefer something more contemporary?"

OK, I doubt you'll ever hear a Christian debating God about celestial mansion decor. Getting bent out of shape over heavenly draperies does sound pretty ridiculous. Yet how many equally trivial things so often trouble our hearts? Once we gain a little perspective, we see them as unworthy of worry. But in the middle of worrisome circumstances, our dismal projections of the future can seem ever so real.

Can you let Christ speak His words of comfort into your heart at those times? Naturally, concerns over finances, children, finding love, or losing a loved one, are legitimate and do trouble every caring heart. At those times it helps to remember: Jesus has prepared a wonderful place for us to spend eternity with Him. In the meantime, He won't leave us to fend for ourselves down here.

Father, I know Heaven is beyond my imagining. But amid my troubles, do give me glimpses of this all-surpassing reality. Through Christ, amen.

What Have You Been Doing?

I tell you the truth, anyone who has faith in me will do what I have been doing. He will do even greater things than these, because I am going to the Father (John 14:12).

Scripture: **John 14:8-14**
Song: **"I Would Be Like Jesus"**

"What have you been doing?" A question like that makes me think of children left unattended for too long. Did they get hold of the dog's dish, Mom's makeup, or the sewing scissors?

Of course, for an adult it can be a good question to hear and answer—especially if we're proud of our work. If asked this question, Jesus might have said, "I healed the sick, lame, blind, and deaf. I comforted the lonely, the mourners, and the forgotten. I brought hope. I spoke truth. I lived out love."

It's amazing to think that we—Christ's ambassadors here on earth—could answer in similar ways as we allow Him to work through us. For with faith in Christ, we can do great things. We even have His promise that whatever we ask, if it will bring glory to the Father, He will do it. So come, brothers and sisters, with our Lord Jesus let us pray the lost into the kingdom, comfort the inconsolable, and fulfill the needs of the needy this day!

Heavenly Father, I want to be like Jesus and do great things in His name for Your glory. But teach me to take the smallest first step toward that end as I hold tightly to Your hand. Wherever I go today, may I be ready to minister with faith. I pray in the name of Jesus. Amen.

My Life: A Parable

He told them still another parable (Matthew 13:33).

Scripture: **Matthew 13:18-33**
Song: **"I Love to Tell the Story"**

"The story of my life!" That's what we say when something unpleasant happens to us. When bad things happen, we ask, "Where are You, God?" When sickness, disappointment, and personal failure come, guilt may wash over us. So I wonder: Why do we persist in the illusion that only comfort and ease betoken God's blessing?

Bad things often happen to God's people. Job had no picnic. Joseph and Daniel sometimes must have wondered. Maybe even John chafed on Patmos (what kind of retirement was that?). While we value the words these men gave us, their lives bear a powerful message.

Fanny Crosby lost her sight when she was 6 weeks old. Some blame an incompetent physician, but hear her words: "Oh, what a happy soul am I. Although I cannot see, I am resolved that in this world, contented I will be."

Fanny Crosby's poems and hymns by the thousands reveal her vibrant relationship with God. Yet while her pen blessed the world, we cannot escape the lesson of her life.

Every life is a parable. What story will I tell today?

God, remind me that more people watch my actions than hear my words. May I be a parable of Your goodness, through Christ my Lord. Amen.

February 19–25. **Lloyd Mattson** is a retired minister and author of Christian camping books. He and his wife, Elsie, live in Duluth, Minnesota.

Let It Shine!

My prayer is not that you take them out of the world but that you protect them from the evil one (John 17:15).

Scripture: **John 17:13-19**
Song: **"Stepping in the Light"**

Frenchy Lamont lived in a weathered cabin just north of town. He couldn't read or write, he'd lost an eye in a fight, and he spent most of his time in a small pub that was walking distance from his home. White-haired and bent over, Frenchy was nevertheless still quite spry after his 80 years on earth.

One evening Paul, a local minister, came upon Frenchy walking home and gave him a lift in his car. Gently, the minister told Frenchy about Jesus—and then offered him a ride to church and dinner at the parsonage the next day.

The congregation took this old man into their hearts, and he became a regular in attending worship services. He was baptized, learned God's love through the love of His people, and soon asked Paul to teach him to read (so he could immerse himself in the Bible).

But one day an anxious church member phoned Paul: "I just saw Frenchy going into that pub!" Paul went and found him there. "Frenchy," he said, "is this really where you want to be?"

The old man looked puzzled. "Didn't you say we should tell our friends about Jesus?"

Heavenly Father, *help me carry the light of the gospel to the dark corners, where so many need Your redeeming love. Through Christ I pray. Amen.*

Where? With You!

See that what you have heard from the beginning remains in you. If it does, you also will remain in the Son and in the Father (1 John 2:24).

Scripture: 1 John 2:24-29
Song: "Lead On, O King Eternal"

During my Boy Scout years, our leader always said, "Trust your compass!" On a few occasions, in real wilderness, that advice came in quite handy. My mind said *go this way;* my compass said *no.* The compass was right.

Perhaps today's Scouts still carry a compass, but that venerable guide seems to have yielded to the Global Positioning System (GPS), an electronic wonder you can carry in your pocket. GPS can pinpoint your precise location anywhere on earth.

I understand fairly well how a compass works, with its deviations from true North. I haven't a clue how GPS works, apart from a vague idea of what it means for satellite signals to triangulate. But, of course, I don't have to know *how* a compass or GPS works, only *that* they work and that I must learn to trust them.

When you know your destination, these devices will keep you on track. God's Word does that too. Keep it close to your heart and consult it often. If that Word remains in you, then wherever you are, Immanuel—"God with us"—is always with . . . *you.*

*Thank You, **Lord,** for giving me Your Word to be a light to my path and a guide toward home when I stray. In Jesus' name, amen.*

Loving, with Due Care

Many deceivers, who do not acknowledge Jesus Christ as coming in the flesh, have gone out into the world. . . . If anyone comes to you and does not bring this teaching, do not take him into your house or welcome him (2 John 7, 10).

Scripture: **2 John 7-11**
Song: **"Jesus, Brightness of the Father"**

My home is my castle, so I am told, which means I can choose my guests and set the agenda for all who visit. One afternoon, two neatly dressed women came to my door. I invited them in, and they immediately asked whether I knew God's name. "Yes," I replied, "His name is Jehovah." The women smiled.

"I know His other name too," I continued without pausing. "It's Jesus." The women frowned.

With enthusiasm I told them how I had met Jesus in my youth, how I had received the gift of eternal life that He purchased for me on the cross, and how Jesus had blessed me with a family, church, and many friends. I told them how I longed for the day when Jesus would return.

My guests grew increasingly agitated before I asked whether I might pray with them. But when I ceased praying, they were gone, without so much as a good-bye.

Perhaps that was the wrong approach. I know it wasn't quite politically correct. But, after all, they came to my castle, a place God calls me to guard with due care.

*Help me, **Father,** to make my home a loving witness to Your grace but to refuse entry to any questioning of Your Son's deity, in Him I pray. Amen.*

All It Takes Is Water

He is like a tree planted by streams of water, which yields its fruit in season (Psalm 1:3).

Scripture: **Psalm 1**
Song: **"Lo! From the Desert Homes"**

A small raspberry patch flourishes close to our back door. For three weeks each summer it provides all the fresh fruit we want—plus pints of jam for the winter. My neighbors, who often struggle with their berries, wonder why my patch never fails.

Water is the secret. Sixty years ago, a small stream flowed through a ravine where three homes now stand, ours in the middle. The developer filled the ravine with red clay, but the stream draining the hillside had to go somewhere. As a result, our backyards have a high water table that requires sump pumps to protect our basements.

All summer, my neighbor's sump issues a gentle, clear flow near my berry patch. I capture the water in a plastic vat and a meandering seep hose directs it to my thirsty raspberry plants.

Like my neighbors, I cultivate, weed, and mulch the patch. I remove spent canes in autumn and stake new growth against the coming snow. But I have a steady supply of water, and my neighbors do not.

It makes me realize a truth of the Spirit: if you want unfailing kingdom fruit, stay close to the living water.

Heavenly Father, *keep me close to the living water, that my life may bear fruit in its season. Through the name of Jesus I pray. Amen.*

Do Something for the Lord

If a man remains in me and I in him, he will bear much fruit (John 15:5).

Scripture: **John 15:1-8**
Song: **"Servant of God, Well Done!"**

Roger Green spent his 79 years as a farmer, cabinet maker, truck driver, logger, and Alaskan gold miner. He was a kind man and my best friend. A craftsman with wood, he sang sweetly and played the accordion (poorly). He always considered himself a man of ordinary gifts. Again and again I heard him say, "I wish I could do something for the Lord!"

Roger died of cancer at home. Among the mourners who packed the large church to say good-bye was a group of Chinese students from the nearby university. The group included a young seminarian, one of several students who learned of Christ in Roger's home. For several years, Roger and his wife, Lois, had hosted a Chinese congregation guided by a missionary from Taiwan.

Roger did far more for the Lord than he knew. His eldest daughter became a career missionary to the country of Chad. And through the integrity of his person and hospitality of his home, scores of young nationals returned home to China with the gospel impressed upon their hearts.

All his life, Roger walked with God, offering the sacrament of friendship. I live with blessed memories.

Father, I desire a legacy of fruit-bearing at the end of my life. Remind me, each new day, that I must stay connected to Jesus, in whom I pray. Amen.

Tall Order Here

My command is this: Love each other as I have loved you. Greater love has no one than this, that he lay down his life for his friends (John 15:12, 13).

Scripture: **John 15:9-17**
Song: **"O Brother Man"**

A young woman, a stranger to me, entered our small church building one Sunday morning. She carried a smiling child, but I found it hard not to stare at the woman's scarred, disfigured face. A friend explained, "Those are love scars. She ran into their burning house to rescue her baby. It nearly cost her life."

Love can be costly, but cheap love is not the love taught in the Bible. We think of love primarily as a warm feeling, a desire to be close to the person of our affections. But that kind of love can be subtly self-serving.

Bible love, though it may well be infused with emotion, ultimately transcends feelings, deferring self-interest to meet the needs of others, no matter who they are or how they respond. That love enables us to reach out to those we may not like, even our enemies. Bible love surely includes sacrifice for those dear to us, and it also calls us to treat everyone in a Christlike manner, no matter how we feel. It's a tall order. But that's how Christian love works.

I know, Lord, that warm and affectionate love is perhaps life's greatest treasure. But the love You give keeps giving even when there is no other warmth. Help me to love that way today, for Your glory. I pray this prayer in the name of Jesus, my merciful Savior and Lord. Amen.

Marital Kindness

Make every effort to add to your faith goodness; and to good-ness, knowledge; and to knowledge, self-control; and to self-control, perseverance; and to perseverance, godliness; and to godliness, brotherly kindness; and to brotherly kindness love (2 Peter 1:5-7).

Scripture: **2 Peter 1:5-11**
Song: **"We All Can Do Good"**

Cheryl was born prematurely 50 years ago before we had the miracle treatments preventing blindness in preemies. She's legally blind, yet she manages to play the piano beautifully and is so sweet that everyone loves her.

One day at a church dinner she set her soda on the floor by her chair and forgot it for a few minutes. When she stood up, her heel knocked the glass over, pouring the contents onto the floor. Her husband, Dave, cleaned up the mess without saying a word—and Cheryl never knew it.

In our passage today, Peter says Christians are "near-sighted and blind" (v. 9) unless they exhibit certain godly traits. When I saw Dave's actions, I thought of brotherly kindness. Amazing! Even in a marriage we can show that special kind of selfless love (a love that's beautiful, too, among all brothers and sisters in Christ).

Father, I can only express the virtues that You grow in my life through Your indwelling Spirit. Work in me today! Through Christ, amen.

February 26–28. **Audrey Hebbert**, freelance writer, lives in Omaha, Nebraska. Her *Dirt Bike Rider,* for kids ages 9-12, is published by Tweener Press.

Surprised by Love

Do not be overcome by evil, but overcome evil with good (Romans 12:21).

Scripture: **Romans 12:9-21**
Song: **"They That Overcome"**

I moved into this house one July 28 years ago, and within a month some "surprise lilies" bloomed—pink ones, with touches of blue on 15-inch stems that rose out of the lawn without any hint they had been hiding there. These old-fashioned darlings have been my favorites for all these years, and I've divided those first bulbs and planted them in all the flower beds for a showy display. In the spring the leaves appear, dark green and about 12 inches long, narrow, with a rounded tip. They die down in May, and I anticipate the August performance.

Could the apostle Paul have known about surprise lilies when he penned today's Scripture? These pink wonders rise from the earth without fail, regardless of what is growing around them, and their perfume sweetens the air. Their matchless beauty brightens the world because of their God-given nature. Paul begins this chapter with the secret to living out verses 9-21: Sink deep into God, be buried in Him as a living sacrifice. Seek Him above all, allowing the Holy Spirit to do His work in you that you may be transformed. Then from your nature will spring a goodness from God that will surely overcome evil.

Lord, I open my heart for the transforming power of Your work in me. Give me courage to confront evil—first, within myself. In Jesus' name, amen.

She Just Adores Him!

Clothe yourselves with the Lord Jesus Christ, and do not think about how to gratify the desires of the sinful nature (Romans 13:14).

Scripture: **Romans 13:8-14**
Song: **"Put Thou Thy Trust in God"**

Gwen is a small woman with beautiful blue eyes that twinkle with love for everyone she meets. She has traveled to many foreign countries on short-term mission trips. Today she talked to a young man as he walked his dog near her apartment building and asked him whether he knew Jesus. She also lovingly prepared a marvelous beef and vegetable lunch for me, though she had cataract surgery yesterday. Little children and adults alike know they are safe with Gwen because she fulfills the apostle's reminder in verse 9: "Love your neighbor as yourself."

I suppose Gwen never even thinks about the deeds of darkness mentioned in verses 12 and 13 of our Scripture today. From all I can tell, she has clothed herself with Christ, for He shines through her eyes and behavior. Her love reaches out to the Chinese restaurant owner who needs prayer and financial advice, to the missionary on furlough from Russia needing a home, to the temporarily unemployed man who has no food. I see all of the love flowing from Gwen, and I am inspired to lift my praises to this same Lord Jesus Christ whom she so clearly adores.

Lord, clothe me in the love of Your Son this day. Let me remember that I am His ambassador to every person I meet. In His name I pray. Amen.

My Prayer Notes

My Prayer Notes

My Prayer Notes

_____

_____

_____

_____

_____

_____

_____

_____

_____

_____

_____

_____

_____

_____

_____

_____

_____

_____

_____

DEVOTIONS

*G*od is the
builder of
everything.

—Hebrews 3:4b

MARCH

Photo © Díamar

Gary Allen, Editor

Devotions® is published quarterly by Standard Publishing, 8121 Hamilton Avenue, Cincinnati, Ohio, 45231. A division of Standex International Corporation. © 2006 by Standard Publishing. All rights reserved. Topics based on the Home Daily Bible Readings, International Sunday School Lessons. © 2003 by the Committee on the Uniform Series. Printed in the U.S.A. All Scripture quotations, unless otherwise indicated, are taken from the HOLY BIBLE, NEW INTERNATIONAL VERSION®. NIV®. Copyright © 1973, 1978, 1984 by International Bible Society. Used by permission of Zondervan. All rights reserved. Where noted, Scripture quotations are from the following, used with permission of the copyright holders, all rights reserved. *King James Version, (KJV),* public domain.

Cute Habit, Holy Fruit

Since we live by the Spirit, let us keep in step with the Spirit (Galatians 5:25).

Scripture: **Galatians 5:13-26**
Song: **"Guide Me, O Thou Great Jehovah"**

Ellie, age 2, and Gracie, 11 months, suffered one respiratory infection after another for three months. Every time Ellie coughed, her parents said, "Cover your mouth, Ellie." Then she placed her hand over her mouth. One day her parents noticed Gracie placing her own tiny, dimpled hand over her mouth, coughing, and pulling her hand away. Now she covers her mouth every time before she coughs.

Gracie's cute habit developed from the influence of her family around her. We individual believers are a reflection of our heavenly family too. Ellie and Gracie's parents instructed Ellie over and over, and the apostle Paul repeated commands like "serve one another in love" (v. 13) in every book he wrote. He also revealed the secret to this life: live by the Spirit, and the result will be love, along with eight other character traits, or fruit of the Spirit. So let us keep in step with the Holy Spirit. Walking with Him this way can become a blessed habit.

Dear God, help me to know how to keep in step with You today. I want to become all You want me to be, through the power of Your Spirit working within me. Through Christ I pray. Amen.

March 1–4. **Audrey Hebbert** is a freelance writer who contributes regularly to devotional periodicals. She lives in Omaha, Nebraska.

One Hundred Percent Sellout

To him be the glory and the power for ever and ever (1 Peter 4:11).

Scripture: **1 Peter 4:1-11**
Song: **"Glory Be to the Father"**

"Why are those people crying?" an American visitor to a Chinese church service asked the minister.

"They're sad because they have not been allowed to suffer for Christ," came the reply.

"Do you mean they *want* to be persecuted and suffer?" the visitor asked, astonished.

"In a sense, yes," replied the minister. "You see, they realize, in the depths of their being, how much Christ suffered for them; they want to give Him glory by suffering too as they live their lives in gratitude."

In verse 1 of our passage, Peter assumes that we will all suffer for Christ because He suffered for us. In the next verses Peter explains the formula for reaching that state where we are allowed to suffer for Christ. Our teacher explained it to our Sunday school class this way: "We are not in this for what we get out of it."

No, it's about what God gets out of it. Therefore, Peter reminds us in verse 11 of the motive for all Christian behavior, "that in all things God may be praised." He deserves all the glory and worship we can give Him.

Dear Heavenly Father, *I can do nothing without You. As I go about my day, let me depend upon Your guidance and wisdom each moment. In all I do, may I somehow demonstrate Your greatness. Through Christ, amen.*

To See or Not to See

Whoever loves his brother lives in the light, and there is nothing in him to make him stumble (1 John 2:7-10).

Scripture: **1 John 2:7-11**
Song: **"Here, O Lord, I See Thee"**

Chance was almost 3 when he discovered his eyelids. "It's dark!" he declared at the dinner table with his eyes squinted shut. "It's dark," he said, and collided with a chair as he crossed the dining room in his self-imposed night. "It's dark," he announced, when he tumbled off the sidewalk with his eyes closed and landed in the grass.

There are indeed times when it is dark, even as the sun shines brightly. John tells us that if we hate our brother, we're swirling around in the shadows. *Forgive him? You don't know what he did!*

John reminds his readers that the command to forgive first surfaced when unforgiveness killed Abel. But forgiveness is difficult! It's like having a car splash mud all over you, the driver roaring on his way, and your choosing to clean up the mess and get over it. Or . . . you let it be dark within; you remain mud-caked and angry.

The mud splasher won't care either way. The question is: would I rather walk in the light or stumble around in the darkness?

Lord, *I need Your help to forgive when my heart feels the sting of unkind words and actions. Thank You for Your mercy and gentleness as I wrestle daily with forgiving those around me. In Christ I pray. Amen.*

Finite Treasures

The world and its desires pass away, but the man who does the will of God lives forever (1 John 2:17).

Scripture: **1 John 2:12-17**
Song: **"Lead Me to Calvary"**

John Wesley, great preacher of heart-deep discipleship, serves even today as an example of the Christian walk. One day his house burned down, and he was soon quietly thankful. "Now I have fewer worldly things to concern me," he said. "I can spend more time serving God."

A modern-day writer echoed John Wesley's sentiments when she said, "When I stand before the King of the Universe, He won't ask me what I owned on this earth, but how I treated His Son." And I heard a minister instruct his TV audience to "create an atmosphere within them that God can dwell in comfortably." His insight, too, seemed to echo John Wesley's desire to please God.

But they are all simply reiterating the most basic message about our relationship with God, the principle John stated so long ago: daily we are becoming a certain sort of person—one oriented primarily to the things of the world, or one whose loves and cares center in the will of the great lover of our souls.

I would be sad if my house were to burn down. But I hope, at least, I would come to see that even my home is a finite treasure, small in the light of God's eternal will.

Father, I'm often tempted to follow the culture with my choices. But may my decisions today please only You. Thank You, in Jesus' name. Amen.

The Three Tenors

These three remain: faith, hope and love. But the greatest of these is love (1 Corinthians 13:13).

Scripture: **1 Corinthians 13**
Song: **"Your Love Compels Me"**

Placido Domingo, Jose Carreras, and Luciano Pavarotti— together they're known as the three tenors. And now you know everything I know about opera. My musical ability stops with playing the radio, but somewhere I heard those three famous names, so, for me, they always go together.

I do know that music basically has three parts that work together too—melody, rhythm, and harmony. When put together artistically, the result is pleasing to the ear.

The Bible tells us of another three: faith, hope, and love. Faith, like rhythm, controls the speed in my life. Hope, like harmony, is the blend, or color. Love, like a melody, makes my life flow. When I practice all three, my life produces a concert that demonstrates just how good the Lord is to His children. Yet without love, faith and hope are nothing more than senseless clatter, an opera with no story, an orchestra with no violins.

Father in Heaven, I give You my life as a blank sheet of music. I want to be more than noise to those around me. I pray You will compose faith, hope, and love into my spirit and make me into something pleasing to Your ears. In the name of Your Son, my Savior, I pray. Amen.

March 5–11. Originally from Nashville, Tennessee, **Kevin Riggs** now ministers in west central Arkansas. He is married to his high school sweetheart, Misty.

New Approach to Love

A new command I give you: Love one another. As I have loved you, so you must love one another (John 13:34).

Scripture: **John 13:31-35**
Song: **"Shine, Jesus, Shine"**

I remember when the governor of Tennessee announced plans for a new car company to be located in a small town outside Nashville where I lived and ministered. I was there when Saturn Corporation set up shop.

Saturn advertised itself as being a "different kind of car company." I didn't see much *difference*, though, in the cars themselves. Was the company being dishonest? No, the difference they were trying to achieve had to do with the basic approach to organizational structure and function. Theirs was a typical car in look and design, but the company was "dedicated to finding ways for people *to work together* to design, build, and sell cars."

When Jesus told His disciples He had a "new command," it really wasn't a *different* command. After all, God had always commanded His people to live in love for one another. The newness was in the basic approach. The old way called for loving others as you wanted to be loved. The new command was to love others the way Jesus loves you—unconditionally, sacrificially. No one had been commanded to love that way before, but that is how He wants us to love. It's a brand new approach.

O Lord, thank You for loving me the way You do. And may my love for others convince them You are real. I pray these things in Jesus' name. Amen.

The Unknown Lady

They all gave out of their wealth; but she, out of her poverty, put in everything—all she had to live on (Mark 12:44).

Scripture: **Mark 12:38-44**
Song: **"We Are an Offering"**

Hundreds of people lined up outside the gates. Children with dirty faces squeezed their heads through the bars to get a closer look. Moms and dads, wearing tattered clothes, showing tired eyes, waited patiently. All, hoping against hope, stood in line to see the doctor.

The makeshift clinic had been set up within a church in Tegucigalpa, Honduras. The people waiting were the poorest of the poor, and some stood there in the hot sun for more than 10 hours.

Near the end of the day, though, something wonderful occurred.

One of the volunteer medical workers gave a piece of bread to a lady who looked like she had not eaten in days. Instead of eating, she broke the bread into smaller pieces, handing them to as many people as she could. As far as I know, she didn't save a single piece for herself. For me, witnessing the scene brought today's Scripture to life. The unknown lady gave out of her poverty. She gave everything. She gave all she had to live on.

Oh God, please forgive me for being selfish. Help me be a giver instead of a taker. May I always be sensitive to the needs around me, and may I give all that I have in service to You and to others. In Jesus' name I pray. Amen.

The Great Bimini Wall

How great is the love the Father has lavished on us, that we should be called children of God! (1 John 3:1).

Scripture: **1 John 3:1-5**
Song: **"Jesus, Lover of My Soul"**

In the Atlantic Ocean, 40 miles off the coast of Miami, Florida, south of Bimini, lies the great Bimini Wall. The Bimini Wall faces the Gulf Stream, starts in 120 feet of water, and drops 1,000 or so feet straight to the bottom of the ocean. Scuba diving along the wall is an exhilarating experience. At about 80 feet, you swim through a beautiful coral reef system, full of aquatic life. Look carefully into the distance and you might see a hammerhead shark. At the edge of the reef is the beginning of the wall. At 120 feet, you can look over the wall—into total darkness. Looking down into the pit is one of the eeriest things I have ever done.

As I was swimming along the reef, looking over into that great chasm, it hit me. My sins are buried at the bottom! God lavished His love on me by sending Jesus to die on the cross so I could be forgiven. He has taken my sins and cast them into the sea of forgetfulness. I now have a visual picture of what that sea looks like. Not only are my sins at the bottom, so are yours; and that is why we can be called the children of God.

Oh gracious Heavenly Father, words are not enough to express how thankful I am for Your love, mercy, and grace. You have forgiven me of my sins. You have adopted me into Your family, making me Your child. I am humbled and speechless. I love You. What more can I say? Amen.

Heavenly Rescue

No one who is born of God will continue to sin, because God's seed remains in him; he cannot go on sinning, because he has been born of God (1 John 3:9).

Scripture: **1 John 3:6-10**
Song: **"There Is a Redeemer"**

As a child I loved the TV show *Gilligan's Island.* So imagine my dismay as an adult when I considered a possible connection between the characters and the traditional "seven deadly sins." Think about it: those sins shipwreck us, keeping us captive on our own little islands.

What's the connection? Gilligan's *laziness* caused the group to become castaways in the first place. Ginger used *lust* to her advantage. Mrs. Howell was often in a *rage* at anyone who didn't meet her demands. The professor knew he was the smartest, and his *pride* clearly showed. Mary Ann never measured up to the glamour of Ginger, leading her to an *envious* spirit, while the Skipper apparently never missed a chance to exercise . . . a little *gluttony.* And Mr. Howell? What better illustration of *greed* than a man who takes a trunk of money on a three-hour tour?

Through three years and 98 episodes, these seven castaways couldn't escape their tropical prison. Likewise, our sins, no matter how beautiful the scenery, can keep us captive forever. But it doesn't have to be that way. Thanks be to God, His Son came to the rescue!

Dear Father, because I am Your child, I have been rescued from continuous sinning. I seek to please You today in all things. Through Christ, amen.

No Surprise Here!

Do not be surprised, my brothers, if the world hates you (1 John 3:13).

Scripture: **1 John 3:11-15**
Song: **"Dear Lord, for All in Pain"**

Sergej Besserab grew up on the mean streets of Tajikistan in the former Soviet Union. A tough street fighter and hardened criminal, he was arrested five times, spending 18 years in prison before giving his life to Christ in 1996.

After his release, Sergej felt called to start a church in the city of Isfara. He and his wife bought a dilapidated house, converted the living room into a small chapel, and planted the first church in that part of the world.

But not everyone was happy about this. The local newspaper started printing "hit piece" articles about Sergej, his church, and his former life of crime. "There is no place in Isfara for Sergej and those like him," said the articles. And then someone accepted an implied challenge to stop the young church. On Monday evening, January 12, 2004, while Sergej prayed inside the small chapel, a masked assailant gunned him down. Nevertheless, the church continues to this day.

Sadly, Sergej Besserab's story isn't unique. Every day believers across the world are persecuted for their faith. Every day the world shows its animosity toward those who love Christ. But are you surprised?

Lord, I pray for my brothers and sisters across the world who suffer because of their faith. May we all stand strong together. Through Christ, amen.

Swing Set Discipleship

If anyone has material possessions and sees his brother in need but has no pity on him, how can the love of God be in him? (1 John 3:17).

Scripture: **1 John 3:16-24**
Song: **"The Servant Song"**

"Wow, Daddy!" exclaimed my 4-year old daughter. "Now I have two swing sets in my backyard."

"Yeah, isn't that great?" I replied, wiping sweat from my face. "I guess so," she said, less than enthusiastically.

I had just finished putting together my second swing set in two years. (Why does it take so many nuts and bolts to assemble those things?) As I placed my tools back in the shed, I could tell my daughter had something on her mind. "Katherine, what's wrong?" I asked.

"Well, I've got two swing sets," she thoughtfully answered. "But my friend Jimmy, who lives down the street, doesn't have any in his backyard. Do you think I could give him one of mine?"

Later that afternoon, my wife and I (and Katherine too) picked up the smaller swing set and carried it down to Jimmy's house. I don't know who was more excited—Katherine, about giving a wonderful gift, or Jimmy, about getting his first swing set. Wait! I was the most excited of all, seeing my daughter teach me how to be a practical disciple of Jesus.

Lord, all good things in my life have come from Your hand. Help me share them with a cheerful heart, at a moment's notice. In Jesus' name, amen.

Whiner or Winner?

We also rejoice in our sufferings, because we know that suffering produces perseverance (Romans 5:3).

Scripture: **Romans 5:1-11**
Song: **"Praise Him! Praise Him!"**

I thought I was a strong person, but I soon learned differently. A friend had invited me to her exercise class, and after just a couple visits, I developed significant soreness. The instructor's take on the situation? "You're finding your weak points," she said. "Just keep working, and your endurance will improve over time."

My goal was to be slimmer and stronger, but discomfort wasn't part of the plan! I became discouraged and began grumbling, until I realized: I have a choice; I can be a whiner or be a winner. The instructor encouraged me to focus on the hoped-for results, not the temporary pain.

Any of us can grow weary of the pain that comes with life's trials. And it's always tempting to complain and look for the easy way out. Paul tells us in Romans 5, though to stay the course and allow the tough times to strengthen our weaknesses. Then one day our reward will be to share in God's glory. That's what I call winning!

God, I'm grateful for the many ways You encourage me each day. When I focus on the struggles, though, help me recognize their perseverance—producing potential. And keep my eyes always on You, the one who provides strength for the journey. I pray through my deliverer, Jesus. Amen.

March 12–18. **Connie Coppings** is a minister's wife and freelance writer in Nicholasville, Kentucky. She enjoys playing the piano, cooking, and gardening.

Settle, and Stay Close

Settle matters quickly with your adversary who is taking you to court. Do it while you are still with him on the way, or he may hand you over to the judge (Matthew 5:25).

Scripture: **Matthew 5:21-26**
Song: **"Moment by Moment"**

Ralph Waldo Emerson said, "For every minute you're angry, you lose 60 seconds of happiness." And we know that, if left unresolved, anger can lead to physical and emotional ill health. Suppressed anger is often the culprit behind headaches, stomach disorders, elevated blood pressure, and even heart attacks. So why would someone hold onto this destructive emotion?

I worked as a counselor for several years, and I was amazed at how much time and energy people devoted to keeping anger alive. One client remarked, "I like the feeling of power my rage gives me." A minor disagreement had sparked his initial anger, but years later it had become a raging inferno.

Admitting to God when we're wrong is the first step to our freedom. Then we can move forward and "settle matters" with our fellow human beings. Jesus points to the very practical results of taking action with our anger. It may well keep us out of jail; it will definitely keep us closer to Him.

O Lord, forgive me for the times I've allowed anger to control my words and actions, making an adversary of a potential friend. May my heart be filled with Your love each minute of this day. In the name of Jesus, amen.

Love That Serves

Jesus said, "Simon son of John, do you truly love me?" He answered, "Yes, Lord, you know that I love you." Jesus said, "Take care of my sheep" (John 21:16).

Scripture: **John 21:15-19**
Song: **"I Will Serve Thee"**

I held my nephews and niece when they were just a few days old. My heart felt such love for them, and I prayed they would grow up to be followers of Jesus Christ. I told them "I love you" many times, but it was important they see those words in action as they grew. I spent time with them, attended significant events in their lives, and supported their dreams over the years.

Our Scripture today shows Peter affirming his love for Jesus with strong words. Three times he was questioned; each time he replied, "You know that I love you." Jesus' response in each instance seems to ask a deeper question, however: "You say the words, Peter, but are you willing to demonstrate their truth through service to me?"

We love many things, don't we? We love our favorite team, we love our pets, we love chocolate, and we love recognition. But if we wish to know what it means to love Jesus, we can always go back to His masterful ever-so-direct description. It's simple, really: "Take care of my sheep."

Gracious God, I am humbled by the depth of love You exercised in the sacrifice of Your own beloved Son for me. Please help my love today reflect the one who first loved me. In the name of my precious Savior I pray. Amen.

Love That Shares

Command them to do good, to be rich in good deeds, and to be generous and willing to share (1 Timothy 6:18).

Scripture: **1 Timothy 6:11-19**
Song: **"Give of Your Best to the Master"**

Have we forgotten the word *share?* It seems most messages coming from the media these days tell me, "You deserve it all; deny yourself nothing." Maybe that's why storage containers fill my closets and garage. Do I look to these things for a sense of security?

We share anytime we give our time, labor, or possessions; however, when we add a grateful heart to our actions, we come closest to the command of Scripture in our passage today. Knowing that God feeds us, we can offer meals to the hungry; knowing He shelters us, we can work to build someone else a home. One Christian woman even gave her kidney, knowing that a friend would shortly be without any!

I am so thankful that God has shared His love in the gift of His Son to me. What better example of what it means to share? And what better motivation to switch off the television commercials for a while and close those ad-filled magazines pages? They promise me security—if only I will get that next precious bauble. God tells me my greatest happiness comes through giving.

Gracious Lord, I know You can use only what I'm willing to share. So give me a grateful and generous heart. Keep my eyes on the security that comes in knowing You. In the name of my Savior, Jesus Christ, amen.

Best of Both Worlds

Dear friends, let us love one another, for love comes from God. Everyone who loves has been born of God and knows God. Whoever does not love does not know God, because God is love (1 John 4:7, 8).

Scripture: **1 John 4:7-12**
Song: **"The Bond of Love"**

I loved receiving gifts as a child. I thought about them even before I received them; and once I opened them, I would spend countless hours playing with my new things. Occasionally, one of my sisters would show interest in what I had, and "sisterly love" would be put to the test.

In the church, we are brothers and sisters in Christ, and our relationships there, too, are often tested. But God is love, and He calls us to be loving with one another.

A wonderful way to express our love for fellow believers is to pray for them—whether they know we're doing so or not. It actually treats them with the kind of personal regard that God holds toward us. Writer Richard Foster put it like this in *Celebration of Discipline*: "We do not pray for people as 'things' but as 'persons' whom we love. If we have God-given compassion and concern for others, our faith will grow and strengthen as we pray."

So . . . we can exercise love while strengthening our own faith? To me, this is the best of both worlds!

Lord, show me any unloving attitudes I may be holding toward my brothers and sisters in Christ. You have bestowed your loving acceptance upon me; help me do the same for those around me. In Christ's name, amen.

Family Resemblance

Love is made complete among us so that we will have confidence on the day of judgment, because in this world we are like him (1 John 4:17).

Scripture: **1 John 4:13-17**
Song: **"O Perfect Love"**

From the day I was born, people have commented on how much I look like my father. At reunions and other family get-togethers, people would say, "You are so much like your dad!" He was a humble Christian, and I was proud to be identified with him. His words and actions demonstrated his love for me, and I found great confidence in them. Long after his death, that love continues to affect my life.

I've counseled with people who tell me they can't remember anyone ever telling them they were loved. How sad! Like a garden without water, they struggle to grow and become what God would have them be. Because they can't seem to feel themselves beloved, they have trouble extending love to others.

Each day we come in contact with people longing to be shown they are valued—longing, really, to have a glimpse of the loving God. Thankfully, as "adopted" children of God's family (see Ephesians 1:5), we can show them what the Father is like in our words and deeds. We simply express our family resemblance.

O God, I grieve for those who feel unloved. Make my heart a vessel of Your love, pouring out to those in need. Through Christ, amen.

God's Perfect Love

There is no fear in love. But perfect love drives out fear, because fear has to do with punishment. The one who fears is not made perfect in love (1 John 4:18).

Scripture: 1 John 4:18-21
Song: "O How I Love Jesus"

My husband and I said vows on our wedding day, promising to love each other "in sickness and health, for richer or poorer." In other words, we'd try to act lovingly, no matter what was happening in our lives. Over the years, I've noticed our love flowing within words of encouragement, through special cards, or in smiles that convey "I believe in you."

When difficult times arise, we try to talk things through. Having built our relationship on love and respect, we can approach each other without fear. No, our love isn't perfect, but our marriage is in the hands of God, the one with perfect love for us.

Romans 5:8 says, "While we were still sinners, Christ died for us." How radical—to be loved *before* I'm able to be lovable! He allows me the freedom to approach Him, confess my sin, and know that I have no reason to fear His rejection. God does that for us and calls us to do our best at treating one another just that way. Which makes me wonder: am I waiting for anyone in my world to "clean up first" before I'll treat him or her with kindness?

Father, I need never fear to coming before You in my sinfulness. You came for just my type of person—the imperfect ones! In Jesus' name, amen.

Am I a Living Lure?

Come ye after me, and I will make you to become fishers of men (Mark 1:17, *King James Version*).

Scripture: **Mark 1:16-20**
Song: **"I Want to Be More Like You"**

This verse reminds me of an advertisement I saw for rattling fishing lures that glow in the dark. Fish come to such a lure from far away because they can hear and see the lure. In similar fashion, as Christian "fishers of men," our lives must provide a stark contrast to the world around us. In fact, our words and actions ought to reflect those of Christ himself. The apostles spent time with Jesus and opened their hearts to Him that He might become a part of their lives. As a result of Christ living in them, thousands were drawn to a new life.

We, too, can spend quality time with Jesus. He has placed us in a darkened world to be a shining light for Him, a glowing lure. So today I'll pause to consider: is my life attractive to the seekers around me? Are people drawn to me—to Christ in me—when they long for truth? Oh, may my life glow with His radiating love!

Dear God, help me reflect Your life and Your love, not in any forced or phony way, not with superspiritual platitudes, but in all genuineness with a real willingness to listen, to care, to reach out with practical encouragement. In all of this, may You be glorified. I pray this prayer in the name of Jesus, my Savior and Lord. Amen.

March 19–25. **Barb Haley** is a teacher and freelance writer who lives with her husband in San Antonio, Texas.

Biblical Bookkeeping

For God so loved the world, that he gave his only begotten Son, that whosoever believeth in him should not perish, but have everlasting life (John 3:16, *King James Version*).

Scripture: **John 3:16-21**
Song: **"Beneath the Cross of Jesus"**

A Christian young man worked as a banker in the days when accounts were kept by hand in a big leather ledger. One day this banker thought about God's Book of Life and imagined a page with his name at the top. As he watched God total the sum of his sins, he realized he could never pay the debt.

But God promptly took the pen and transferred the complete debt to the account of Jesus Christ. Thinking God was finished, the banker was further amazed when God proceeded to credit his account with the total righteousness of Jesus Christ (see Philippians 3:9).

Love can mean so many things in our world today. But God's love goes beyond all we can imagine, for His love calls us to be what we could never become on our own—a perfect creature in the likeness of His Son. And since we can't produce that marvelous work by our own effort, He gives us His indwelling Spirit to accomplish it, from beginning to end.

No, we will not perish but have everlasting life. Because He loves us just that much.

God, I'm amazed at the work You've done for me and also within me. Let its excellence shine through in my world today! Through Christ, amen.

Soli Deo Gloria

I have glorified thee on the earth: I have finished the work which thou gavest me to do (John 17:4, *King James Version*).

Scripture: **John 17:1-5**
Song: **"Lord, Prepare Me to Be a Sanctuary"**

Johann Sebastian Bach, the famous composer, once said, "All music should have no other end and aim than the glory of God and the soul's refreshment." The titles of his works usually began with "J.J." (*Jesus Juva*, the Latin for "Jesus, help me") and ended with "S.D.G." (*Soli Deo Gloria*, or "to God alone, the glory"). Bach apparently didn't consider his compositions to be his work alone. He prayed for God's help and then gave credit where credit was due. Really, what do any of us have to offer God that God hasn't already given us?

The situation reminds me of a small child who wishes to buy her father a birthday present. She innocently asks for the money and later joyfully delivers the gift. In the same way we can joyfully return to God the fruits of all His goodness toward us, the exercise of all the gifts He's given. It doesn't matter whether we travel as missionaries or clean office buildings or write beautiful orchestral pieces. Let us make our goal one thing on this earth: to finish the work He gave us to do.

Father, Your Son, Jesus, lived to glorify You, and that is how I also wish to live. I offer my time, my talents, and my will for Your use. Work through me to accomplish the tasks You have set before me. And bless the work of my hands that it might lead others to You. In Christ's name I pray. Amen.

What a Start!

If the Spirit of him that raised up Jesus from the dead dwell in you, he that raised up Christ from the dead shall also quicken your mortal bodies by his Spirit that dwelleth in you (Romans 8:11, *King James Version*).

Scripture: **Romans 8:9-17**
Song: **"Bring Your Vessels, Not a Few"**

A missionary tells of being given a car that wouldn't start without being pushed. For two years, the man enlisted neighborhood children to get the car going and then had to either park on a hill or leave his engine running once he got the car started.

When it came time for the missionary to move on, he passed the car on to the man who would take his place. The new owner promptly looked under the hood, tightened an engine cable, and started the car with no problem at all. For two years, the power had been there, and only a loose connection had kept the missionary from putting it to work.

Paul says the same powerful Spirit who raised Christ from the dead dwells within us even now. The Holy Spirit enables us to put to death all those impulses that work against His will and frustrate our own joy. By this Spirit—and only through Him—we've gotten our start in God's kingdom. Now we can move forward with Him always.

Dear Father, *You sent Your Spirit to empower me for the life You've called me to live. Thank You in the name of Jesus, my Savior. Amen.*

Daddy Will Carry It

Because ye are sons, God hath sent forth the Spirit of his Son into your hearts, crying, Abba, Father (Galatians 4:6, *King James Version*).

Scripture: **Galatians 4:1-7**
Song: **"I Know Whom I Have Believed"**

Young Corrie ten Boom once asked her father, "What is sex sin?" Not answering, he instructed her to carry his case—full of watches and spare parts. "It's too heavy," Corrie responded.

"Yes," he said. "And it would be a pretty poor father who'd ask his little girl to carry such a load. It's the same way, Corrie, with knowledge. Some knowledge is too heavy for children. When you're older and stronger, you can bear it. For now you must trust me to carry it for you."

"I was more than satisfied," Corrie remembers. "Wonderfully at peace. There were answers to this and all my hard questions. But now I was content to leave them in my father's keeping."

Life is tough, and our minds often swirl with questions for *Abba*, our "Daddy" in Heaven. *Why don't You heal me? Why did You let her die? Why don't You help me find a job?*

God carries the answers. He loves us; He knows our limits. Could we leave our heavy questions for a moment today and simply relax in His presence?

Abba, I come to You as a child—full of questions, doubts, and worries. Fill me with Your peace as I surrender them all to You. Through Christ, amen.

Stable Priorities, Changing World

This is love for God: to obey his commands (1 John 5:3).

Scripture: **1 John 5:1-6**
Song: **"Change My Heart, O God"**

When Truett Cathy opened his first Chick-fil-A restaurants during the days of segregation, he disregarded public opinion and hired employees without racial consideration. Doing the right thing was important to him.

"I believe the Bible to be a road map for our life and a blueprint for our life, and we could do very well to not only read the Bible, but put the Bible into practice," Cathy says. Today he does just that. Forfeiting millions of dollars, he closes all 1,200 of his restaurants every Sunday, believing the day ought to be reserved for rest rather than business.

"I'd like to be remembered," he says, "as one who kept my priorities in the right order. We live in a changing world, but we need to be reminded that the important things have not changed, and the important things *will* not change if we keep our priorities in proper order."

John the apostle tells us that we show God our love by obedience, even in a changing world that demands our time and attention. As for me, I'm inspired to take a minute sometime today to examine my priorities.

Heavenly Father, do continue to speak to me through Your Word, revealing areas in my life that I have not yet surrendered to You. Transform my heart and make me what You created me to be. In the holy name of Jesus, my Lord and Savior, I pray. Amen.

Yes, You May Know

I write these things to you who believe in the name of the Son of God so that you may know that you have eternal life (1 John 5:13).

Scripture: 1 John 5:7-13
Song: "How Can We Sinners Know?"

I looked at the question again. "Would you go to Heaven if you died today?" The answers included *Yes, No,* and *I'm not sure.* A seventh-grader in a parochial school, I had become a Christian years before. I loved God and tried to keep His commands. But was that enough? Marking my answer, I turned in my test.

I'll never forget that day. All but two of the students had marked *I'm not sure.* My teacher walked us through the Scriptures. "We are all sinners in need of God's grace," she said. "God is so good! He provided for our forgiveness through the death of His own Son, Jesus." After a little more explanation, she concluded by reciting our Scripture verse for today, stressing the KNOW.

We prayed a prayer of thanks and belief. Then we wrote the following in the covers of our Bibles: "I rededicate my life to Christ today. I believe He is the Son of God. Therefore, I now have eternal life. If I were to die today, I would spend eternity with my Lord and Savior."

Dear God, Your grace is unfathomable, too much for me to comprehend. Yet in the waters of baptism, You have extended it to me with all the benefits of forgiveness and acceptance in Your family. How I praise You in this moment of quietness! In the name of Jesus, Son of God, I pray. Amen.

A "Living" Stone?

As you come to him, the living Stone—rejected by men but chosen by God and precious to him—you also, like living stones, are being built into a spiritual house to be a holy priesthood, offering spiritual sacrifices acceptable to God through Jesus Christ (1 Peter 2:4, 5).

Scripture: **1 Peter 2:4-10**
Song: **"Because He Lives"**

As a child, I felt so important sitting by my father in his old Ford dump truck. Having made arrangements with retired farm owners, Pa rumbled up dirt roads, backed up to crumbled stone walls, and loaded the rocks he later sold to masons and builders. New England is stone-wall country, and I still enjoy driving scenic Route 169, passing one wall after another.

The first epistle of Peter (whose name Simon, Jesus changed to Rock), reminds me of my native rocky countryside, especially when I read the words "living stones." But I wonder, isn't that a contradiction in terms?

Upon closer inspection, however, I realize: it's all about Jesus! He is the one who rose from the dead, alive forevermore. Knowing Him as my Savior and Lord, living my daily life in His love and power, I too become a "living stone."

Gracious Father, today keep me aware of my identity in the living Lord Jesus. For I pray in His name, with all thankfulness. Amen.

March 26–March 31. Having retired from 30 years of classroom teaching, **Blanche Gosselin** is now "refired" in the areas of prayer, Bible teaching, and writing.

Builder at Work

Every house is built by someone, but God is the builder of everything (Hebrews 3:4).

Scripture: **Hebrews 3:1-6**
Song: **"His Name Is Wonderful"**

"We've decided to build our retirement home now, while we're young and able to make the mortgage payments," my nephew told me. He and his wife had found the right builder and eagerly anticipated the completion of their dream house.

The Bible has a lot to say about houses. The prophet Nathan assures David, "The LORD himself will establish a house for you" (2 Samuel 7:11). "Unless the LORD builds the house, its builders labor in vain," states Psalm 127:1. And Hebrews 3:4 tells us that God is a builder—"the builder of everything."

In the Bible the word *house* sometimes refers to a building; elsewhere it means a household, a community of people related by blood or common responsibilities. In our passage, "God's house" refers to His obedient children.

That's where you and I come in. Jesus was a faithful Son over God's house, carrying out the Father's plan of salvation. He began a new family, God's household of redeemed believers. As we fix our thoughts on Jesus, we gain much more than a dream house. The heavenly home awaiting us is more real than anything in the world.

Master Builder, I fix my heart on Jesus, knowing You will complete in me what You've begun. All praise to You, in Christ's name. Amen.

Embarrassing? No!

When the chief priests and the teachers of the law saw the wonderful things he did and the children shouting in the temple area, "Hosanna to the Son of David," they were indignant (Matthew 21:15).

Scripture: **Matthew 21:14-17**
Song: **"Hosanna, Loud Hosanna"**

For years Rita taught first grade. Whenever we met for lunch, she'd regale me with stories of student antics. Being quite creative, Rita devised all kinds of learning fun and also used her own brand of time out. In a corner, hidden by an upright piano, was a small stool; any offender knew that to sit there, away from all activity, was just no fun.

One day the school supervisor, Mrs. Jordan, visited Rita's class. All seemed to go well, and Rita felt she had passed the test. Then, as the visitor prepared to leave, one little, squeaky voice piped up from the corner: "Mrs. Jordan, I bet you don't know who's behind the piano."

Children can be embarrassing at times. But Jesus didn't seem to mind. "Let the little children come to me, and do not hinder them, for the kingdom of heaven belongs to such as these," He said (Matthew 19:14). As He entered Jerusalem on a humble mount, how pleased Jesus must have been to hear jubilant "hosannas" ring from the lips of innocent children, their praise a far cry from the indignation of His religious enemies.

Father God, Your Son called us to humble ourselves as little children. By Your grace, initiate that change of heart in me. In Christ I pray. Amen.

Marvelous Mercy (for Losers)

The stone the builders rejected has become the capstone; the LORD has done this, and it is marvelous in our eyes (Psalm 118:22, 23).

Scripture: **Psalm 118:21-28**
Song: **"Praise to the Lord, the Almighty"**

It was our final high school men's basketball game. Two county rivals tied for . . . last place. Only a few seconds to go, with the scoreboard showing the game tied up at 50 points each. But all of our starters had fouled out! On the court: pigeon-toed, undersized Kevin and his lackluster second-stringers.

Suddenly, the ball flew high into the air, right into Kevin's upraised hands. A little lay-up—the winning basket! I still remember the uncontrolled applause as Kevin's teammates hoisted him into the locker room.

That unforgettable scene taught me something important about appearances and reality. Jesus, the capstone, was never a second-stringer, but He did know the pain of rejection. Yet He accomplished the most awesome feat in cosmic history—the salvation of the lost . . . of the losers.

When I consider this amazing reality, my heart swells with thanksgiving. Every day becomes a marvelous mercy in my eyes.

Gracious Heavenly Father, *thank You for providing in Jesus the perfect capstone for the building of Your kingdom. May I never take for granted the marvelous accomplishment of Your divine deeds on my behalf. I pray this prayer in the name of Jesus, my Savior and Lord. Amen.*

Why a Donkey?

Those who were sent ahead went and found it just as he had told them. As they were untying the colt, its owners asked them, "Why are you untying the colt?" They replied, "The Lord needs it" (Luke 19:32-34).

Scripture: **Luke 19:28-34**
Song: **"I Surrender All"**

Do you see the rich symbolism here? We might ask, after all, why Jesus would enter Jerusalem—for His final week on earth—riding an unused, unbroken donkey. Why not choose a strong horse, emblem of might and honor, the mount of kings, officials, and generals?

Yet Jesus himself planned His entrance into the holy city, and in so doing, He fulfilled prophecy: "Rejoice greatly, O Daughter of Zion! Shout, Daughter of Jerusalem! See, your king comes to you, righteous and having salvation, gentle and riding on a donkey, on a colt, the foal of a donkey" (Zechariah 9:9).

The meaning? Horses represented war; Jesus was coming to restore peace between creator and wayward creatures. He needed the donkey, but many onlookers missed the point. They expected a warlike leader to free them from Roman rule.

Of course, Jesus is often "missed," going unrecognized in our lives. Let us turn to Him in this moment. He's right here with His peace.

God of Peace, let me bring Your Word to others, not in a spirit of conflict, but with the mind of the prince of peace. In His name I pray. Amen.

Give, or Sleep?

They brought it to Jesus, threw their cloaks on the colt and put Jesus on it. As he went along, people spread their cloaks on the ground (Luke 19:35, 36).

Scripture: **Luke 19:35-40**
Song: **"Give Me Thy Heart"**

In biblical times, the cloak served as an essential outer garment—usually a large square of cloth with two arm-holes—worn over other clothing. An average person owned only one such precious wrap. "If you take your neighbor's cloak as a pledge, return it to him by sunset, because his cloak is the only covering he has for his body. What else will he sleep in?" (Exodus 22:26, 27).

I imagine the crowd as Jesus enters Jerusalem: those who fetched the requested donkey throw their cloaks upon it and help Jesus mount. The procession moves on; people spread their cloaks on the road before Him. . . .

I want to call out, "Wait a minute! Think about what you're doing. You're going to need that cloak to keep warm this very night!"

Nevertheless, this throng of disciples "began joyfully to praise God in loud voices for all the miracles they had seen: 'Blessed is the king who comes in the name of the Lord!'" (vv. 37, 38). So I ponder: is there indeed more joy in selfless, sacrificial giving than in a comfortable night's sleep?

God of Heaven, serving You wholeheartedly because of who You are is the greatest joy of my life. I praise You in Christ's name. Amen.

DEVOTIONS

*T*hose who
seek the LORD
lack no good
thing.

—Psalm 34:10

APRIL

Photo © Díamar

Gary Allen, Editor

Devotions® is published quarterly by Standard Publishing, 8121 Hamilton Avenue, Cincinnati, Ohio, 45231. A division of Standex International Corporation. © 2006 by Standard Publishing. All rights reserved. Topics based on the Home Daily Bible Readings, International Sunday School Lessons. © 2003 by the Committee on the Uniform Series. Printed in the U.S.A. All Scripture quotations, unless otherwise indicated, are taken from the HOLY BIBLE, NEW INTERNATIONAL VERSION®. NIV®. Copyright © 1973, 1978, 1984 by International Bible Society. Used by permission of Zondervan. All rights reserved. Where noted, Scripture quotations are from the following, used with permission of the copyright holders, all rights reserved: *King James Version (KJV)*, public domain. *New American Standard Bible (NASB)*, © 1960, 1962, 1963, 1968, 1971, 1972 The Lockman Foundation. *The New King James Version (NKJV)*, Copyright © 1982 by Thomas Nelson, Inc.

The First and the Last

"I am the Alpha and the Omega," says the Lord God, "who is, and who was, and who is to come, the Almighty" (Revelation 1:8).

Scripture: **Revelation 1:1-8**
Song: **"Jesus Is Coming Again"**

Exiled on the island of Patmos, John received from God a prophetic vision: the revelation of, and from, Jesus Christ. John assures all believers: "Blessed is the one who reads the words of this prophecy, and blessed are those who hear it and take to heart what is written in it, because the time is near" (v. 3). The book of Revelation centers on the sovereignty of God, on the primacy of Jesus, and on the certain judgment God will execute on all evil—including Satan himself.

In our passage today, using the imagery of the first and the last letters of the Greek alphabet, Jesus declares that He is the beginning and the end, the originator and the consummator, of all things. Therefore, I can rely on His powerful presence, now and in the future. Such knowledge is almost too wonderful for me to grasp! In silence, I meditate on this truth, sincerely thanking the divine author and finisher of my faith.

Lord, grant me a thirst to know more fully the alpha and the omega of my life. And guide me each day, in wisdom and love, as I await the coming of Your glorious kingdom. Through the Lord Jesus Christ, I pray. Amen.

April 1. Having retired from 30 years of classroom teaching, **Blanche Gosselin** is now "refired" in the areas of prayer, Bible teaching, and writing.

Bread for Life

He took bread, gave thanks and broke it, and gave it to them, saying, "This is my body given for you; do this in remembrance of me" (Luke 22:19).

Scripture: **Luke 22:7-23**
Song: **"We Plow the Fields and Scatter"**

Because I live in a city, I rarely think about the origin of the food that ends up on my local supermarket shelves. Two years ago, however, on a summer train trip to Wisconsin, I had ample opportunity to view the "amber waves of grain" growing in high-plains states where so much of our food originates.

As our train threaded through Montana and North Dakota, I marveled at how vast—how lonely—this landscape appeared. In the midst of acre upon acre, brimming with wheat, oats, and barley, only an occasional tractor, trailing its plume of smoke, puttered through the scene.

Would I be able to endure the loneliness of farming? In spite of the solitude, would I take comfort in knowing that my solo efforts would, in time, feed many?

I also wonder, did Jesus, at that holy Thursday meal, facing His difficult, singular task just ahead, take comfort in knowing that the bread of His body would, in time, give eternal life to multitudes?

*Thank You, **Father,** for the bread of life, given for me. Help me always remember the source of my soul's nourishment. In Jesus' name, amen.*

April 2–8. **Phyllis Nissila**, of Springfield, Oregon, teaches high school English and community college GED and citizenship classes.

Sacrificial Masterpiece

Christ died and returned to life so that he might be the Lord of both the dead and the living (Romans 14:9).

Scripture: **Romans 14:7-12**
Song: **"I Gave My Life for Thee"**

Having been punched, whipped, and kicked, Jesus slumps—torn, bleeding, and gasping for breath. The ragged chant of His accusers—"Crucify Him! Crucify Him!"—pierces His ears. Then He glimpses someone twisting a thorn-studded branch into a grotesque mockery of a crown for His skull. All the while, the clank of hammer and nails punctuates the horror.

Jesus waits, alone, as unfettered evil closes in. Even His disciples have left Him.

Yet He is *not* alone.

Where time stands still, an invisible crowd, robed in white, surrounds the scene. We are from every nation, denomination, and era; our ranks stretch beyond Jerusalem into eternity. Each in our own way, we worship the perfect Lamb, the Lamb of God, now awaiting His sacrificial altar, our altar.

Lord of both the living and the dead! Yes, beyond time Jesus summons strength, shoulders the cross, and works an eternal masterpiece as He ascends the hill of our salvation.

God and Father of my Lord Christ, how can I thank You for the work of atonement You planned for me from eternity? I can only bow my knee and my heart in this moment of gratitude. In the name of my Savior, amen.

While Still Dark

Early on the first day of the week, while it was still dark, Mary Magdalene went to the tomb and saw that the stone had been removed from the entrance (John 20:1).

Scripture: **John 20:1-9**
Song: **"In the Garden"**

From all accounts, Jesus, You rose early that morning. By the heavenly power that brought Your dead body to life, You left the dark of the cave for the dark of the day, the promise of the first Easter morning not yet purpling the sky.

Magdalene was yet to bring her ministrations. The disciples were yet to race to the tomb. It was just You, alone, at the dawn of the day that split time.

Scriptures indicate Your frequent desire for solitude. I wonder, did You, even then, want a little time to yourself? Before the acclaim and controversy of the new era, did You want to check on Your mother as she slept, no doubt a fitful sleep, thick with grief? *(Soon, Mother, soon.)*

Did you gaze on Peter, too, so lately devastated by denying You, so constantly loved by You? *(Soon, Peter, soon.)*

Did You visit Gethsemane once more, that place where the full impact of Your sacrifice bled through Your pores? And did You stand one last time—trembling and triumphant—at Golgotha? I know this: You rose early, Jesus, in the fullness of time, to accomplish all.

Father, *while it is yet early, I draw near to You. Fill my heart with love for Your Son and for those He loves. In His precious name I pray. Amen.*

In Failure, Fellowship

"They have taken my Lord away," she said, "and I don't know where they have put him." At this, she turned around and saw Jesus standing there, but she did not realize that it was Jesus (John 20:13, 14).

Scripture: **John 20:10-18**
Song: **"Never Alone"**

Mary Magdalene's first post-crucifixion glimpse of Jesus certainly wasn't what she expected. She looked for Him in the grave; she found Him in the garden. In fact, she thought He was the gardener.

Until He spoke her name—"Mary."

The confusion was understandable. The last time Mary saw Jesus, His battered body had just been removed from the cross so that she and the others could prepare Him for burial. Her last view—through eyes blurred with tears, no doubt—was of His lifeless body wrapped in burial linens and laid on a stone slab. In other words, her last, lingering view of Jesus was at the scene of His seeming defeat.

And now He was here. Transformed. Alive!

Plagued by the twin torments of guilt and regret, we often linger at the "grave" of our own seeming defeat. It is hard to see Christ glorified here, too, hard to recognize Him in the midst of our failure. But He is here, as well, alive and inviting our fellowship. And He knows us each by name.

Dear God, help me to remember the promise of Your Son never to leave me—even when I stumble, even when I fall. For this, I am eternally thankful. In Christ's holy name I pray. Amen.

Power Within

Again Jesus said, "Peace be with you! As the Father has sent me, I am sending you." And with that he breathed on them and said, "Receive the Holy Spirit" (John 20:21, 22).

Scripture: **John 20:19-23**
Song: **"Peace, Perfect Peace"**

As the disciples broke bread on that first Easter evening, I imagine them recalling the last three years with Jesus, recalling the power: how they tasted superb wine from a water jug, saw a dead man stumble from his tomb, and heard the shouts as demons fled.

Yet having been in the midst of all that power wasn't enough to shake the grip of anxiety here and now, not enough to soothe the sting of cowardice.

Afraid of Christ's enemies, the disciples kept hushed tones, locked doors, close guard. I imagine the tension: *Where is He? What do we do now? If our enemies find us, what will they do?*

Then Jesus amazes them again. In one physics-defying instant, doors still bolted, He appears in their midst. Perhaps more amazing, He extends not condemnation for cowardice, but peace; not criticism for doubt, but proof of His reality by showing His pierced hands and side.

And He gifts them with the power they long for—the Holy Spirit, the power within that would revolutionize their world and revolutionizes ours.

*Thank You, **God,** for the peace that flows from You. May I walk in Your ways today. Through Christ my Lord, amen.*

Faith-Building in Progress

[Thomas] said to them, "Unless I see the nail marks in his hands and put my finger where the nails were, and put my hand into his side, I will not believe it" (John 20:25).

Scripture: **John 20:24-31**
Song: **"Falter Not"**

The first time my husband and I saw our house, it was little more than a foundation and a frame. Yet we could still envision the completed structure and appreciate its unique design. Amid the lumber stacks, cable coils, and rolls of pink insulation strewn about and covered in sawdust, the building looked wonderful to us, and we knew it would eventually be a warm and inviting home.

Like our house in progress, Thomas, doubts on display, was a believer in progress. But he wasn't the only one in need of finishing touches. Peter, for example, was still recovering from a glaring miscalculation of loyalty. And the other disciples, intimidated by the enemies of this "spiritual project," were behind schedule in the construction of the new church. Their faith foundations also needed serious shoring up.

Jesus responded by offering Thomas a hands-on opportunity to build his faith. Jesus also provided the rest of the disciples—and us—with many other signs and miracles, that our faith also might be completed, right on schedule (see Philippians 1:6).

*Remind me, **Lord,** to keep a hard hat and a soft heart in my spiritual construction zone. Through Christ's name I pray. Amen.*

Blessed Reassurance

When I saw him, I fell at his feet as though dead. Then he placed his right hand on me and said: "Do not be afraid. I am the First and the Last. I am the Living One; I was dead, and behold I am alive for ever and ever!" (Revelation 1:17, 18).

Scripture: **Revelation 1:9-12, 17, 18**
Song: **"Leaning on the Everlasting Arms"**

I recall once entering a busy airport terminal and imagining what it might be like to one day enter the temple in the new Jerusalem to see Jesus. I envisioned a similar scene, an excited, bustling crowd. I heard shouts and laughter, saw tears and smiles as people, like those around me in the terminal, anticipated greeting their beloved one, the Son of God.

As soon as my mind's eye focused on Jesus, however, I caught my breath. In a split second, I realized I'd never be able to stand under my own power at such an extraordinary event. Face-to-face with the one through whom all things were made—how could I possibly maintain my footing?

Like John on Patmos, I too would surely fall at His feet "as though dead." However, I imagine Jesus reassuring me too, as He did with John. "Do not be afraid," He'd say then, even as He reassures me now when I sometimes lose my footing over life's ordinary trials and challenges.

*Thank You, **Lord,** for Your reassurance, for Your help in all circumstances. And thank You, especially, for the vision of Your awesomeness that comes through to me today in Your Word. Through Christ Jesus, amen.*

The Fledgling

The LORD is good to all, and His mercies are over all His works
(Psalm 145:9, *New American Standard Bible*).

Scripture: **Psalm 145:8-12**
Song: **"God Will Take Care of You"**

The homely fledgling squawks incessantly. After falling from its nest, it calls to the parent. The tiny bird flaps its wings in an attempt to reach safety; however, those small wings just can't work a self-rescue.

Quickly, the plump mama robin darts down to feed its baby a bite of worm. The young bird quiets down, hops close to mama, and follows her along a hedge to hide. This act of care and provision repeats itself throughout the afternoon until the sun settles below the horizon.

As I watch this scene unfold on my front lawn, I consider how God provides for all His earthly creatures—and that includes me. When life causes me to stumble and fall, the Lord reaches to care for me with everlasting mercy. He hides me in the shadow of his wings (see Psalm 17:8).

When our lives tremble with chaotic circumstances, erratic emotions, or rocky relationships, may we look to this merciful Lord. He hears and responds, quieting our souls as we rest in Him.

O Lord, I thank You for taking such good care of Your creation. Help me to know and sense Your presence, even when I feel alone and desperate. Grant me Your mercy each day. In Christ's name, I pray. Amen.

April 9–15. **Susanne Scheppmann** lives in Nevada with her husband, Mark. She is an author and speaker for Proverbs 31 Ministries.

For a Moment, Revere Him

The fear of the LORD is the beginning of wisdom; all who follow his precepts have good understanding. To him belongs eternal praise (Psalm 111:10).

Scripture: **Psalm 111**
Song: **"O Master, Let Me Walk with Thee"**

Thunderstorms once terrified my young son. Now he loves loud firecrackers. My little boy once feared high bridges too. Now he rides the highest and jerkiest roller coasters. He enjoys the thrill of fear when the metal car slides down the heights and races around a tight corner.

Fear comes in many forms and meets us at various places. Some fears can paralyze us into immobility; others may well enhance our lives. The fear of the Lord is an enhancer.

What is fear of the Lord? It isn't a trembling in your shoes in dread of what God is going to do next. Rather, it's the reverent honor we render to our all-powerful king. Such fear not only acknowledges His power over our lives but also His unfailing love for each of us.

According to the psalmist, reverence for God starts us on the path to wisdom. And this godly wisdom gives us the ability to make good decisions on a daily basis. I would like to walk that path today. Will you join me in a moment of reverence?

Dear God, *let me fear You in a way that opens my heart to Your incomparable wisdom. Give me understanding as I read Your Word and seek to obey it. In the name of Jesus, my Savior, I pray. Amen.*

Aching Arms

In him and through faith in him we may approach God with freedom and confidence (Ephesians 3:12).

Scripture: **Ephesians 3:7-13**
Song: **"Still, Still with Thee"**

Justin, my toddler nephew, whimpered away from me. He feared coming into outstretched arms for a squeeze from his adoring aunt. Instead, he darted away to Mom's familiar lap. My arms ached to hold this strawberry-blond cherub; he wouldn't come within reach of me.

It made me realize how often I fear a kind of closeness with God. If I draw close, will He ask me to do something outside my comfort zone? Will He call me to let go of something dear to me? Or even worse, perhaps God is displeased with me. Does He then stand ready to exact punishment?

The words of two apostles confront my anxious thoughts. Paul tells me I can approach God with freedom and confidence. Then James encourages me with, "Come near to God and he will come near to you" (4:8).

The next time I want to shy away from God, I hope to remember what a fatherly hug He's extending to me, always. Even when He calls me to repent, He does it from His fathomless love. I like to think His arms ache for me, even now.

Father, because of Jesus, I may approach You with a joyful heart. Let nothing hinder me from developing a closer relationship with You, my loving heavenly Father. In the name of Jesus, amen.

What's in a Name?

There is none like Thee, O LORD; Thou art great, and great is Thy name in might. Who would not fear Thee, O King of the nations? Indeed it is Thy due! (Jeremiah 10:6, 7, *New American Standard Bible*).

Scripture: **Jeremiah 10:6-10**
Song: **"Blessed Be the Name"**

Do you know Shania Twain's real name? This pop music diva's actual given name is Eileen. The music industry thought "Eileen" didn't evoke a superstar image, though—hence the change.

I'm fascinated by names. I like the way you can guess someone's generation just by knowing his or her first name. For example, Brittany rings of Generation X. However, Ebenezer recalls to our minds a century gone by. Another fascination: celebrities may be known just by their first names—think of Elvis, Tiger, or Cher.

The Lord's name is above all other names, disclosing supremacy in all things. What images come to your mind as you read these names of God: Father, Lord God Almighty, Christ Jesus, Savior, the Lamb, Abba, and Sovereign Lord? All of these names reflect certain truths about our mighty God and—thankfully!—they define who He is in our relationship with Him.

So what's in a name? Everything, if we speak the names of our God.

Lord of All, thank You for revealing yourself to me through Your many wonderful names. In Christ I pray. Amen.

Just like Father

Be imitators of God, as beloved children (Ephesians 5:1, *New American Standard Bible*).

Scripture: **Ephesians 4:25–5:2**
Song: **"Take My Life and Let It Be"**

"You sound just like your mother!" remarked a friend of the family. This was news to me. My mother passed away when I was young, and I have no memory of her voice. Yet her tone and inflections come through in my adult speech. Somehow, many years ago, perhaps my young ears listened and then imitated my mother's words.

Just as we mimic our parent's words, as children of a heavenly Father we should sound like Him. Hmm, but what does He sound like?

Thankfully, the Bible provides a few examples of God's speech patterns. Ephesians 4 calls us to be kind, compassionate, forgiving, and encouraging. It also reveals communication that is clearly unlike God's, such as slander, bitterness, or any unwholesome speech. Mimicking the good isn't always easy for me to accomplish every day!

Yet I recall a children's song, "Practice Makes Perfect." It persuades hearers to keep improving their behavior until it becomes a habit. Will you practice godly speech patterns with me today? Then one day we will no doubt hear, "You sound just like your Father!"

Heavenly Father, teach me to pattern my speech in a manner that sounds like Your heart. Remind me to be kind and encouraging with my words today and always. I pray in the sweet name of Jesus. Amen.

Wired Tired?

You have persevered and have endured hardships for my name, and have not grown weary (Revelation 2:3).

Scripture: **Revelation 2:1-7**
Song: **"Art Thou Weary?"**

"You look tired," says a concerned friend. My response? I puff up with pride, wearing my exhaustion as a badge of honor. I know sometimes I wrongly perceive my tiredness as spirituality, especially if I've been overly busy with kingdom work. Then I excuse my fatigue by saying, "This is the way God made me. He wired me tired."

But has the Lord really called us to lives of weariness? He certainly wants us to persevere, but Christ also called His disciples to refresh and renew themselves: "Come with me by yourselves to a quiet place and get some rest" (Mark 6:31). Here's what I find truly remarkable: the disciples were busy doing wonderful things for God, yet Jesus called them away to a *better* venture—to rest for a time.

I needed a daily reminder of this truth, so I pasted Isaiah 40:31 on my mirror: "Those who hope in the Lord will renew their strength. They will soar on wings like eagles; they will run and not grow weary, they will walk and not be faint." How do these words encourage you?

God, help me to realize that my weariness—even from my attempt to serve You—is hardly a badge of honor. Nudge me to rest and to restore myself from the busyness of daily life. Call me away that I might simply be still and enjoy being in Your presence. In the name of my Lord Christ, amen.

How Worthy!

Thou art worthy, O Lord, to receive glory and honor and power: for thou hast created all things, and for thy pleasure they are and were created (Revelation 4:11, *King James Version*).

Scripture: **Revelation 4**
Song: **"All Things Bright and Beautiful"**

"All things bright and beautiful . . . the Lord God made them all." Cecil Alexander created this familiar hymn refrain in 1848 while staying in Ireland's spectacular Markree Castle. The nobility of this old stone fortress, coupled with the beauty of the surrounding landscape, urged her to inscribe words that would stand the test of years. And these are, indeed, memorable words sparked by her awe of the Lord's creative hand.

It makes me consider: how often do I neglect the myriad evidences of God's handiwork in my life? Life passes by in a scurry of daily activities. However, His creation calls out to me to slow down for a moment of enjoyment and wonder. Look! A hummingbird whizzes by my window. The wet fragrance of newly mowed grass wafts through the screen. Sips of steamy jasmine tea revive my afternoon. God bestows these graces as a reminder to stay aware of His marvels on earth.

Yes, today I will slow down a bit. Praise will flow from my tongue to the Lord God who made all things. How worthy He is!

Lord, *I praise You for the beauty of creation. The flowers, the animals, the sunshine, and moonlight declare Your magnificence. In Jesus' name, amen.*

Those Blessed Beetles

They cried out to the Lord in their trouble, and he delivered them from their distress (Psalm 107:6).

Scripture: **Psalm 107:1-9**
Song: **"Enough"**

I was a sophomore in college when my family's financial burdens started weighing heavily upon me. My parents had three children in college, and Dad had health problems. We were in debt.

I'd seen God answer prayers in my life, but this was overwhelming to me. With the medical bills and college expenses piling up, the situation seemed hopeless. I didn't know anywhere else to turn, but to God. I asked for the money to cover it all.

Why are we surprised when God answers our big requests? I certainly was. We discovered beetles in the trees on our farm, so after selling the trees from 60 acres, we could pay all the bills! But, you see, we weren't in the tree-growing business and would never have thought of selling those trees. Except for those blessed beetles.

God is a bit more creative than we are, isn't He? I considered this entire unfolding of events to be quite miraculous. For this I know: He answers when we cry out to Him.

Father, You are so good. You are faithful. Your love endures forever. Forgive me when I forget just who You are. In the name of Jesus, amen.

April 16–22. **Carol Bradfield** has taught Sunday school and numerous small-group Bible studies. She and her husband, Jim, live in LaGrange, Georgia.

A Clean Fix

Let us draw near to God with a sincere heart in full assurance of faith, having our hearts sprinkled to cleanse us from a guilty conscience (Hebrews 10:22).

Scripture: **Hebrews 9:11-15**
Song: **"Nothing but the Blood"**

"Mom, the sink's leaking again."

"That's it! I'm calling the plumber," Mom said.

Dad had tried numerous times to fix those leaking pipes, slathering plumber's cement all over. (I'm sure he must have used his ever-at-hand gray duct tape too.) The leaks kept coming back, though, awaiting a proper fix.

The plumber and his helper arrived. After replacing the pipes, the assistant, John, said, "Miss Eva, you'll save yourself a lot of money, if you call us before your husband tries to help."

The pipes had rusted on the inside, and the rust was wearing through to the outside. Dad's surface fixes only helped for a time; the plumbers fixed all the previous problems in one attempt. Now Mom had new kitchen pipes, good inside and out.

Jesus does something similar within all who love Him. He corrects all of our cover-ups, our futile attempts to right our wrongs. He clears away all the surface fixes and goes straight to the internal cleansing we need.

Abba, thank You for doing such a great work for me and in me. Thank You for the blood of Christ that justifies me and then frees me from sin. Help me keep my heart pure and my conscience clear today. In Jesus' name, amen.

No Turning Back

I press on to take hold of that for which Christ took hold of me (Philippians 3:12).

Scripture: **1 Peter 1:13-21**
Song: **"Follow Me, the Master Said"**

"I'll take the grilled chicken salad with fat-free ranch dressing," Pam said.

After the waitress left, I asked her, "Why don't you celebrate with a big pasta dish?" Pam had reached her weight-loss goal, having lost 20 pounds and droped two sizes. She looked fantastic.

"I still want to be careful. I worked too hard, and I don't want to gain any of it back!" she replied.

"I guess that means we're not splitting a dessert," I said. She rolled her eyes, laughed, and shook her head.

For four months, Pam planned meals and walked around her neighborhood. She obediently followed the plan and determinedly said no to many and various temptations. She kept focusing on the envisioned results. And the results were indeed spectacular—a new appearance and a new attitude.

Pam's experience reminds me of the scriptural principle before us today: Let us stay alert, follow Christ's plan, say no to the things that so easily weigh us down, and focus on the goal—becoming more like Christ.

O Father, thank You for such a priceless and wonderful gift, the gift of Your Son. Keep me from going back to my old ways and old loves. Help me press on, through Christ who strengthens me. Amen.

Let the Music Begin!

He put a new song in my mouth, a song of praise to our God; many will see and fear, and will trust in the Lord (Psalm 40:3, *New American Standard Bible*).

Scripture: **Psalm 40:1-5**
Song: **"I Will Sing of the Mercies"**

"I'd never heard people sing like that," my friend Jennifer said. "As a musician, it intrigued me. They really *meant* what they were singing."

I listened as Jennifer told me about the first time she'd visited a particular church. She was 25, and her sister had invited her. That was also intriguing because her sister had been as wild and rebellious as Jennifer was.

Church was nothing like Jennifer had expected—not just the music, but the people too. The way they treated each other, how they loved each other . . . it all drew her back to the services, week after week.

Jennifer had long viewed Christianity's claims with skepticism. Yet, because those believers sang with such heartfelt intensity and loved one another so deeply, she decided to investigate further. She started reading the Bible, looked into its historicity and authority, opened her heart to its callings. Before long, she had entered the waters of baptism.

It all began with the music.

Heavenly Father, Your wonders are many. Your thoughts are too great for me. Your mercies are new every morning. Help me not only to sing of Your mercies but also to declare them daily. In the name of Christ, amen.

Heartfelt Affection

It is right for me to feel this way about all of you, since I have you in my heart (Philippians 1:7).

Scripture: **Philippians 1:3-11**
Song: **"Bind Us Together"**

"So, how long have you two known each other?" a new acquaintance asked my suite mate Carla and me. It was the October after we started college, and without hesitation we both replied, "Since August." We were as surprised as everyone else at our simultaneous answer.

Carla and I thought alike and often spoke together like that, sometimes stating whole sentences in unison. The summer before attending college, each of us had prayed for a best friend. We were each other's answer to prayer. We lived in the dormitory together for four years, through good times and bad.

I've been out of college for almost 15 years now, and every time I think of Carla, it is with thanksgiving and affection. Although we don't see each other often, she's in my heart and will always be a special friend.

I am thankful for Paul's words in this passage, and I can understand them more powerfully when I put faces to them, faces of those whom God has placed in my life. I don't think Paul would mind if I used his prayer on their behalf—and let them know of my intentions.

Dear Lord, I thank You for the wonderful people You have placed in my life. May I not only remember them but also remember to pray for them. In the name of the Father, the Son, and the Holy Spirit, I pray. Amen.

Earning the Position

We pray . . . that you may live a life worthy of the Lord and may please Him in every way (Colossians 1:10).

Scripture: **Revelation 5:1-5**
Song: **"Worthy Is the Lamb"**

"So, how did you arrive at your current position?" I asked the architect seated at our banquet table.

"I was with a firm in the Midwest when an employment agency called and asked whether I'd be interested in this job. The position required licensing in several states, which I had, along with experience in a specific industry, which I also had."

"How many other candidates also met the criteria?"

"Only two or three others, as far as I know. Our qualifications arose from the work we'd been doing to that point. My previous jobs required the licenses. I was blessed to be one of the few who had what was required for this position."

Very few had what was required for such a specialized job. In Revelation, I find another specialized job—that of breaking the seals and opening the scroll. No one in Heaven or earth could do it except Christ. He alone was worthy, having earned the right through His triumph over sin and death. So consider this: if He has earned the right to such a great position in Heaven, what has He earned the right to do in and through our lives?

O God, show me any part of my life that does not honor You. Your Son died for me; help me to live for Him. In His name I pray. Amen.

A Worthy Lord

From Him and through Him and to Him are all things. To Him be the glory forever. Amen (Romans 11:36, *New American Standard Bible*).

Scripture: **Revelation 5:11-14**
Song: **"Blessing, Honor, and Glory"**

I stepped to the counter and ordered my meal "to go" at the busy fast-food restaurant. When I got back in my car, though, I noticed I had no fork . . . or salad dressing. I went back; the counter lady seemed genuinely embarrassed. "I'm sorry. I must have overlooked them," she said. "I try to double-check to make sure I haven't left anything out." I thanked her, knowing that being in a hurry makes it easier for any human being to leave something unintentionally undone.

In Revelation, John tells us Christ is worthy to receive many things: power, riches, wisdom, might, honor, glory, and blessing, not just for now but forever. The elders, living creatures, and angels were *intentional* as they praised Him.

But are we? How often do we take the time to "double-check" our hearts, lifestyles, and praises? Do we intentionally give Him all of the things the heavenly hosts say He is worthy to receive?

Almighty Creator and Lord of my life, You are worthy of power and riches. You are full of might and wisdom. Help me intentionally and continually give You all the praise You deserve. I pray this prayer in the name of Jesus, my all-worthy Savior. Amen.

Nov. 1 '10

They'll Know

We have heard of your faith in Christ Jesus and of the love you have for all the saints (Colossians 1:4).

Scripture: **Colossians 1:3-8**
Song: **"They'll Know We Are Christians by Our Love"**

Have you Googled today?

The Internet search engine called Google™ is now so well known that its name has become a common verb. Like many successful companies, Google™ used advertisements and other promotions to establish a brand that represents its product with a single word.

As Christians, what is our brand? For what are we known? Just think how powerful our witness would be if the label of Christian became synonymous with love! And not just love as a concept or feeling, but love as an action verb.

Of course, we are not a business, and love isn't a sales technique that we can use to attract people to our church. We love because Christ loved us and because it is what God calls us to do. Love is one way of manifesting His mercy and grace in our daily lives and expressing it to everyone we come in contact with. It asks for nothing in return. It was happening in the ancient city of Colosse. Could it happen your town too?

*Thank You, **Lord,** for loving me. Grant me boldness and creativity as I seek to share Your love with the people in my life. Through Christ, amen.*

April 23–29. **Beth Huber** is a pianist and piano teacher as well as a freelance writer and editor. She resides in Chester County, Pennsylvania.

Look Up

I will lift up mine eyes unto the hills, from whence cometh my help (Psalm 121:1, *King James Version*).

Scripture: **Psalm 121**
Song: **"Jesus, Lord, We Look to Thee"**

In the past when people asked my opinion or advice about ethical matters, I would begin my response by saying "If it were me . . ." or "Well, I would. . . ." It's as if I were presenting myself as an expert, somebody with all the moral answers. But I came to realize that God's perspective on right and wrong might hold a little more weight! He is the expert with all the answers.

So I've been making an effort to stop using those phrases. I now try to direct people's eyes upward to God when they're struggling with a tough quandary or facing a decision-making challenge. As I seek to filter all of life's choices and situations through the truth of the gospel, I want to help others do the same thing.

That's really where we need to look, isn't it? Up to the hills, up to Heaven itself, where God sits enthroned in glory. Yet it gives me a thrill to know that this same Lord of all chooses to dwell within me as well. What an awesome Lord we have! He is our help and He is our hope.

Gracious God, when I face times of confusion or trouble, may I look to You for the way through. And when I advise others, may I encourage them to keep their focus on You as well. Thank You that we can rely on the truth of the gospel and the wisdom of Your Word. All praise to You, in Christ's holy name. Amen.

Everyday Blessings

I lie down and sleep; I wake again because the LORD sustains me (Psalm 3:5).

Scripture: **Psalm 3**
Song: **"Great Is Thy Faithfulness"**

Traveling in a foreign country can be unsettling. Everything is so different! The unfamiliar language, the new food, the "strange" customs—all force us to rethink every move we make. The simplest, formerly routine actions now seem to require extra effort. Ordering a beverage, finding a restroom, and even crossing the street suddenly require an added measure of awareness, concentration, exploration, and discovery.

What if we approached this day as if we were in a foreign country? What if we took the time to notice every small comfort and provision with fresh eyes, with new appreciation for God's grace and care? He is behind these everyday blessings of life that we take so much for granted. Every breath, every heartbeat—every hour of every day—is a gift from the Lord who sustains our being. "His compassions never fail. They are new every morning; great is your faithfulness" (Lamentations 3:22, 23). As fellow travelers, as pilgrims in this foreign land, let's give thanks for His great faithfulness.

Heavenly Father, I am so grateful for all the blessings that You supply every day. Forgive me for the times when I take those things for granted. I pray for an attitude of gratitude and a spirit of thanksgiving for Your faithfulness and all that You provide for me. In Jesus' name, amen.

Whom Shall I Fear?

Fear the LORD, you his saints, for those who fear him lack nothing. The lions may grow weak and hungry, but those who seek the LORD lack no good thing (Psalm 34:9, 10).

Scripture: **Psalm 34:1-10**
Song: **"Great and Wonderful"**

Some Bible translations use words other than "fear" in Psalm 34:9, including "honor," "revere," "respect," and "worship." Dictionary definitions of *fear* reflect those ideas but also include the phrases "anxiety caused by real or possible danger" and "to expect with misgiving."

That kind of fear is something we might have trouble reconciling with our understanding of God as a loving and gracious Father. Yet God also loves justice, provides discipline when it's necessary, and allows us to face the negative consequences of wrong choices. That kind of fear can prevent us from falling into sinful attitudes, words, and actions.

Christian author Elisabeth Elliot wrote, "The more we learn to fear God, the less we fear anything else." When we are in right relationship with the Lord, when we honor His authority, our day-to-day fears and anxieties lose their lion like power to bring us down.

*How awesome and powerful You are, **Mighty God!** Thank You for reminding me that when I fear You—when I give You the honor and authority You deserve—I have no need to fear anything or anyone else. I bow down before You in worship and praise. In the name of the Father, the Son, and the Holy Spirit, I pray. Amen.*

The Best Offense

Because you have kept My command to persevere, I also will keep you from the hour of trial which shall come upon the whole world, to test those who dwell on the earth (Revelation 3:10, *New King James Version*).

Scripture: **Revelation 3:7-13**
Song: **"Who Is on the Lord's Side?"**

Perseverance is one of those unsung, underrated character qualities. It implies a sense of plodding or treading water, making little if any visible progress. That just doesn't seem very thrilling or impressive, does it? And yet, according to this passage from Revelation, that type of endurance is going to be rewarded by God.

Consider the role of the defense in a sport like football. In my own limited understanding of the game, I've always appreciated the glory of the big offensive plays. To my untrained eye, those dramatic plays are easier to understand and get excited about. (In fact, I've always felt that the teams should be running touchdowns every few minutes in order keep the game action packed.)

But a friend recently gave me some insight into the value of the defensive role. He described the strategy, teamwork, courage, and determination necessary for a successful defense. Denying victory to the opposition can prevent the defeat of our team. As they say, "The best offense is a good defense."

Dear Lord, *I pray for a greater appreciation of a persevering defense against evil. Please give me courage, faith, and strength. Through Christ, amen.*

The Power of One

I looked and there before me was a great multitude that no one could count, from every nation, tribe, people and language, standing before the throne and in front of the Lamb. They were wearing white robes and were holding palm branches in their hands (Revelation 7:9).

Scripture: **Revelation 7:1-3, 9, 10**
Song: **"To the Lamb"**

In 1999 the world's population reached six billion people. To get a handle on that enormous number, think about this: In 1972, the *Pioneer 10* spacecraft lifted off into space, and it took 25 years to reach the distance of six billion miles from earth, with round-trip communications at that point taking more than 18 hours (at the speed of light, 186,000 miles per second).

Now picture the size of the crowd worshiping at the feet of the Lord as He sits on His throne in Heaven. Try to imagine the number of believers over the entire scope of human history past, present, and future. The sights and sounds of that experience are unfathomable—the splendor of God, the mass of diverse peoples, the echoes of praise and worship.

It is an awesome thing to belong to the family of God! There we will all be, along with every tribe, every people, every language represented. That is the glory, supremacy, and majesty of our Lord. That is the power of One.

God, I can hardly imagine the glorious spectacle of all believers worshiping You. What a wonderful day that will be! Through Christ my Lord, amen.

Touch of God

The Lamb at the center of the throne will be their shepherd; he will lead them to springs of living water. And God will wipe away every tear from their eyes (Revelation 7:17).

Scripture: **Revelation 7:11-17**
Song: **"He Touched Me"**

The sense of touch is said to be the first sense we experience in the womb and the last sense we lose before we die. While the other four senses (sight, hearing, taste, and smell) are located in specific areas, the sense of touch encompasses the entire body. Research has shown that babies who are frequently touched and held will fuss less, sleep better, and even have stronger immune systems as adults. That's how important touch is to human beings.

Our Scripture verse for today conveys the image of an affectionate, personal Lord who touches us. He goes beyond making sure our sorrows cease; He touches our faces, gently wiping away our tears like a parent comforting a child.

Our God is spirit, so we can't know His literal, physical touch. But He is not removed or distant. Through the comfort of the indwelling Holy Spirit—and through loving friends, our family, and church members—we do indeed experience the touch of God in our lives.

*Thank You, **Father,** for this beautiful picture of Your tender kindness. I long for the time when there will be no more sadness. Thank You, too, for the comfort You give me in this life. In the holy name of Jesus, my Lord and Savior, I pray. Amen.*

What to Do with Grace

Tell those who have been invited. . . . Come to the wedding banquet (Matthew 22:4).

Scripture: **Matthew 22:1-14**
Song: **"Come, Let Us Use the Grace Divine"**

This parable tells us what to do with grace by telling us what *not* to do with it. Do not turn down its invitation to attend God's banquet. Show up for the feast of God's lavish blessings. As the roll is taken at the table of God's bounty, answer when your name is called.

Grace is given to be accepted. The biblical record is clear about that. A woman taken in adultery, a tax collector up a tree, a hopeless paralytic let down through a hastily torn up roof—all of them discovered it. A man whose sight had gone, a man who never had any, a woman who got her dead son back. They accepted grace.

And then there's the disciple who vehemently denied Jesus but was restored and commissioned by Jesus to feed His lambs. It's all the same for them. It's all the same for us. Grace is given to be received.

Respond affirmatively to God's creating grace that gives life. Say yes to God's saving grace that offers eternity. Receive the sustaining grace that keeps you each day.

*Your grace is everywhere, **O God,** and I am most grateful. I open my heart today to receive every offer of Your goodness. Through Christ, amen.*

April 30. **Phillip H. Barnhart,** retired minister, has written 13 books, compiled 5 others, and contributed numerous articles to various publications. He lives on Perdido Bay in Florida with his wife, Sharon.

My Prayer Notes

DEVOTIONS®

Gary Allen, Editor

***T**he grace of the Lord Jesus be with God's people.*

—Revelation 22:21

MAY

Photo © Díamar

Devotions® is published quarterly by Standard Publishing, 8121 Hamilton Avenue, Cincinnati, Ohio, 45231. A division of Standex International Corporation. © 2006 by Standard Publishing. All rights reserved. Topics based on the Home Daily Bible Readings, International Sunday School Lessons. © 2003 by the Committee on the Uniform Series. Printed in the U.S.A. All Scripture quotations, unless otherwise indicated, are taken from the HOLY BIBLE, NEW INTERNATIONAL VERSION®. NIV®. Copyright © 1973, 1978, 1984 by International Bible Society. Used by permission of Zondervan. All rights reserved. *New American Standard Bible (NASB),* © 1960, 1962, 1963, 1968, 1971, 1972 The Lockman Foundation. *The Contemporary English Version (CEV).* Copyright © 1991, 1992, 1995 American Bible Society. Used by permission. All rights reserved.

A Song to Sing

They were singing, "Lord God All-Powerful, you have done great and marvelous things. You are the ruler of all nations, and you do what is right and fair (Revelation 15:3, *Contemporary English Version*).

Scripture: **Revelation 15:1-5**
Song: **"Majesty"**

When we belong to God, we have a song to sing, a song of testimony to the greatness of God in our lives. It is a song of grace and glory that counters philosopher Friedrich Nietzsche's taunting of the church: "They would have to sing better songs to make me believe in their Redeemer." We sing wonderful songs because we have a wonderful God. Our music starts on earth and ascends to heaven on the wings of our love for Him and our faith in His promises. Like those John saw in his vision, we play our instruments and lift our voices in praise.

When we belong to God, we do not keep our music inside us. We let it out every day, in every way. Just as the Israelites sang a song of deliverance to God, we sing a song of thanksgiving to the one who made us, died for us, and keeps us company throughout the day.

All-Powerful Lord in Heaven, You have done such great things! All Your ways are right and fair, as You extend perfect justice combined with infinite mercy. How can I keep from singing Your praises? In the name of Jesus, Lord and Savior of all, I pray. Amen.

May 1–6. **Phillip H. Barnhart,** retired minister, is also a prolific writer, contributing articles to various publications. He lives in Florida with his wife, Sharon.

Bow Now!

The kingdom of the world has become the kingdom of our Lord and of His Christ; and He will reign forever and ever (Revelation 11:15, *New American Standard Bible*).

Scripture: **Revelation 11:15-19**
Song: **"I Exalt Thee"**

In New York's Rockefeller Center stands a famous bronze statue of the Greek god Atlas carrying the globe of the world on his mighty shoulders. He is bending forward, straining greatly under the tremendous weight. Every muscle and tendon stands out in agonizing relief. Just across the street, at Saint Patrick's Cathedral, is another statue depicting the Christ child. Here the baby Jesus serenely and effortlessly holds the globe of the world in the palm of His tiny hand.

God—not *a* god—is in charge. The control knob is in His hand; His management holds sway throughout the cosmos. And if the entire universe is already His kingdom, then it makes sense to await the coming day announced in Revelation 11:5. Then, visible to all, Christ will reveal himself as sovereign ruler of the world as well.

He holds back for a while, letting human will have its say. But He will not restrain himself forever, as Revelation powerfully reminds us. The question is, am I bowing my knee to this sovereign ruler *now*, so it won't be a shock when I must do it *then*?

Sovereign Lord, throughout the whole universe, all things are under Your authority. I acknowledge: that includes me too. Through Christ, amen.

Raise Your Praise

Praise the LORD. Praise the LORD from the heavens, praise him in the heights above (Psalm 148:1).

Scripture: **Psalm 148:1-6**
Song: **"Oh! Say, but I'm Glad"**

A minister had just started his Sunday sermon when thunder roared in the heavens, lightning flashed across the sky, and rain poured down in pounding torrents. Always one to recognize God's blessings in everything, the preacher said to the congregation, "Isn't God wonderful? While all of us are sitting in here, dry and comfortable, He's out in the parking lot washing our cars!"

Great reasons to raise our praise to God pop up everywhere. No turn of the head or touch of the heart escapes the call to thanksgiving for the excesses of God's grace. We could go on for an hour, lifting up every word of thanksgiving for what God does for us, and still remain far from exhausting our inventory of praise. The psalmist clearly felt the impact of God's goodness as well. He plumbs the depths of vocabulary and syntax to find phrases sufficient to honor Him.

The primary *focus* of the spiritual life is what God does for us and who God is to us. The foremost *obligation* of the spiritual life is to express our gratitude.

Dear God, I raise my praise to You for the full cupboard of my life and the adventures with You in my journey. Because of Your bounty, I come to You with a hallelujah heart and an amen attitude. I fall down before You, overwhelmed by Your blessings. In the name of Christ, amen.

Don't Hold That Applause!

Let them praise the name of the LORD, for his name alone is exalted; his splendor is above the earth and the heavens (Psalm 148:13).

Scripture: **Psalm 148:7-14**
Song: **"O for a Thousand Tongues"**

During the opening ceremonies of a state fair, the governor was honored with a 19-gun salute. When the emcee explained to the crowd that a 21-gun salute would mean the president was in attendance, a bright 8-year-old girl asked her grandfather what it would mean if it had been a 100-gun salute. "I don't know, honey," he said.

She responded, "It would mean *God* is in town!"

God is always in our town. Let us take up the psalmist's invitation and respond accordingly, as Arturo Toscanini once did when he visited the Grand Canyon. A companion watched as the great conductor stood motionless, contemplating the miracle of what stretched before him. Suddenly, after a long and silent meditation, the maestro burst into applause.

What God does for us each day is what might be called "shouting news." Breath of life, vista of opportunity, gift of skill and talent, touch of friends and family—the list goes on and on, and each item deserves and demands our exuberant response.

Magnificent God, You give me so many reasons for praise! You bring gifts to me in such a variety of creative ways, and I am grateful for each of them. In the holy name of Jesus, my Lord and Savior, I pray. Amen.

You're the Greatest!

The twenty-four elders and the four living creatures fell down and worshiped God who sits on the throne (Revelation 19:4, *New American Standard Bible*).

Scripture: **Revelation 19:1-5**
Song: **"The Great God of Heaven"**

God is larger than our concepts of Him, and no finite dogma or creed can capture God's infinite vastness. God is not even in space; space is in God. He sits at the head of creation, high and holy on the throne of dominion. And like the elders and creatures of our verse today, wherever we turn we must acknowledge the ultimate power and boundless presence of God. God minus the world equals God. The world minus God equals nothing.

At the funeral of Louis XIV, the cathedral overflowed with those who came to pay their tribute to a monarch they perceived as great. The room was dark, save for one candle illuminating the king's golden casket.

At the appointed time, the court preacher stood to address the people. He reached from the pulpit and snuffed out the single candle that had been placed there to symbolize the greatness of the king amid all else.

Then from the darkness came four words, "God only is great."

Infinite and Sovereign God, I come to bow down before Your magnitude and magnificence. I open my mouth to say what I think of You but cannot speak. You are so much more than mind can reflect or tongue can recite. Let this silence reveal my thankful heart. Through Christ I pray. Amen.

Where to Kneel

I knelt at the feet of the angel and began to worship him. But the angel said, "Don't do that! I am a servant, just like you and everyone else who tells about Jesus. Don't worship anyone but God" (Revelation 19:10, *Contemporary English Version*).

Scripture: **Revelation 19:6-10**
Song: "For the Healing of the Nations"

Soon after signing the Emancipation Proclamation, Abraham Lincoln took a trip up the river to Richmond. When he got off the boat on the river bank at the edge of the Confederate capital, a group of former slaves recognized him from half-remembered pictures they'd seen over the years. One of the men ran several yards to where Lincoln stood with his advisers, knelt directly in front of him, and attempted to kiss his shoes. But the president spoke quickly and graciously. He said, "Do not kneel to me. You must kneel only to God."

Imagine if, on the day that happened, the apostle John could have watched from Heaven. He might recall the angel's word of caution to him, too, and heartily approve of Lincoln's words.

All of us humans stand before God on level ground, created excellently, loved equally and fully. Misguided human will makes some of us slaves and some of us rulers . . . for now. In the kingdom to come, we will all be free—at liberty to worship our Lord forever, side by side.

God, You reign among all peoples and circumstances. And I, among my fellow servants, kneel before You. All praise to You, in Jesus' name. Amen.

He's All in All

As I have often told you before and now say again even with tears, many live as enemies of the cross of Christ. Their destiny is destruction, their god is their stomach, and their glory is in their shame (Philippians 3:18, 19).

Scripture: **Philippians 3:17-21**
Song: **"Be Thou My Vision"**

John's heart attack struck at noon, and by 4:30 doctors had placed two stents into a main artery, assuring much better cardiac blood flow. Three days later he returned home with a new lease on life—but still facing battles with his addiction to cigarettes.

In the following days, John realized how much of his life, night and day, centered around his smoking habit. Trying hard to quit, he didn't know what to do with his hands, his time, his thoughts; he felt a great loss of control.

I feel for John, knowing that we are all addicted to some finite "god" in one way or another. The challenge of life is to free ourselves from what some have called the false infinites that demands inordinate affection. The apostle Paul writes that as long as these earthly things are so important to us, God remains less than our all in all.

Father God, when I am weak, I ask for strength. When I am tired, I ask for rest. When I fail to put You first, I ask for intervention. I am not in control, and I give thanks that You are! Through Christ my Lord, amen.

May 7–13. **Geneva Rodgers** is a rural grandmother embarking on her third career of writing. She's active in her church and views every day as a new beginning.

Hourly Battle

He must reign until he has put all his enemies under his feet (1 Corinthians 15:25).

Scripture: **1 Corinthians 15:20-28**
Song: **"Jesus Shall Reign"**

John is in his second week of battle against those cigarettes that likely contributed to his heart attack. I'm cheering him on, but he finds it no easier to quit today than when he started. It's an hourly fight . . .

Across town, Sarah stands in her kitchen, preparing the evening meal, and her battle rages too. It's in her smell, taste, and touch as she handles the food. There's that leftover piece of pie on the counter, ice cream in the freezer, gravy to taste for seasoning—and what tempting mashed potatoes! It's a regular boxing ring here, and Sarah, fighting in the heavyweight class, fights hard . . .

And here's Jane. Her good friend has just dropped by for a little gossip session. Jane has tried to conquer the habit but wants so badly to share what she overheard in the post office about the Smiths. It's a *war!*

Have you learned yet that willpower doesn't work against those kinds of internal enemies? Yet if we can sit still with our temptations long enough, we'll sense a deeper "I want" bubbling up in our hearts. We want *Him*, the source of our deepest longing, the one who won't let us go until He reigns within, free and clear.

Dear Father, *waiting in Your presence, I feel the pull of this habit. Let Your "pull" within me be stronger just now. In Jesus' name, amen.*

It's Not About Me

We make it our goal to please him, whether we are at home in the body or away from it (2 Corinthians 5:9).

Scripture: **2 Corinthians 5:1-10**
Song: **"Lord of the Dance"**

One more word about my friend John: he loves God, attends church, prays, and studies his Bible. But he fails to realize that abusing his lungs with smoke hardly pleases God. His focus is on himself at the moment—how hard it is to quit, how much he's giving up, how scary the prospects if he doesn't stop. That load gets pretty heavy on a daily basis. What are the chances he can continue?

Will, on the other hand, has taken a different approach. He knows without a doubt he can't quit on his own. He acknowledges his weakness and seeks daily strength from God and loving encouragement from God's people. I've noticed that his load seems to lighten each day. What are the chances he will continue?

These bodies of ours aren't really about us. They're about our stewardship, our call to stay fit for God's work through us. (I, too, need much help there!) With John and Will, and all my brothers and sisters in Christ, I come before God to humbly confess my failures. But I also come to renew my fondest hope: that I might please Him.

None of us knows how long our bodies will last. But to please Him—*whether here or there*—what a great goal!

Father, You have given me this body to keep ready for Your service. Help me to care for it as You care for me and my friends. In Christ, amen.

One Step at a Time

By faith Abraham . . . considered him faithful who had made the promise (Hebrews 11:11).

Scripture: **Hebrews 11:10-16**
Song: **"My Faith Looks Up to Thee"**

My daughter, a physical therapist, tells stories of patients struggling to regain their health after suffering strokes, automobile accidents, and other crises. She's a nurturing, caring soul, but often these patients begin to dread her appearance in their doorways. Why? Because they know whatever she has in store for them that day will likely hurt. No pain, no gain.

The therapy may involve just lifting an arm, taking a small step, pushing a ball, or simply trying to sit up. But the early treatments usually hurt, nevertheless.

And they hurt my daughter's heart! She feels her patients' pain as they try so hard. But she also knows that weeks later much of the pain will be replaced by the joy of freer movement and better coordination. That's when she's greeted with smiles (and an occasional piece of pie). They had faith in her ability; they persevered in the promise of regained health.

In our relationship with God, our hurts are just as real, just as painful. He is faithful, though, and calls us to have faith in His saving ability. We are rewarded with wholeness, fullness, a complete turn around.

God, You made me Your child. Now help me take each step toward becoming in practice what I am in position. Thank You, in Jesus' name. Amen.

What Kind of Life?

The heavens will disappear with a roar; the elements will be destroyed by fire, and the earth and everything in it will be laid bare. Since everything will be destroyed in this way, what kind of people ought you to be? You ought to live holy and godly lives (2 Peter 3:10, 11).

Scripture: **2 Peter 3:10-18**
Song: **"Amazing Grace"**

It had been such a good day. Lots of friends had called to visit. Lots of news had flown over the wires; sadly, most of it was hearsay. But Jane was elated to know that she was the hub of the group, the confidante of all. She would listen, absorb, and eventually pass on certain "information" to whomever she thought needed to hear.

Things came to a screeching halt at the post office later in the afternoon. As circumstances would have it, all four friends were there as Jane entered. Their faces were not pleasant, and their bodies quickly turned inward to close her out. Apparently Jane's gossip had somehow trampled on the feelings and reputations of her friends. It wasn't supposed to happen, but it did.

As we consider Peter's words in our verse, each of us must look at our lives to see what Jesus will find there when the earth and heavens finally melt away. What He sees—now and *then*—ought to be holy and godly lives.

*Renew my heart, **O God,** that I might walk ever closer to You. Make my actions loving and self-giving, and cloak my words in kindness. Your Son, Jesus, is my best example! In His name I pray. Amen.*

Let Him Hear Your Cry

Before they call I will answer; while they are still speaking I will hear (Isaiah 65:24).

Scripture: **Isaiah 65:17-19, 23-25**
Song: **"I Want to Be Ready"**

Sarah is 76, a beautiful 76 years old. She doesn't know why she's been so blessed with good health, a sharp mind, her original teeth, and very few ailments. Sarah is afraid of dying . . . and also afraid to let anyone know it.

Chad, 33, divorced, had found a supportive Bible study group. He called for help, for peace, for meaning. Just recently he told several friends he felt his time on earth was short. He had finally gotten his life in order and was content. Chad died this past week.

A child dies in an auto accident, a nursing home resident turns 100, a father of three succumbs in a fire, and a fiancée is raped and killed. Their stories all appear together in my newspaper, and I know I could search my whole life to make sense of these puzzling patterns. Yet I must content myself with this: only God can know my own readiness, when my spirit is "done" and ready to leave this earthly existence. We can theorize, we can mathematize, we can philosophize. But until the cry of our heart is surrender, perhaps we have not yet called to Him.

Loving Father, on bended knees I cry out to You for the peace that passes understanding. I cry for joy at Your patience with me and Your continued love. How I thank You for hearing me! And I do want to be ready for Your call to service, whatever it may involve. I pray in Jesus' name. Amen.

Worth the Fight

He will wipe every tear from their eyes. There will be no more death or mourning or crying or pain, for the old order of things has passed away (Revelation 21:4).

Scripture: **Revelation 21:1-8**
Song: **"When We All Get to Heaven"**

It's now been six weeks. John, Sarah, Will, and Jane have all walked rocky paths, fought daily battles, lost hope and regained hope, lost strength and found strength. They encountered ferocious warriors and ministering angels in their walks with God. They grew, sometimes two steps forward and one step backward.

Nevertheless . . . progress! Each has broken another dubious chain of command on their spirits, giving God more room to operate in their hearts. Were they successful in each battle? No. But they dared to fight, knowing the prize was worth the struggle. The tears and pain, the death—and all the old things—will soon pass away. Knowing this, we, like them, can take the next step forward.

When we think of a whole "order of things" passing from the scene, we may assume we're required to take giant leaps of faith each day. But God is patient with us. He knows we can usually manage only the next small step in front of us. He waits, He encourages, He picks us up when we fall. If tears need wiping away, He's there for that too. What awesome love!

O Precious Father, when my road seems too rough to travel and my load too heavy to carry, turn my gaze heavenward. In Jesus' name, amen.

Exercise Those Muscles!

I keep asking that the God of our Lord Jesus Christ, the glorious Father, may give you the Spirit of wisdom and revelation, so that you may know him better (Ephesians 1:17).

Scripture: **Ephesians 1:15-23**
Song: **"There Is Power in the Blood"**

Muscles are an amazing part of God's creation. They are elastic, snapping back when exerted. All they do is shorten and lengthen, but these organic rubber bands are responsible for every bodily movement.

But have you ever pulled a muscle? I started a strength-training exercise program using weights a few years ago. When I first worked one of the upper-body machines, I discovered how weak my arm muscles were and how quickly they became sore. Ouch!

Yet after a few months of strength training, I realized how much easier the arm machine had become. I could push harder and faster because the more I used my muscles, the better they worked.

Perhaps Paul had this concept in mind when he prayed that the Ephesians would learn to know God better. These believers could "exercise" their belief in God's own "muscle"—the power that raised Christ from the dead.

Almighty God, thank You for exerting Your power in the resurrection of Your Son. Give me discipline to exercise a daily life of prayer so our fellowship might grow stronger and deeper. Through Christ I pray. Amen.

May 14–20. **Jane Cook** is the former White House Deputy Director of Internet News Services for President George W. Bush. She lives in Alexandria, Virginia.

Crediting the Creator

The sun will no more be your light by day, nor will the brightness of the moon shine on you, for the LORD will be your everlasting light, and your God will be your glory (Isaiah 60:19).

Scripture: **Isaiah 60:18-22**
Song: **"God of Wonders"**

My little boy loves to watch videos from a popular series for babies and toddlers. His favorite part is the puppet that acts as tour-guide narrator. The puppet introduces each new concept, such as the sky or a new color or the next number. Then the puppet steps out of the picture so the child can view videos of the sky or different colored scenes.

Even as young as 4 months, my son would coo with delight whenever the puppet appeared. Like most movies, these videos end with credits. They show the name and face of the puppeteer who gave form and function to the puppet. My son is still too young to understand that someone is guiding the puppet. But someday he will distinguish the creator from the creation.

In Genesis we learn that God created the sun to guide us by day and the moon to give us light at night. He gave the sun and moon their form and function. Isaiah reminds us that when life's "video" is over, it is the puppeteer, not the puppet, who deserves our recognition and praise.

Magnificent Creator, I praise You for Your glorious creation of the earth and sky. You are a God of far-flung wonders, yet You promise to stay close to me in deep communion. I offer my praise through Your holy Son. Amen.

Digging for Reality

Since we are receiving a kingdom that cannot be shaken, let us be thankful, and so worship God acceptably with reverence and awe (Hebrews 12:28).

Scripture: **Hebrews 12:22-28**
Song: **"Rock of Ages"**

Can you imagine proving the existence of an imaginary place? That is exactly what German archaeologist Heinrich Schliemann accomplished in 1870. He uncovered Troy, the ancient city of Homer's *Iliad.* Because Homer described Troy as a seaside town, historians concluded it was an imaginary place, since no seaside city or ruins existed in the region.

Schliemann proved the doubters wrong. He studied Homer's descriptions and eventually discovered the ruins of Troy buried inland, below other cities, in western Turkey. Clearly, although Troy was once a thriving city, it could be shaken and destroyed. Uncovering its ruins only proved its existence, not its invincibility.

Some people think Heaven is as imaginary as the Wizard's oz, Santa's workshop at the north pole or Alice's wonderland. All of these places disappear as soon as we close a book or turn off the television set. The book of Hebrews, however, promises us that we are receiving a real kingdom that cannot be shaken. Our response is to worship its king.

King of kings, I can't fathom the immensity of Your kingdom, which is and is yet to be. May I worship You in an acceptable way, with reverence and awe for Your solid invincibility. In the name of Jesus I pray. Amen.

Incremental Glory

We, who with unveiled faces all reflect the Lord's glory, are being transformed into his likeness with ever-increasing glory, which comes from the Lord, who is the Spirit (2 Corinthians 3:18).

Scripture: **2 Corinthians 3:7-18**
Song: **"He Leadeth Me"**

Several years ago Washington, D.C., residents witnessed a series of unveilings when the city became home to a new major league baseball team. To build a fan base, the new franchise sponsored a series of press events over many months. At the publicity kick off, the mayor hit a home run when he unveiled the team's name: the Washington Nationals.

A few weeks later he unveiled the team's colors and uniforms. Soon the streets and subways were filled with red T-shirts and caps boasting a curly *W*. Then a spokesperson walked around town in an egg costume to encourage fans to guess the identity of the team's mascot. When the egg hatched, out came a costumed eagle, delighting young children. Opening-day crowds proved the effectiveness of this incremental strategy.

God employs a kind of unveiling strategy with us. He doesn't make one announcement and then exit the stage. Instead, He provides us with frequent unveilings of His love, plan, and purpose for us—an ever-increasing glory.

Lord, thank You for giving me daily opportunities to grow and become more like You. May I respond in trust and obedience. In Jesus' name, amen.

Radiant Rebirth

It [Jerusalem] shone with the glory of God, and its brilliance was like that of a very precious jewel, like a jasper, clear as crystal (Revelation 21:11).

Scripture: **Revelation 21:9-14**
Song: **"By the Grace of God We'll Meet"**

Ruby and sapphire mining turned a Blue Ridge Mountain town in North Carolina into a commercial diamond in the 1870s. For years these gemstones brought a sizable profit, but the town eventually lost its sparkle when synthetic minerals replaced the commercial need for authentic stones. So, one by one the mines closed.

Years later the mines opened again, this time for tourism. Mine owners sold buckets of stoney dirt, promising visitors they could keep whatever jewels they found there. The stones were washed and held up to the sun; anything that sparkled was a precious find. When these folks began taking their newfound gems to jewelry stores to turn them into rings and necklaces, the town was reborn.

Similarly, Revelation predicts that another town will be reborn because of sunlight. The new Jerusalem will sparkle like a precious jewel, with the Son of God as its light source. Whether it's a jewel, a town, or a human being, wiping away some mud and reflecting the Son delivers a radiant rebirth.

Lord, give me a makeover; wipe off any debris and hold me up to Your light. By the power of Your indwelling Spirit, may I reflect even a fraction of Your brilliance today. Thank You, in Jesus' name. Amen.

Living Temple

I did not see a temple in the city, because the Lord God Almighty and the Lamb are its temple (Revelation 21:22).

Scripture: **Revelation 21:22-27**
Song: "Behold the Lamb"

One of my favorite buildings in Washington, D.C., is the National Cathedral. This Gothic marvel sits atop the capital city's highest hill. I love the symbolism of its cross-shaped floor plan, towering stained-glass windows, pointed arches, sky-high ceiling, giant bells, and flying buttresses. All of these characteristics encourage visitors to worship, pray, and sing to the Lord.

Most church buildings use architecture and interior design to point us toward God. A white, wooden church building in the countryside makes a simple statement about the call to a simple liftestyle. Another building's full-scale fountain pours forth a picture of the river of life. Some congregations display banners on their worship wall, the bright fabrics emblazoned with various names for God or truths of His character.

Revelation tells us the new Jerusalem will not have a temple though. The Lord himself will be its temple. No longer will we need visual symbols and architectural inspirations to motivate us to worship. The Lord's presence will be closer to us than a ring on our finger.

*You are the great architect, **God,** the builder of Your temple. Show me how to worship You in spirit and truth each day, with a sincere heart and dedicated priorities. In the name of Your Son, my Savior, I pray. Amen.*

Heavenly Imprint

They will see his face, and his name will be on their foreheads (Revelation 22:4).

Scripture: **Revelation 22:1-5**
Song: **"On My Heart Imprint Thine Image"**

When I was pregnant, my son's soccer like kicks bonded me to him before his birth. And although my husband is grateful that it's the *woman* who actually bears the child, he also needed a way to bond with his son. Would the little guy at least *look* like him?

When Austin was born, we immediately compared his tiny features to our own baby pictures. Austin's nose and ears are near duplicates of mine, but his most dominant features scream "I look like my daddy!" His forehead, hairline, hair color, skin tones, mouth, eyes—and even the dimple above his upper lip—clearly came from my husband.

Five days after Austin's birth, my husband was holding him in a doctor's office waiting room. Another patient commented that Austin looked exactly like his dad. My husband just beamed because from Austin's forehead to his toes, he bears his father's likeness.

God promises us in Revelation that from our foreheads on the outside to our hearts on the inside, we will bear our Father's imprint. How much more will our heavenly Father beam when we arrive to see His face.

Father, *thank You for loving me so much that You placed Your birthmark on my forehead. I seek to return Your love today! In Jesus' name, amen.*

Trading My Sorrows

You will grieve, but your grief will turn to joy (John 16:20).

Scripture: **John 16:17-24**
Song: **"Trading My Sorrows"**

The death of our newborn son devastated me. A year later, I was pregnant again, but fear grew within me too. What if this child contracted the same illness as our son's? I couldn't bear the thought of burying another child. I certainly didn't want to miss the miracle of this pregnancy; however, I found it hard to see past my pain.

With a heavy spirit, I forced myself to attend a praise service at our church. The words of Psalm 30:5b spoke to my frightened soul, "Weeping may remain for a night, but rejoicing comes in the morning." As I began repeating that verse, I sensed God asking me to do that very thing, to give Him my sorrow so He could exchange it for His joy.

That thought became my theme throughout the pregnancy and birth of our new son, whom I now refer to as my "joy boy." This new life is a constant reminder to me of how God delights in exchanging for joy our most disappointing and painful life experiences.

Comforting Father, *thank You for this life of adventure with You, filled with all forms of joy and sorrow. I don't expect You to remove every source of suffering while I'm on this earth. But I do look forward to the day when eternal joy is my settled home. Through Christ I pray. Amen.*

May 21–27. **Stacy Rothenberger,** mother of five, homeschools, works part-time as a speech language therapist, and enjoys writing and speaking about what God is teaching her along the way.

Why, Lord?

In this world you will have trouble. But take heart! I have overcome the world (John 16:33).

Scripture: **John 16:25-33**
Song: **"Through It All"**

"Why, Lord? Why can't my life be going as I had planned? My marriage isn't everything I expected. My kids aren't perfect. Even my friends and family have disappointed me!"

God allowed me to finish my long tirade of complaints before I sensed a tender and gentle reply: "But if everything had gone as you had planned, our intimacy wouldn't have matured. As a result of those disappointments and struggles, you are learning to depend on me. Instead of making demands, you are receiving what is given. Continue clinging to me. I will never leave you or forsake you."

Have you found these things true in your own life? In the times I've stopped complaining, and offered thanks in the midst of tough circumstances, I've experienced a renewed closeness to God. He allowed me to learn something new about myself, about others, and about His character. Yes, on the spiritual journey, hindsight is clearer than the road ahead; we're called to walk by faith. But take heart! Instead of complaining, praise Him for another opportunity to see His power revealed.

Lord, thank You for the powerful lessons hidden in each trial I face. Remind me to take heart and trust You in every situation. In Jesus' name, amen.

Bearing with One Another

Be completely humble and gentle; be patient, bearing with one another in love (Ephesians 4:2).

Scripture: **Ephesians 4:1-6**
Song: **"Cast Thy Burden Upon the Lord"**

He did it again. How could I forgive my husband for making (what I thought was) a poor decision? The Bible instructs us to "[bear] with one another in love," but what, exactly, does it mean?

I went to my dictionary and found that bear with can mean "to exert pressure or effort on." I hadn't thought of it that way before. Armed with this rather obscure definition, I felt I could at least approach my husband with my concerns rather than stuffing them into the pit of unresolved conflict.

Later, I came across another definition that surprised and encouraged me even more: "to give birth to." By my willingness to withstand, endure, support, approach, and exert, God could eventually give birth to something new—in me and in my relationships at home.

Just as a pregnant woman bears down to bring forth new life, God was allowing me the opportunity to bear with my husband in love. The result: new life sprang up within our marriage.

Dear Lord, thank You for bearing with me in love! Help me do the same for others, especially with my husband and other family members. Please breathe new life into every relationship plagued with conflict today. In the holy name of Jesus, my Lord and Savior, I pray. Amen.

Well Suited Now!

Clothe yourselves with compassion, kindness, humility, gentleness and patience. . . . And over all these virtues put on love, which binds them all together (Colossians 3:12, 14).

Scripture: **Colossians 3:12-17**
Song: **"Make Me a Blessing"**

A battered T-shirt, a mismatched pair of socks, a winter scarf, and fuzzy earmuffs—each item became a memorable teaching tool for my young children. The lesson: the importance of putting on the Lord Jesus Christ.

You see, being cooped up together for seven days a week could tax anyone's KQ (kindness quotient), and I needed something to help my children remember to model Jesus. So I labeled each item with a characteristic of Jesus. The socks were "kindness" and "gentleness," for without these it could be easy to tread on others as we climb the ladders of our own success. "Humility" and "patience" went to the earmuffs; without their covering we might hear things that make us irritable. The warm scarf symbolized "compassion," which needs to be draped over those who are hurting.

Finally, the well-worn T-shirt, symbolizing "love," was placed over all of these godly characteristics. As my children put each item on, it was as if they were actually clothing themselves with Jesus' righteousness. They were now well suited to model God's love to others.

Heavenly Father, *keep clothing me with the best of virtues that I might learn to model Your life to others. In Your loving name I pray. Amen.*

Properly Prepared

Behold, I am coming soon! Blessed is he who keeps the words of the prophecy in this book (Revelation 22:7).

Scripture: **Revelation 22:6-11**
Song: **"What If It Were Today?"**

"I'll be right over." Panic jolted me into action. My new friend mustn't see my house in such disarray! But how could I clean up the mess before she arrived? I began hiding things, shoving toys under the sofa, slamming pans into the oven and squeezing dirty clothes into dresser drawers. I even sprayed window cleaner into the air, in hopes of achieving a just-cleaned aura.

By the time she arrived, I was exhausted. And instead of enjoying our visit, I worried. What if I missed something? Would she see through my squeaky clean facade? (And what if she inadvertently took a look under the sofa?)

Jesus is coming back. In fact, He'll "be right over" (we just don't know exactly when). Instead of waiting until the last moment, we can be practicing an interior preparation, day by day. Developing a little more compassion. Opening to a deeper sense of peace, a less harried run at success. I would like to be ready with a free and joyful heart to greet my heavenly visitor when He arrives. Or, will I go to Him first?

Father, I desire to live each day in hopeful anticipation of Your Son's return. Show me the kinds of preparation that would please You most—and give me the will to put them into practice. Come, Lord Jesus. Amen.

A Sacrifice of Praise

My reward is with me, and I will give to everyone according to what he has done (Revelation 22:12).

Scripture: **Revelation 22:12-16**
Song: **"We Bring the Sacrifice of Praise"**

As a new Christian I struggled with the thought of meeting God face-to-face when I died. Would I have to hang my head in shame? I hadn't led anyone to Christ, my tithing was minimal, and I failed to reflect Jesus on many occasions. I seemed to possess nothing of significance to offer Him.

God used my biggest fear, the death of a child, to help me understand what it means to offer a sacrifice of praise. In Hebrews 13:15 we are encouraged to "continually offer to God a sacrifice of praise." A sacrifice always requires a death. It may not include a physical death but may involve the death of a desire, death of an ideal, or death of a dream. If pain weren't involved, it wouldn't be a sacrifice.

God was providing me an opportunity to offer Him a sacrifice of praise *in* and *through* my pain. Even though my heavy heart didn't want to rejoice, I deliberately chose to do so. God taught me that my response to this trial could someday be transformed into a crown of righteousness (see 2 Timothy 4:8), a crown I'll gladly lay at His feet.

Dear God, *I offer my praise for the free gift of salvation. Yet I know You call me to good works as Your grateful child. Give me the wisdom and strength to serve You well. In the name of Jesus my Savior I pray. Amen.*

Amen!

The grace of the Lord Jesus be with God's people. Amen
(Revelation 22:21).

Scripture: **Revelation 22:17-21**
Song: **"God of Grace and God of Glory"**

"Mom, do you know what the last word of the Bible is?" My 8-year-old son had me stumped, so he smiled as he answered his own question, "Amen."

Most of our prayers end with this simple word, but what does it mean? We decided to look up the definition and found that it means "May it be so." Four simple words.

Suppose we really meant our amens? Would we live differently? For example, when I read a verse such as Philippians 4:4—"Rejoice in the Lord always"—if I say amen to that, may it be so, then I don't have any excuse for not praising God at all times.

And what about Revelation 22:20 where Jesus says, "Yes, I am coming soon"? Amen, may it be so.

If I took seriously every word in the Bible, and lived as if it were so, how much of my doubt, fear, worry, anger, and self-centeredness could I easily let go? That grace-filled life Jesus promised me—how I could live it!

May it be so.

Dear Lord, may it be that You will find me faithful and waiting for Your return. In the meantime, may I share to a hurting and needy world the grace You have lavished on me. Amen, amen, amen, may it be so. I pray in Your most precious name!

Too Messy?

Rescue the weak and needy; deliver them from the hand of the wicked (Psalm 82:4).

Scripture: **Psalm 82**
Song: **"More Like the Master"**

The other day I was driving to church when traffic slowed considerably. In the closed lane ahead was a familiar red car, now dented and smashed on one side. Instantly I recognized the driver who was talking to police officers along the roadside. We had just given money to this driver for engine repairs—on a now totaled car! In my frustration, I made a choice not to stop. Everyone was OK, so rather than offering assistance or comfort, I hurried on to church.

In the busyness of daily life, it is sometimes easy to turn away from the needy. We find quite rational reasons to stay uninvolved because we are busy with family or work, lack financial resources, or feel that folks should be able to meet their own needs. What's more, other people's problems can often complicate our own lives! Yet it is just such forms of complication that make the call to service what it is: an often inconvenient giving of our self—the whole of us—including our schedules and plans.

God, may I refuse to turn away from people in need when it seems too messy to get involved. Renew my compassion, in Christ's name! Amen.

May 28–31. **Karen Lusby** is a Colorado girl—born and raised amid the beautiful mountains and clear, blue skies.

No Faking It!

Our offenses are many in your sight, and our sins testify against us. Our offenses are ever with us, and we acknowledge our iniquities (Isaiah 59:12).

Scripture: **Isaiah 59:9-15**
Song: **"Come Ye Sinners, Poor and Needy"**

When I confronted my teenage son with a missed curfew, he replied defensively "I wasn't late *on purpose*; I fell asleep. Besides, other kids are doing much worse things than I am!" How like us human beings to minimize or justify our wrongdoing!

Sadly, sin separates us, not only from one another but from God. When Israel sinned, the prophet Isaiah called the nation to repentance. Their sins were many, but God would redeem and bless the people if they sincerely and honestly owned up to their misdeeds. The principle holds for all of us: No matter our offense, we can confess our sin and be cleansed with God's forgiveness.

How much easier it would have been for my son to say "Sorry, Mom; I was wrong." Rather, he sought redemption without the necessary step of confession. Yet the two always go together. The apostle John clearly affirms: "If we confess our sins, he is faithful and just and will forgive us our sins and purify us from all unrighteousness" (1 John 1:9).

Father, help me to be perfectly genuine with You—no hiding, no faking, no covering up. How thankful I am that You call sinners into fellowship with You! Through the name of Jesus, amen.

Ruinous Disobedience

If you do not obey these commands, declares the Lord, I swear by myself that this palace will become a ruin (Jeremiah 22:5).

Scripture: **Jeremiah 22:1-5**
Song: "Joy Unspeakable"

Two young college-age Christians recently chose to date one another. With excitement, they deliberately asked their family and friends to hold them accountable to God's standards in their relationship. They are committing to physical purity as an act of obedience, claiming 1 Corinthians 6:13 as their guiding principle: "The body is not meant for sexual immorality, but for the Lord, and the Lord for the body." Although challenging in today's world, their obedience is joyful for them.

In contrast, I chose disobedience when young and dating. I tested God's limits rather than trusting His Word. In hindsight, I regret opting for instant gratification (with its resulting misery).

Through the prophet Jeremiah, God long ago made clear the benefits of following His commands. And the blessings are many: wisdom and guidance for daily life, encouragement, hope, comfort, purity, freedom, peace, protection. And, of course, we avoid the ruin of living only for ourselves.

Almighty Lord in Heaven, *my heart is sometimes weary with disobedience. In those times, give me strength and courage to turn toward You. I know Your help is available, if I will only accept it. I pray this prayer in the precious name of Jesus. Amen.*

Sometimes Walking Alone

Do two walk together unless they have agreed to do so?
(Amos 3:3).

Scripture: **Amos 3:1-10**
Song: "Faith Is the Victory"

For years I'd heard debates on how to stay in fellowship within the church while disagreeing on points of theology. The answer was to focus on Jesus Christ and on spreading the gospel rather than giving energy to divisive disputes. However, some issues have become so nationally visible that they are now splitting churches.

For example, in more than one denomination, the idea of expanding the definition of marriage seems to hold some appeal for certain members. And thus the orthodox must decide whether to walk together (and perhaps work for renewal from within) or walk away. I heard one national church leader recently recite what God asks in Amos 3:3, "Do two walk together unless they have agreed to do so?" Holding his Bible high, he said, "Those who do not uphold this—I will not go with them." I admire a person like that, one who knows that a line can be crossed by others, beyond which he cannot go.

The principles apply to all. If we align ourselves with those who have walked away from God, we are surely witnessing to our agreement with them. And we walk on dangerous ground.

O Lord, keep me walking close to You this day that I might discern truth from error and always delight in Your ways. Through Christ, amen.

DEVOTIONS®

*T*he ways of the
LORD are right;
the righteous
walk in them.

—Hosea 14:9

JUNE

Photo © Liquid Library

Gary Allen, Editor

New Start Available

The LORD has sworn by the Pride of Jacob: "I will never forget anything they have done" (Amos 8:7).

Scripture: **Amos 8:4-8**
Song: **"Amazing Grace"**

When my children were betrayed by a friend, they responded angrily: "That was unfair! I'll *never* be his friend!" Betrayed by an office colleague, I was hurt and vowed never to trust her again. When we're treated unfairly, we can hardly believe it, and we nurse our hurt.

God doesn't hold onto hurt in self-destructive ways as we so often do. However, He does remember the unfaithfulness of His people as He calls them back, over and over, to His heart of love.

How it must have hurt when Israel breached its covenant with Him! In Amos's day, the nation engaged in empty religious ritual, abusing the poor and needy. God abhors such evil; He knows and remembers the pain it causes. But we can be thankful for this: He extends the opportunity for repentance. He consistently provided warnings so the people could see their sin, repent, and receive the great blessing of forgiveness. A new start lay ahead for them, just as it does for you and me.

Dear Lord, when I am hurt and eager to judge, let me forgive as I have been forgiven. Remind me of Your mercy. I pray these things in the precious name of my Savior, Jesus Christ. Amen.

June 1–3. **Karen Lusby** is a Colorado girl—born and raised amid the beautiful mountains and clear, blue skies.

Brick by Brick

Though you have built stone mansions, you will not live in them (Amos 5:11).

Scripture: **Amos 5:10-15**
Song: **"Mansion Over the Hilltop"**

I once took great pride in being self-sufficient. I wore my apparent independence like a comfortable, well-loved sweater, a favored possession that I pulled out of the drawer and put on whenever I felt vulnerable or wasn't in complete control. Although I had given my life to Christ, I unwittingly held on to my sweater-of-sufficiency as a kind of armor of relational protection.

Slowly, over time, my sweater became tattered with age and use. I married, became a parent, divorced, and remarried. Then, months after taking a lucrative but stressful job, I was diagnosed with a potentially debilitating autoimmune disease. I couldn't protect myself from the sickness. Emotionally exposed and vulnerable, I turned to God and sought answers.

I learned that my protective sweater was really a "stone mansion" sheltering my heart. God lovingly dismantled it, brick by brick. How difficult it was to let go! Yet, finding my sufficiency in Him, how could I ever go back to the old way of being? As the apostle Paul put it in 2 Corinthians 3:5, "Not that we are competent in ourselves . . . but our competence comes from God."

Father, I know I'm often stubborn, wishing to run my own life without interference. But be my sufficiency this day. Through Christ, amen.

Openhearted?

"Even though you bring me burnt offerings and grain offerings, I will not accept them. Though you bring choice fellowship offerings, I will have no regard for them" (Amos 5:22).

Scripture: **Amos 5:20-25**
Song: **"Here I Am to Worship"**

Sunday services in our congregation begin with contemporary music worship followed by the minister's sermon. I like the music because it helps me prepare my heart to hear the scriptural message.

Recently our worship minister stood before the church and expressed his concern that our worship had seemed to become routine for us. Were we just going through the motions? Were our lips expressing what was truly in our hearts?

He challenged us gently, inquiring whether our familiarity with the service had caused us to become less than genuine. In response, we put music aside for a month during Sunday services. Instead, we worshiped together through prayer and sharing Scripture with one another.

How easy to become complacent! As God's people found long ago, when life is always the same, when worship is predictable and giving becomes routine, our hearts can drift from God. Thankfully, He knows our hearts. He keeps knocking there until we open wide once again.

My Father, God, I seek to worship and praise you with an authentic heart, open to all Your wisdom, guidance, and care. Help me to avoid being complacent with You when life is routine. I pray in Jesus' name. Amen.

The Kids Are Watching

He did evil in the sight of the LORD, as his fathers had done; he did not depart from the sins of Jeroboam the son of Nebat, which he made Israel sin (2 Kings 15:9, *New American Standard Bible*).

Scripture: **2 Kings 15:8-12**
Song: **"Father in Heaven, Who Lovest All"**

"One more minute and I'll have the bolt off this gate."

Samuel looked past his dad, afraid the police would show up. Yet he loved the feel of adrenaline pumping through him. When he was younger, he'd hated the fact his father was a thief. He laid in bed every night not knowing whether Dad would be in jail or at home when he woke up. Now Samuel understood the rush his father felt every time he made off with something valuable. What could be easier than working two hours a week to support his family? He knew stealing was wrong, but he just didn't want to stop.

Our parents play a huge role in how we think, don't they? When Israel had kings, the people could never know whether a king would "turn bad." But to make matters worse, a son would often follow in the footsteps of an evildoing dad. It's no different today. The children are watching us; they will pick up our ways, for good or ill.

Father, *thank You for being my example of what an earthly parent should be. Today and always, may I follow only You! Through Christ, amen.*

June 4–10. **Darlia Hill** lives and writes in Grand Junction, Colorado. Her three children have blessed her life immensely since she lost her husband in 2004.

No Need to Stumble

Whoever is wise, let him understand these things; whoever is discerning, let him know them. For the ways of the Lord are right, and the righteous will walk in them, but transgressors will stumble in them (Hosea 14:9, *New American Standard Bible*).

Scripture: Hosea 14
Song: "Gentle Shepherd, Thou Hast Stilled"

Water cascades over the rocks, foaming and frothing in the small pool below on its journey down the mountainside. Mist swirls over the creek as the roar of rushing water shuts out all other sounds in the forest.

Then I see a doe walking amid the fast-moving creek, each step sure and graceful. Her fawn rushes into the water, too, but ignores the path her mother took. The little one, on spindly legs, stumbles over the rocks with each step. By the time she reached her mother, her little hooves must have been bruised and sore.

When we take our eyes off the one who leads us, we lose our footing. We trip over pebbles and twigs in our way—all the daily troubles we encounter. But according to Hosea, we can walk a righteous path without stumbling. The problems won't go away, but we won't need to face them with hopeless despair. God is there with us. He leads us through the creek beds of our crises, over the mountains, through the streams, onward to glory.

Dear Father, *thank You for being my guide, for holding my hand as I follow the path You've placed before me today. In Jesus' name, amen.*

Our Humble God

I led them with cords of a man, with bonds of love, and I became to them as one who lifts the yoke from their jaws; and I bent down and fed them (Hosea 11:4, *New American Standard Bible*).

Scripture: **Hosea 11:1-5**
Song: **"At Thy Feet, Our God and Father"**

A vast desert lies behind and before me, and the sun shows no mercy as it burns into my skin. My legs no longer hold me, so I fall to my knees for a rest. My canteen is a lifesaver on this rigorous wilderness trek. Water is no longer simply a need but the difference between living and dying.

But suppose I'm without water or food, languishing in a hot, dry desert? I have felt that way at times, spiritually thirsty, longing for a sense of the Lord's care. Yet I'm sure He wants to lead us out of our deserts, just as the prophet tells us. For God is always there to offer us living water, the fellowship of His presence. With Him, every desert will come to an end.

He cares about us enough to "bend down" to feed us. What an amazing thing! When the load we're carrying threatens to overwhelm, He asks us to give it to Him. He is just that humble in His great love.

Dear Father, thank You for not leaving me in the desert places of my days. I am so grateful that You bend Your love to me, even when I fail to look to You for help and guidance. Today, may I leave all my struggles with You and drink deeply from the wellspring of Your goodness. Through Christ, amen.

Hear the Bugle?

My people are bent on turning from Me. Though they call them to the One on high, none at all exalts Him (Hosea 11:7, *New American Standard Bible*).

Scripture: **Hosea 11:6-11**
Song: **"Our Guilt Do We Confess Today"**

The snowpacked earth held the weight of the burro and the shivering man. At least there weren't any storm clouds in the Colorado sky—and just three more miles to go before Daniel would reach the next town. He'd made this loop through the mountains many times in the past four years, being the only preacher in the 1870s who made it to the few remote mining towns. As he entered the center of each town, he blew his bugle and then headed to the saloon to hold services. There he would call hardened miners to repent and be baptized in Christ's name.

Many realized this "mountain minister" brought the answer they'd searched for. The Lord he proclaimed became more precious to them than any riches they'd hoped for in the hills.

That is how I want Christ to be for me, today and always. Unlike the people of Hosea's day, I want to hear Him when He calls. And I hope that someday we two will be so close that even His most gentle whisper will be as a trumpet call to my ever-listening spirit.

O God, thank You for ministers who faithfully preach Your Word, even in the most difficult places. Help me to hear Your call through them and turn my heart to Your goodness and guidance. Through my Lord Jesus, amen.

A Land Without God

Listen to the word of the LORD, O sons of Israel, for the LORD has a case against the inhabitants of the land, because there is no faithfulness or kindness or knowledge of God in the land (Hosea 4:1, *New American Standard Bible*).

Scripture: **Hosea 4:1-5**
Song: **"Lord, Thou Hast Greatly Blessed Our Land"**

Another program filled with the sad things we do to each other. I listen to a story about a father who tried to take his own son's life. I turn off the television set.

Has the kindness left our land? We call a baby in its mother's womb a "mistake" and do away with it. When someone is sick without much hope for recovery, we begin considering euthanasia. When men or women grow "too old," we take them away from us to be cared for by strangers.

And what about the knowledge of God in our land? We've made prayer in schools illegal. We've banned the Ten Commandments from public display in our courts of law. Are we trying to erase God as if He never existed?

Have we become like Israel of old? Yet then, as now, God preserved a faithful remnant. May we be in that number! May we desire more of God each day, not less. Only then will faithfulness, kindness, and godly knowledge bloom once again in our midst.

God, thank You for loving the sinners of this world, those just like me. Now help me be an ambassador for You, an agent of change for the good in my culture. In the name of the Father, the Son, and the Holy Spirit, amen.

Already Favored

The thief enters in, bandits raid outside, and they do not consider in their hearts that I remember all their wickedness (Hosea 7:1, 2, *New American Standard Bible*).

Scripture: **Hosea 7:1-7**
Song: **"Thus Speaks the Lord to Wicked Men"**

"Brandon, they won't know if you don't tell," Kyle said, laying the stolen video game on his bed. "I deserve this game; Mom and Dad promised it to me months ago."

As Kyle threw his shirt in the corner, a pack of cigarettes fell out, and Brandon picked them up. "Now you're smoking? You know Grandpa died of lung cancer."

"That was him, not me." Kyle grabbed the cigarettes. "In fact, I think I'll smoke one right now."

Brandon backed to the door. "If you won't tell them you're stealing and smoking, then I will."

"Go ahead. You just want to be their perfect child. I'll never be that." Kyle slammed the door shut.

None of us will ever be that perfect child, neither for human parents nor for our heavenly Father. Yet God sent prophets like Hosea to tell us that God sees and cares about what we do. And when the time was just right, He offered us the perfection of His Son, Jesus. In Him and His strength, we can carry out good works that please Him—not to earn His favor, but because we already have it.

Father, forgive me for not considering how my sins make You feel. Thank You for the forgiveness that comes through Christ. In His name, amen.

Our Lighthouse

Return to your God, observe kindness and justice, and wait for your God continually (Hosea 12:6, *New American Standard Bible*).

Scripture: **Hosea 12:5-10**
Song: **"They That Overcome"**

Waves crashed upon a rocky shore as a lone figure sat in the sand, his head resting on bent knees. "How did I lose everything so fast?" Matt wondered. He thought the money he provided as breadwinner of the family would be enough. Now his family life lay in pieces around him. The corporate prestige and power that had once mattered so much now meant nothing. If only he could have back the family he'd neglected for so long. But they were miles away, living in a different state.

Matt had loved God as a boy but thought he'd outgrown Him. Now he realized he needed God to shine His light upon him and guide him home. He'd go to his family and ask their forgiveness.

Matt knew it might be a long time before his wife and kids would believe he really was a changed man. But he'd wait—continually wait in God's presence—knowing his life was secure only in that harbor of heavenly peace.

Lord, thank You for never giving up on me. I often make foolish plans, poor decisions, and self-destructive choices. But in Your mercy and goodness You stay close nevertheless. So in the next crisis that awaits me, give me grace and courage to wait patiently for Your guidance and to carry out Your will as You reveal it. In the name of Jesus, Lord and Savior, I pray. Amen.

Soon, in Heaven

You answer us with awesome deeds of righteousness, O God our Savior, the hope of all the ends of the earth and of the farthest seas (Psalm 65:5).

Scripture: **Psalm 65:1-8**
Song: **"Only Trust Him"**

A strong hurricane bore down on the Florida coastal town. Preparation time had ended, and now the people headed inland to seek safety.

A television reporter spotted one family cramming their car with all the belongings they could squeeze in. He approached the mother and asked her what she was feeling. "Hope," she replied. "We've done as much as we could to protect our house and our land. But this is such a powerful storm, we have no idea what may happen to it. It might be all gone when we get back, and we may have to start all over again. But right now there's nothing more to do. Now we can only hope."

No one knows what tomorrow holds. One of life's storms may be bearing down on us. Or sunny skies may be waiting to burst forth from gray clouds. But in all circumstances, our ultimate hope rests in our precious Savior. He has promised to be with us forever—in storms now, in Heaven soon.

Dear God, no matter what troubles may come, I know You will never leave me. I place my hope in You for now and for eternity. In Christ, amen.

June 11–17. **Jeff Friend**, big fan of the Baltimore Orioles, is also an award-winning writer and speaker who lives in Largo, Florida, with his wife, Nancy.

Worthy Example

Following the example of his father Uzziah, Jotham did what was pleasing to the Lord (2 Kings 15:34, *Good News Translation in Today's English*).

Scripture: **2 Kings 15:32-36**
Song: **"Let My Life Be a Light"**

As we sat around the table counting the money collected in the morning service, I came upon two little offering envelopes that jingled with the sound of coins. The envelopes displayed the names of young sisters and the word "Tithes" written across them in childlike scribblings.

When I opened the envelopes, four pennies fell from each and plopped on the table. I stared at the little pile of coins. I had been opening envelopes for several minutes, pulling out checks and paper money without a thought.

But these eight pennies held my attention. Was it silly for a child to give four cents? Not at all! Their parents had taught them about tithing, and the children were simply following the example of obedience to God.

The amount of the girls' contribution may seem insignificant, but the spiritual foundations being built into their lives are a matchless gift of love to them. I am sure God receives their offering with pleasure—and with joy in Mom and Dad's good work.

Heavenly Father, may I live following good examples that are pleasing to You. I thank You for placing godly people in my path. May I be an example to others as You give me opportunities each day. In Jesus' name, amen.

Ready, Set, Go

I heard the voice of the LORD saying, "Whom shall I send?
And who will go for us?" And I said, "Here am I. Send me!"
(Isaiah 6:8)

Scripture: **Isaiah 6:1-8**
Song: **"Send Thou, O Lord, to Every Place"**

As the preschool teacher gathered the children around
her, looking into all the eager faces, she softly said, "I
have a very special job for someone to do." Before she
could speak another word, each child shot up an arm and
started waving it excitedly. Each hoped to be selected for
the special task.

"But I haven't even told you what the job is!" said
the teacher. "What if it's something hard, or something
you don't like to do?" Not a hand went down, and the
children continued to call out to their teacher. The details
didn't matter to them. All they knew was that this beloved
woman was asking for a volunteer; they simply wanted
the chance to please her.

When the Lord said, "Whom shall I send?"(Isaiah 6:8).
Isaiah immediately responded, "Send me!" Although
he didn't know what he was going to be sent to do, he
jumped at the opportunity to serve his Lord. And for
good reason. There is a sense in which, whatever we are
doing, if we have turned our hearts to God's presence in it
with us, we will find joy there. Have you found it so?

Holy God, *I make myself available to serve You today, joyfully saying,*
"Here I am!" Through Christ the Lord, I pray. Amen.

God's Got You Covered

"My favor will shine on you like the morning sun. . . . I will always be with you to save you; my presence will protect you on every side" (Isaiah 58:8, *Good News Translation in Today's English*).

Scripture: **Isaiah 58:6-12**
Song: **"Surround Me, O Lord"**

Whenever the president of the United States appears in a public place, he's surrounded by secret service personnel. They watch for signs of trouble and are ready to respond at the first hint of something amiss. They blend in with the crowd and draw little attention to themselves.

They are trained to go to any lengths, even sacrificing their own lives, if necessary, to ensure the president's safety. Because of their presence, he can move about freely, without fear.

We also live in a world of danger. Yet God protects us on every side. What does that mean, in practical terms? For one thing, even though we cannot see Him, He constantly watches over us. But He ensures our safety in a deeper way than the guardians of a human president—not by sanitizing our existence or by denying any physical harm to us in our fallen world. He aims higher. In all situations, even our most painful ones, He seeks to grow our souls in holiness. His good and great goal is to prepare us for eternity. What an awesome protection!

Lord, *how thankful I am that You guard my soul against attack, that you protect my faith in You. Bring me home safely! Through Christ, amen.*

The Comforter Has Come

Comfort, comfort my people, says your God (Isaiah 40:1).

Scripture: **Isaiah 40:1-5**
Song: **"The Comforter Has Come"**

As the result of a venomous spider bite, I had 12 surgeries over six years and suffered extreme pain during most of that time. Finding it difficult to express to my family what I was going through, I would often become frustrated. It just seemed that no one could truly understand my situation.

During this time I learned the supreme value of comforting words and deeds. My family and friends would do whatever they could to soothe my suffering, both physically and emotionally. Although they could not help bear my pain—and they really couldn't understand it or feel it the way I did—they were able to encourage and support me in all kinds of practical ways.

The Israelites had endured years of hard times, and God had heard their cries of grief. Finally He proclaimed that it was time for them to be comforted and encouraged out of their misery.

God is also aware of our sufferings, even when we may think we're struggling alone. And there is, indeed, a time for those sufferings to come to an end. God has appointed that time. Be assured; relief is on the way.

God, You have promised a day when every tear will be wiped away. In the meantime, give me the peace of Your presence and the comfort of Your indwelling Spirit. In Christ's name I pray. Amen.

Delight in the Best

"Stop bringing meaningless offerings! Your incense is detestable to me. New Moons, Sabbaths and convocations—I cannot bear your evil assemblies" (Isaiah 1:13).

Scripture: **Isaiah 1:10-14**
Song: **"I Am Thine, O Lord"**

When I played football in high school, I found our coach to be very demanding. As we prepared for the upcoming season, he would run us through a variety of training drills every day. The first couple weeks we practiced with such great intensity that we could hardly lift our arms and legs by the end of the day. But every afternoon it was the same drills, over and over again.

Coach soon realized we were only doing those drills because we had to, not because we wanted to become better players. Truth be told, we just wanted the pain to end for that day.

After one particularly lackluster drill, Coach called us together and vented his frustration. "If any of you are just going to walk through this practice, then get off the field right now!" he bellowed. "I'm sick of this laziness!"

God does not want our half-hearted attempts to worship Him. He's not interested in lackluster routines. But He's *very* interested in you and me. I'm sure that's why He constantly invites our sincere worship and praise. What delight He must know when we give Him our best!

Father, You are worthy of my sincere worship. May my offerings be acceptable in Your sight. In the name of Your Son, my Savior, I pray. Amen.

Keeping It Simple

"Stop doing wrong, learn to do right!" (Isaiah 1:16, 17).

Scripture: **Isaiah 1:15-20**
Song: **"Trust and Obey"**

We're bombarded by slogans these days, those catchy little phrases advertisers use to highlight the main features of their products or services. Marketers spend a lot of money developing those cute ditties to help consumers understand and remember a basic concept.

Likewise, we tend to greatly condense information. After reading a 300-page novel, we may simply tell a friend, "It was about a man and his dog trapped in the mountains." We certainly left out a few details, right? But our friend at least caught a glimpse of the plot.

In Isaiah we find such an example of a basic concept God wants us to understand. It is nicely condensed, easy to remember: stop the wrong; do the right. What could be easier to recall? (The difficulty comes in the details.)

God constantly called the Israelites to trust Him and worship Him with sincere hearts. And Jesus' message was to repent of our sins and follow Him. Not difficult concepts, but impossible to carry out under our own power. Thus, centuries later, the apostle could say in Galatians 2:20: "I no longer live, but Christ lives in me. The life I live in the body, I live by faith in the Son of God, who loved me and gave himself for me."

Great God, sometimes I tend to lose sight of the essence of Your Word. Help me simply focus on doing what is right today. In Jesus' name, amen.

God's Invitation

"He has brought me to his banquet hall, and his banner over me is love" (Song of Solomon 2:4, *New American Standard Bible*).

Scripture: **Luke 14:15-24**
Song: **"Jesus Is Calling"**

One December, several years ago, I decided to host a fancy Christmas party. I planned the menu and decorated the house with all the trimmings of the season. I could picture my friends laughing and enjoying themselves around the beautifully decked-out Christmas tree.

When I called my friends to invite them, one by one they . . . declined! One was ill, another was having surgery, and another would be out of town. All gave excellent excuses, but, to say the least, I was quite disappointed. Never again would I plan a party until I was sure my friends could attend.

I didn't think of inviting the poor or the lonely into my home. Yet Luke tells us that is exactly what the Lord did (the man in the parable represents Jesus). He invited the people to come, but they were all too busy.

God still goes out into the highways and byways to call the poor and the lost. I was lonely and hurt when He called me to His banquet table. I will be forever grateful.

Father God, *I want to be at Your great banquet in Heaven. Prepare me so I will be ready when You send out the invitations. In Jesus' name, amen.*

June 18–24. **Marty Prudhomme** has been writing and teaching Bible studies for the past 20 years. She leads a friendship evangelism ministry called "Adopt-a-Block" for her church in Covington, Louisiana.

Day of Rejoicing

Surely our griefs He Himself bore, and our sorrows He carried
(Isaiah 53:4, *New American Standard Bible*).

Scripture: **Isaiah 25:6-10**
Song: **"Rejoice Today with One Accord"**

Several years ago I went on a mission trip to the Philippines where I constantly saw children begging in the streets, even at midnight. In the city of Manila, thousands of people live in a gigantic garbage dump. It's referred to as Smokey Mountain because of the fires that continually smolder under the mound. The citizens of this horrific city live in cardboard houses and survive off the trash. Many die of disease and hunger.

I was amazed to find so many people on Smokey Mountain who had faith in God. They know what it means to trust the Lord for their very existence. And they long for the day when their suffering will end, when their sorrow will be defeated forever.

Not everyone suffers like these people of the Philippines, but many of us are emotionally neglected, brokenhearted, abused, and wounded. Isaiah tells us about a day when the Lord of Hosts will prepare a lavish banquet for all of us who look to Him. All of God's people will rejoice together and be glad in His salvation. What a day of rejoicing that will be!

Father, I believe there will be a day when heartache, and sorrow, and suffering will cease forever. Give me the will to help those who suffer until then. I pray through my deliverer, Jesus Christ the Lord. Amen.

Good News for Now

He began to say to them, "Today this Scripture has been fulfilled in your hearing" (Luke 4:21, *New American Standard Bible*).

Scripture: **Isaiah 61:1-6**
Song: **"Spirit of the Living God"**

As I was growing up, at times depression would overwhelm me. I hoped marriage would rescue me from my troubles, but my problems became even more difficult. Often I felt hopeless, unloved, wondering, "Is this really all there is to life?" I didn't know that Jesus was my way out of this downward spiral.

Jesus stood in the synagogue 2,000 years ago and proclaimed that Isaiah's prophecy was fulfilled in Him. He was called to bring good news to the afflicted and to give a spirit of praise to those who mourn. I know there was no time limit to His heavenly mission, because I still remember the day I accepted Jesus' gift of salvation. He began healing my depression and my marriage. Now I can praise the Lord for my husband, children, and grandchildren. Yes, Jesus is still restoring lives.

Only He can repair our broken hearts. If we allow Jesus to take our junk, He will make something beautiful. The Spirit of the living God dwells in all who will receive His salvation. The Scripture is fulfilled in our hearing—now.

Lord, thank You for the gift of salvation. Help me comfort those who mourn and long for wholeness. I want to bring them the good news of Your grace so they will praise You forever. Glory to You, in Christ's name! Amen.

Known by Joy

"Their descendants will be known among the nations and their offspring among the peoples. All who see them will acknowledge that they are a people the LORD has blessed" (Isaiah 61:9).

Scripture: **Isaiah 61:7-11**
Song: **"Therefore the Redeemed of the Lord"**

My friend Shannon grew up with an abusive father who terrorized her family. At 13 years of age, she fought her way out of the house with a baseball bat, rescuing her mother and younger sister in the process.

When I first met Shannon years ago, she was serving as head of our local pregnancy crisis center. She was so much fun to be around that laughter followed wherever she went. Since that time, she has traveled for several years teaching children and adults God's Word in Indonesia, the Philippines, and Mongolia. Though the people of these nations live under terrible oppression and fear, Shannon can relate to their sorrows: "I know God can heal a wounded heart; He healed mine."

I believe God calls each of us to rise above our circumstances, relying upon His provision of daily strength. In fact, Isaiah tells us that God's people will be known among the nations because of their rejoicing in the Lord. They will be like a well-watered garden with seeds springing up into praise before all the earth. What a powerful image of our witness for Christ!

Dear Lord, *no matter what heartache comes into my life, I rejoice in Your presence with me. Thank You, in Jesus' name. Amen.*

Blessings Come Back

In their prayers for you their hearts will go out to you, because of the surpassing grace God has given you. Thanks be to God for his indescribable gift! (2 Corinthians 9:14, 15).

Scripture: **2 Corinthians 9:10-15**
Song: **"The Gift of Love"**

Four months ago I began an "Adopt-a-Block" ministry in my community. With a team of volunteers, we introduced ourselves to the people on Slemmer Road by distributing Easter baskets. The residents were a little puzzled, but we soon made friends. We didn't carry Bibles or talk in religious language. We simply explained that God cares for them, and so do we. Returning weekly, we prayed for them and brought food to the sick and needy. Soon we began to see answered prayers in their midst. One man even gave his neighbor a car.

Last month I had a stress test and angiogram. One of the families whose lives had been changed by our outreach effort phoned to let me know they were praying for me every night. I know God heard those prayers—they certainly gave my heart a boost.

God tells us to minister to others' needs and that they in turn will bless God and us. What a wonderful way—through blessing our neighbors—to add a few trinkets to the heavenly treasure chest.

Good and merciful God, may I always see others through Your eyes of compassion. Use me as a vessel to pour out Your love to the hurting and the lost in my world. In the name of Your Son, my Savior, I pray. Amen.

Come, Be Satisfied

"Why spend money on what is not bread, and your labor
on what does not satisfy? Listen, listen to me, and eat what
is good, and your soul will delight in the richest of fare"
(Isaiah 55:2).

Scripture: **Isaiah 55:1-5**
Song: **"Springs of Living Water"**

My daughter-in-law and I have the same love for
chocolate—all kinds of gooey chocolate confections, candy
bars, and ice cream. When we first met, I coaxed her into
the family with chocolate cakes. During my childhood,
when there was no money for extras, I could never get
enough chocolate. I remember standing outside the ice
cream parlor begging Mom for a cone.

Today, I can buy all the chocolate I want, but it makes
me gain weight. So, you see, I'm never satisfied.

Many people try to fill their lives with substitutes for
genuine spiritual life. They "self-medicate" their soul-
hurt, their deep longings, with things that temporarily
dull the pain. These only fill the gap for a few moments;
afterwards, there's a price to pay. Have you been there?

Isaiah says we can be content with the abundance
God provides. It may not seem like gourmet food at first
glance. But as we settle down in peace before the Lord, we
find a table spread with just the right food for nurturing
life within us. He gives living bread, himself, forever.

*Lord, may I never be disappointed with Your daily provision in my life, for
You know just what I need. In the name of Christ I pray. Amen.*

Bitterness, Good-bye

"As the heavens are higher than the earth, so are my ways higher than your ways and my thoughts than your thoughts" (Isaiah 55:9).

Scripture: **Isaiah 55:6-11**
Song: **"Higher Ground"**

One night, while on a mission trip to Panama, I met a woman named Mary. Several years before she had lost her 6-year-old daughter to cancer. Her husband left her soon afterwards because he couldn't handle the grief. Now Mary was very bitter; everyone could see it on her face. In fact, bitterness and anger had consumed her life for a long time. And she wanted nothing to do with God anymore, assuming He had cruelly taken her child away from her.

A friend of Mary's virtually dragged her to our church service one night. She heard this message: God sees the hurts of our hearts. She heard that God was calling her to give up the bitterness, for He was pouring out His compassion on her hurting soul. Though everyone in town could see only her bitterness, He saw her grieving heart.

Mary suddenly realized that God's ways were not her ways. She called on Him while He was near and received His transforming love that night. Mary let go of the bitterness in her heart and began a new life.

Dear Lord, I know that human sin has brought much pain and suffering into our world—and that You're allowing it to continue for a time. But it still hurts. Nevertheless, lift my eyes to my neighbors today. Give me the courage to help ease their pain in some small way. In Jesus' name, amen.

Clinging to the Rock

Thou shalt fear the LORD thy God; him shalt thou serve, and to him shalt thou cleave, and swear by his name (Deuteronomy 10:20, *King James Version*).

Scripture: **Deuteronomy 10:12-22**
Song: **"Rock That Is Higher Than I"**

My fingernails dug into the leather of the saddle horn as my horse plunged down the riverbank, bucking frantically. I could see more rocks than water, so I clung to what I had, desperately.

Is it like that between God and us? He invites His people to cleave to Him, to stick close and form an unbreakable bond with Him. He knows we'll face times of desperation more serious than landing headfirst in a river. Therefore, He promises never to leave us (see Hebrew 13:5).

Sometimes my first reaction to difficulty is to pull away from God. "Why me?" I ask. Why must I face financial insecurity, physical or emotional pain? Yet, in those times, I hear His invitation to cleave. I hear Him whisper His promise—not that I might have a better life, but that I might have a better relationship with Him. After all, cleaving, joining, and staying close result in companionship. And what could be better than companioning with God?

God of relationship, thank You for being my Rock to cleave to when the rocks of life's trials threaten to loosen my grip. In Christ I pray. Amen.

June 25–30. **Ron Silflow** works as an educator in the area of human and animal biotechnology. He resides in Bozeman, Montana, with his wife, Laura. His passions include being with his three children, caring for people, and journaling.

In Great Distress?

Wherefore lift up the hands which hang down, and the feeble knees; and make straight paths for your feet (Hebrews 12:12, 13, *King James Version*).

Scripture: **Hebrews 12:6-12**
Song: **"No Other Name but the Name of Jesus"**

I've just read the Bible story in which King David and his men came back to their city and found it burned to the ground. The city's families had been taken captive, including the wives and children of David and his men. It was so bad that there was talk of stoning David for the lack of protection while he was away. Yet here's the statement that sticks with me so powerfully: "But David found strength in the Lord his God" (1 Samuel 30:6).

David didn't deny the reality of great distress. Instead, he used it as a good reason to look to a higher source than himself for courage. He had to let go of the weight of self-reliance and look to God. When our hearts are heavy, our hands will hang down.

When our hearts look up, our hands can arise in surrender, in trust, in courage. As the great preacher Charles Spurgeon once said, "The refiner is never far from the mouth of the furnace when his gold is in the fire, and the Son of God is always walking in the midst of the flames when his holy children are cast into them."

*You are my strength, **Almighty God of glory,** when I am weak. Lift up my head and hands before You when distress fills my days. And set my feet on a solid path. Through Christ my Savior I pray. Amen.*

Jealous Love

Woe to them that devise iniquity, and work evil upon their beds! when the morning is light, they practice it, because it is in the power of their hand (Micah 2:1, *King James Version*).

Scripture: **Micah 2:1-5**
Song: **"Saviour, Thy Dying Love Thou Gavest Me"**

I arrived at the high-school social late and quickly scanned the room for the girl I was to meet there. No sign of her. Had she tired of waiting and returned home? Then my eyes caught her talking to another boy, their eyes locked on to each other, oblivious to my presence as they walked into a nearby garden, hand in hand. My face flushed red, my heart sank, and, 30 years later, I still feel the jealous crush.

Despite many warnings, God's people, during the time of Micah, were becoming more openly rebellious. God was about to manifest a part of His nature that is inseparable from His spirit of love: His righteous jealousy. "For thou shalt worship no other god: for the LORD, whose name is Jealous, is a jealous God" (Exodus 34:14, *KJV*). Of course God is the only one in the universe with the right to be jealous of worship. Why? Because He's . . . *God!*

The wonderful thing is that God is jealous for our fellowship, which is for our good, for our best. He loves us so much that He guards this relationship with His life. The cross of Calvary proves it.

Loving, jealous God, forgive me for turning elsewhere for satisfaction in life. You gave Your life for my love. Thank You, in Christ's name. Amen.

No Hiding Here!

Then shall they cry unto the LORD, but he will not hear them: he will even hide his face from them at that time, as they have behaved themselves ill in their doings (Micah 3:4, *King James Version*).

Scripture: **Micah 3:1-7**
Song: **"I Lay My Sins on Jesus"**

To be chastened by God is, to say the least, unpleasant. To have Him hide His face, though, is unbearable. Chasten us, judge us, but, O God, please don't abandon us!

Yet He cannot look on our sin. Therefore, like David, in repentance we cry out, "Cast me not away from thy presence; and take not thy Holy Spirit from me" (Psalm 51:11, *KJV*).

So often the pressures of life and the guilt of our sin lead us to question God . . .

"Are You really enough for me?"

"Do You have what it takes to carry me through?"

"Will You turn Your face from me?"

The good news chimes in at just this point: Because our sin was placed on Jesus when He hung on the cross, God hid His face—once and for all. Christ not only bore the judgment for the world's sin, He was abandoned by the Father so we would be accepted. When we come to God in repentance, we hear the resounding reply to our deepest plea: "No, I will not turn my face from you!"

Father, how I love You for the mercy of Your saving plan! How I praise You for my forgiveness! Glory to You, through Christ the Lord. Amen.

Inconvenient Surrender

Therefore shall Zion for your sake be plowed as a field, and Jerusalem shall become heaps, and the mountain of the house as the high places of the forest (Micah 3:12, *King James Version*).

Scripture: **Micah 3:8-12**
Song: **"Come, O Come, Thou Quickening Spirit"**

Have you noticed? God's plow will turn your life upside down. The purpose of His plow is to prepare good ground to receive His good seed. Good ground plus good seed lead to good fruit.

Is your ground wild and untamed? Or, perhaps, has your ground recently produced a fruitful crop? To the plow, it doesn't matter. The plow will bury what can be seen on the surface and reveal what has been hidden.

Saul, apprehended by Jesus, had his life turned upside down on the road to Damascus. What was visible on Saul's surface—a life of persecuting Christ's followers—got buried by this miraculous encounter. What had been hidden in Saul's depths, Christ brought to the surface, "for [Saul] is a chosen vessel unto me, to bear my name before the Gentiles" (Acts 9:15, *KJV*). What a transformation! His name even changed. Now he was Paul, the apostle.

I want my heart to be ready for that plow in coming days. It isn't an easy surrender. It might be uncomfortable, might be inconvenient. But it's the only way to grow.

O Lord, move upon my heart today and prepare me to be a more productive fruit bearer in Your kingdom. Through Christ I pray. Amen.

Walk in His Paths

Let us go up to the mountain of the Lord, and to the house of the God of Jacob; and he will teach us of his ways, and we will walk in his paths (Micah 4:2, *King James Version*).

Scripture: **Micah 4:1-5**
Song: **"The King of Love My Shepherd Is"**

It looked like my grandpa was teaching me to braid a three-strand rope from baling twine. But he was teaching me much more. He was teaching me of God's ways. As we braided, he spoke of lives being entwined together. He talked about the entwining of a husband and wife with Christ.

I held in my hand a three-strand rope. In my mind I saw a picture of a Christ-centered marriage relationship—"a threefold cord is not quickly broken" (Ecclesiastes 4:12, *KJV*).

What an invitation! God calls us to take a journey in His *paths,* not highways. Paths of learning. Paths of companionship and intimacy.

Can you recognize the path God has you on at the moment? He doesn't promise our paths will be easy. But He invites us there anyway, because He's been there before and will lead us now. There is great intimacy in that kind of walk with Him.

My Lord and shepherd, I join You for the journey on Your paths. I thank You that I can declare, like the psalmist, "Though I walk through the valley of the shadow of death, I will fear no evil: for thou art with me" (Psalm 23:4, KJV). In the name of Your Son, my Savior, I pray. Amen.

My Prayer Notes

_____

_____

_____

_____

_____

_____

_____

_____

_____

_____

_____

_____

_____

_____

_____

_____

_____

_____

_____

DEVOTIONS

*T*he earth will be filled with the knowledge of the glory of the LORD.

—Habakkuk 2:14

JULY

Photo © Stockbyte

Gary Allen, Editor

God's Goodness

O my people, what have I done unto thee? And wherein have I wearied thee? testify against me (Micah 6:3, *King James Version*).

Scripture: **Micah 6:3-8**
Song: **"Within the Veil"**

"God, if You are good, then why . . . ?" Like me, you've probably asked this question many times, under many difficult circumstances. Is it OK to question of God, "Are you good?" David said, "I had fainted, unless I had believed to see the goodness of the Lord in the land of the living" (Psalm 27:13, *KJV*). David got his answer, and we each long to hear our answers, individually, from God. Why? Because it is difficult to hold to the goodness of God when our circumstances scream differently. This was a problem in Micah's day, and it still plagues us too.

I am comforted by the fact that God invites such questioning, just as He invited the ancient Israelites to "testify against" Him. So join me in responding to God's invitation to meet with Him in every circumstance—whether we are joyful or in pain, whether confident or confused. As you plead for His response, let Him answer you personally. He has shown us His love by saving us through Christ's blood. He will reveal His goodness right where our hearts need Him today.

O Lord, *You have shown me what is good: to walk humbly with You each moment. That is my desire this day. Through Christ, amen.*

July 1. **Ron Silflow** loves to journal his conversational relationship with Jesus. He and his wife, Laura, live in Bozeman, Montana. They have three children.

Pie in the Sky?

I would have lost heart, unless I had believed that I would see the goodness of the LORD in the land of the living (Psalm 27:13, *New King James Version*).

Scripture: **Psalm 27:7-14**
Song: **"God Will Take Care of You"**

Ministers are sometimes accused of preaching a "pie in the sky" brand of Christianity. The downtrodden are encouraged to keep their focus on Heaven and all the blessings to come in the afterlife. For most of us, though, as precious as that blessed hope is, it's not enough just to imagine it coming to pass . . . someday. We need hope for *today*, assurance that God is working on our behalf in the here and now. David was a man after God's own heart, but even he admitted he would have lost heart if he couldn't count on seeing God's goodness here on earth—in the land of the living.

Ironically, it may be easier to have faith for life beyond the grave. We may have to press in closer to the Lord to gain that same assurance for our daily walk in this life. When we draw close to Him, He will draw close to us, and we will see His goodness at work in our lives to give us the strength we need today.

God of all goodness, thank You for Your promise to be with me every step of the way, in this life and in the life to come. In the name of Jesus, my Savior and Lord, I pray. Amen.

July 2–8. **Rosalie M. LoPinto** is a freelance Christian writer. She lives in Riverside, Rhode Island, and works with several ministries in the area of communications.

Whom Do You Trust?

Stop trusting in man, who has but a breath in his nostrils. Of what account is he? (Isaiah 2:22).

Scripture: **Isaiah 2:12-22**
Song: **"No One Ever Cared for Me Like Jesus"**

Ancient Egyptians believed their kings, the pharaohs, were actually gods. They also believed their own continued existence in the afterlife was connected to that of the pharaohs, and thus gave great care to preserving their rulers' bodies after death. Mummification was crucial because one could only survive in the afterlife as long as the body survived.

We Christians view things differently! We know our spirits will remain when our bodies have returned to the dust. And we don't rely on another human being to usher us into the afterlife. Yet in this life we still sometimes place people on pedestals, looking to them for our own survival. We expect politicians to fix this troubled world, ministers to mend our wounded hearts, friends to cure our loneliness, and spouses to meet our deepest needs.

In reality, it is the prince of peace, the healer, the friend of sinners who sticks closer than a brother. He is the lover of our souls, in whom we can place our ultimate confidence. He is the only one on whom we can depend completely.

Lord, it seems easier to turn to the phone instead of the throne. Forgive me for all the times I look for answers from everyone else. Help me to remember to seek counsel from You, first and foremost. Through Christ, amen.

Heavenly Plans

The plans of the LORD stand firm forever, the purposes of his heart through all generations (Psalm 33:11).

Scripture: **Psalm 33:1-11**
Song: **"God Is Still on the Throne"**

In his book *1776*, David McCullough cites repeated instances when the colonial army survived almost certain defeat at the hands of the British by what seemed like divine intervention. Winds would shift, switching the advantage to the Americans. Or a sudden fog would keep them from detection by the British. Ultimately the Americans prevailed, and a nation was born.

For all its flaws, the United States of America has been a beacon of gospel light through much of its history. In fact, I believe God has allowed this nation to survive for His plans and purposes. Over the decades, thousands of missionaries have gone out from this land to every corner of the globe.

Whether for nations or for individuals, God's plans are indestructible. True, a certain amount of chance and probability infuse our fallen world for now. Yet we are never its victims, for all that enters our lives is only what God allows. Even more encouraging is this: "He who began a good work in you will carry it on to completion until the day of Christ Jesus" (Philippians 1:6).

*I thank You, **Lord,** that You knew me when I was in my mother's womb and You had a plan for me. I ask You now to fulfill Your purpose in me and through me, and I will give You all the glory. In Jesus' name, amen.*

Housecleaning

He . . . crushed the idols to powder and cut to pieces all the incense altars throughout Israel. Then he went back to Jerusalem (2 Chronicles 34:7).

*Scripture: **2 Chronicles 34:1-7***
*Song: **"Burn in Me, Fire of God"***

I don't like superficial cleaning jobs. Shoving things in closets, sweeping dirt under a rug, hanging clean curtains on dirty windows—that's not my thing. I never feel as if a house is really neat and clean until every window gleams and every closet displays order.

In our text, Josiah determined to utterly destroy every remnant of Israel's previous idolatry. He wanted to restore righteousness to the land, and he knew all of the evil reminders of Israel's sin had to be obliterated before he could restore the temple in Jerusalem.

If you're like me, you want your house to pass the "white glove test." But more importantly, you want your *life* to pass muster with your Lord. Let's take an inventory together in the week ahead. Anything needing to be cleaned up, straightened out—or even completely "crushed to powder"? I certainly want the temple of my body to be a clean and comfortable place for the Spirit of God to dwell.

***Dear Lord,** please show me if there is a habit or practice, or even a possession or a relationship, that shouldn't be in my life. Help me to be determined to destroy that which displeases You. I pray this prayer in the name of Jesus, my merciful Savior and Lord. Amen.*

The Problem of Pain

The LORD within her is righteous; he does no wrong. Morning by morning he dispenses his justice, and every new day he does not fail, yet the unrighteous know no shame (Zephaniah 3:5).

Scripture: **Zephaniah 3:1-7**
Song: **"I Want to Be Like Jesus"**

"Why would a good God allow children to starve to death?" My friend Leif's question was nothing new. Human beings have struggled over "the problem of pain" since the beginning. Adam and Eve were the first to wonder about God's goodness and intentions.

A young Christian at the time, I offered up a quick and silent prayer before responding to my friend. "There is more than enough food in the world to feed every single person, with plenty left over," I said. "People starve because of the greed, hatred, and lack of concern for their fellow creatures." I don't know how you'd have answered, but I was as startled at my words as Leif apparently was. For the moment, at least, his latest assault on God's character had been squelched.

The point is, God is good—let's just settle the matter. We, on the other hand, are not always so good. We often fail to meet a need when it is in our power to do so. Much of the problem of pain results from our problem with sin.

Dear Lord, keep me from turning my eyes from the needs that swirl around me. Move me with Your compassion today! Through Christ I pray. Amen.

Can You Blush?

Never again will you be haughty on my holy hill. But I will leave within you the meek and humble, who trust in the name of the LORD (Zephaniah 3:11, 12).

Scripture: **Zephaniah 3:8-13**
Song: **"In My Life, Lord, Be Glorified"**

As a child, I loved Red Skelton. His funny and poignant characters, like Clem Kadiddlehopper and Freddy the Freeloader, could make me laugh and make me cry. Commenting on the Freeloader, Red once said that Freddy was "nice to everybody because he was taught that man is made in God's image. He's never met God in person, and the next fella just might be Him." Every night Red closed his show the same way, "Good night, and God bless."

You can't listen to most of today's comedians for more than a minute or two without realizing that Red would be way out of his element in today's entertainment business. Crudeness and vulgarity are the standard fare, served up with arrogance but without shame. Jeremiah 6:15 refers to such folks as those who "do not even know how to blush" over their sin.

Today I'm asking myself: What do I find entertaining and amusing? What am I willing to allow into my living room—and into my spirit? And . . . do I still know how to blush?

Father, help me remember today that You are present when I am watching TV, listening to the radio, or hanging around the watercooler at work. Let me recall that Your Spirit dwells within me. In Jesus' name, amen.

Treasure Hunt

"He will take great delight in you, he will quiet you with his love, he will rejoice over you with singing" (Zephaniah 3:17).

Scripture: **Zephaniah 3:14-20**
Song: **"May I Never Lose the Wonder"**

Let's be honest. For many of us, Bible reading can sometimes be a chore. Oh yes, we love the Word, and we know God wants to speak to us through it. Still there are days when it feels like a mandatory assignment.

Some years ago, I was having one of those days and feeling justly convicted. I put my Bible down and opened my heart to God. "Lord, make Your Word come alive to me," I prayed.

Returning to my Bible, I saw it for the first time—God sings! Not only does He sing, but I'm the *reason* He sings; He sings over me! The lover of my soul is so enthralled with me that He bursts into song. (Wouldn't you love to hear the song He is singing over you today?)

God's Word is full of precious jewels like that. If we live a hundred years, He will still be able to surprise us with some shining nugget of truth and wisdom we never saw before. Every time we read the Bible, we can approach it as a thrilling treasure hunt.

Lord of all truth and wisdom, show me something new in Your Word every time I pick it up. Thank You for this awesome book that nourishes me and helps me see You more clearly. Truly, it is the bread my soul requires, and nothing else can fill me so completely. In the name of the Father, the Son, and the Holy Spirit, I pray. Amen.

Waiting for God

Wait for the LORD and keep his way. He will exalt you to inherit the land (Psalm 37:34).

Scripture: **Psalm 37:27-34**
Song: **"It Is Well with My Soul"**

When I came home from the hospital to recuperate from cancer surgery, I was eager to get on with life. I wanted to pick up right where I'd left off. Reality set in quickly, however. I was weak; I was tired; I had no strength. When I sat down in my chair, I promptly fell asleep. It seemed I could do nothing that required even the smallest effort.

Time moved slowly. I felt bored and useless. Finally I struggled to my desk and began shuffling through bills and papers. *If I could just walk down the driveway to the mailbox. . . .* But my wife had to bring the mail to me.

I opened one of the cards she handed me. The cover displayed these words: "Be still, and know that I am God" (see Psalm 46:10). I stared at the words and let them sink in.

"Wait," I heard. "Wait for God's healing time, and savor this period of quietness. Wait for your body and your spirit to be restored. Listen to the voice that whispers when you wait. Then you will find the healing you need."

Patient God, teach me the importance of resting in the moment, for I am so prone to rush off and leave You behind. Give me the serenity that comes with pausing to hear Your voice. In the name of Christ, I pray. Amen.

July 9–15. **Drexel Rankin** served as an ordained minister for more than 35 years before his recent retirement. He and his wife, Patty, live in Louisville, Kentucky.

Are You Jesus?

To this you were called, because Christ suffered for you, leaving you an example, that you should follow in his steps (1 Peter 2:21).

Scripture: **2 Kings 23:31-37**
Song: **"I'm Gonna Live So God Can Use Me"**

The busy executive was rushing to catch his plane. He had almost given up living a *personal* daily life because of the great time demands of his *work* life—including speaking engagements along with all the administrative duties of his company. But on this particular morning, he had promised himself he'd try to at least act the part of a Christian as he went through this day.

By the time he had reached the airport terminal and checked his bags, he was running late. Charging down the concourse, he heard the last call for boarding. In his haste, he bumped into a small boy carrying several toys in his arms. The toys scattered across the waiting area.

The executive paused, saw the child in tears, and, with an inward sigh, remembered the promise he'd made to himself earlier. He stopped, picked up the child's toys, put them back in his arms, ruffled the lad's hair, and said, "I'm sorry."

The boy looked at the man with awe and said hesitantly, "Mister, are you Jesus?"

Lord, help me to be a shining token of Your love wherever I will be this day. May I reflect Your compassion to others. May I remind those whom I meet today of the love that You have for all people. Through Christ, amen.

Can You Detect Him?

Your eyes are too pure to look on evil; you cannot tolerate wrong. Why then do you tolerate the treacherous? Why are you silent while the wicked swallow up those more righteous than themselves? (Habakkuk 1:13).

Scripture: **Habakkuk 1:12-17**
Song: **"Immortal, Invisible"**

We human beings are tantalized by mysteries. Detective novels fascinate many of us, and even public television has a weekly program called, simply, *Mystery*.

God and His ways were a mystery to Habakkuk—and still are to us in many ways. The mystery of God, however, isn't so much *secretive* as it is *vast*. My wife and I rediscover this each time we visit another national park.

God's vastness encompasses the entire world, and it seems there just isn't enough time to understand it all. Yet answers are set before us everywhere—in nature, in science, in our own deeds. We too are each a part of God's mystery when we gather in worship, offer friendship to a stranger, or feed the hungry.

Echoing the prophet, our own "why's" will never cease, though. Not until the mystery is fully revealed when, as the Scripture says, we shall see Him face to face. For "now I know in part; then I shall know fully, even as I am fully known" (1 Corinthians 13:12).

Immortal, invisible God, in all the places You are, in all the things You do, in all the great and glorious mystery that is You, may I stand in awe today. In Christ's name, I pray. Amen.

Living with Questions

"The revelation awaits an appointed time; it speaks of the end and will not prove false. Though it linger, wait for it" (Habakkuk 2:3).

Scripture: **Habakkuk 2:1-5**
Song: **"Spirit of God, Descend Upon My Heart"**

My wife, Patty, is a more patient person than I am. I learn from her as she prepares her several gardens in our yard. The heat of the summer is now past as Patty plants the bulbs in the ground—tulips, daffodils, hyacinths. Carefully she chooses the right location. Gently she tamps the soil around them.

Through the cool days of autumn, into the first chilled days of winter, beneath the snow and the ice, those tubers will sleep in the darkness. The bulbs—and my wife—patiently wait for frozen days to pass. The ground will soon thaw, and sprouts will emerge.

This process of life parallels living for God. There is always a time of waiting in the darkness, living with questions that beg for answers. This was Habakkuk's situation when God encouraged him to hold on patiently.

Like the flowers of spring, I need that time for God to form me from within—to create something new and beautiful. In God's time, the answers to my questions will emerge in their own season.

Patient God, teach me the secret of the planted seed—to wait on You. Give me Your gift of patience as I wait for You to form me as You wish. In the name of the Father, the Son, and the Holy Spirit, amen.

The Eyes of a Child

"The earth will be filled with the knowledge of the glory of the LORD, as the waters cover the sea" (Habakkuk 2:14).

Scripture: **Habakkuk 2:6-14**
Song: **"For the Beauty of the Earth"**

Recently, my friend Jerry wrote about his little girl and the summertime dandelion season. He said that, like many people, he and his wife pay a lawn service to come to their home once a month to spray their yard. The service isn't cheap, but he thinks it's worth it to keep his lawn up to the standards of those who live around him.

But Jerry's 4-year-old daughter, Gracie, has a favorite yard in their neighborhood—the one down the street that is covered with dandelions. Gracie told her dad, "I hope we can have pretty little flowers like that in our yard some day!"

Oh, to see the world through those little eyes, to see the beauty of dandelions and to feel special because you're certain the sun is following you. I wonder how much of the glory of the Lord I miss on any given day. How much beauty, how much goodness? Maybe Gracie and all other children around us can teach us truly to see. I am sure that if we look closely enough we will see not only a wonderful creation but the face of the creator as well.

God of creation, I am thankful for the eyes of children who behold You in such a sincere and innocent way. Help me to learn from them as they teach me about seeing You everywhere in life. In the holy name of Jesus, my Lord and Savior, I pray. Amen.

In Silence

"The LORD is in his holy temple; let all the earth be silent before him" (Habakkuk 2:20).

Scripture: **Habakkuk 2:15-20**
Song: **"This Is My Father's World"**

Miss Graham, my first piano teacher, exercised infinite patience as she tried to teach me the rudiments of musical knowledge and performance. Among the concepts she attempted to clarify for me was the musical rest.

"Do you understand what a rest is?" she asked.

"A rest," I offered, "is a time filled with nothing."

Wrong answer!

She launched into an extended oration, explaining how the composer, in his genius, had placed the rest in a particular passage of the music to be part of the grand design of the composer's work. To the uneducated ear it might seem like "nothing" was happening. In truth, the composer used that silence to build the power of the music and to bring the entire score to a grand finale. "Something" was indeed happening in each silence.

I've pondered that lesson many times. A rest in a portion of human existence—silence—is hardly *nothing*. It is part of God's grand design. In the silence, if we listen closely with our hearts, we will surely hear something wondrous from on high.

Let me be still, O Lord. Let me push aside, at least for a time each day, the many swirling voices and noises that fill my mind. Today I want to hear Your whispers in the silence. In the name of Jesus, amen.

God for All Seasons

Though the fig tree does not bud and there are no grapes on the vines, though the olive crop fails and the fields produce no food . . . I will be joyful in God my Savior (Habakkuk 3:17, 18).

Scripture: **Habakkuk 3:13-19**
Song: **"Joy to the World"**

It came as a bit of a shock when the folks in the congregation opened their hymnals for the opening song: "Joy to the World." A Christmas carol in the middle of July? Was this a joke?

As their minister, I had chosen the hymn, not as a prank, but as a way to express the truth that rejoicing in the Lord knows no season. And it worked.

This was a song that we all knew, and we sang it boisterously, joyfully. In fact, there was spontaneous rejoicing—a praising of God that burst with life from deep within our souls. And why not? Christmas isn't the only season to sing gladly about God's coming in our midst.

Yet, as Habakkuk demonstrates, joy and happiness are not always the same. Circumstances can cause us deep pain and consternation, and we won't be happy about it. That's why happiness is usually a temporary, emotional condition based on "things going my way."

Joy is deeper. We can be joyful regardless of an unhappy situation. We have Christ within us. Even when those troubles seem to endure, He and His joy remain.

God who brings joy to heavy hearts, You are my God for all seasons. All glory to You, in the name of Jesus the king. Amen.

In the Sunshine, Draw Near

We must pay more careful attention, therefore, to what we have heard, so that we do not drift away (Hebrews 2:1).

Scripture: **Hebrews 2:1-4**
Song: **"Leaning on the Everlasting Arms"**

I find drifting in a rubber raft on a slow-moving river one of the most relaxing things to do. No white-water rapids for me! I just like to lie back, soak up sunshine, and watch dragonflies dart over the placid surface of the water.

Floating in a raft provides great summertime relaxation, but drifting away from church can sabotage our spiritual lives. Neglecting private devotional time or worship services can set us up to meander in the direction of our culture—which is often less than spiritually healthy.

Ask your minister and he'll probably tell you attendance and giving typically decrease during the summer months. But instead of sliding into a slump, I'm finding creative ways to keep God first this summer. My kids and I schedule outings so we won't miss services with our church. And picnics with small groups offer pleasant fellowship. I'm beginning to see that summertime is a wonderful season to draw near to the Lord.

Father, this summer I don't want to drift but to press closer and hear Your heart more clearly. I love You. Through Christ I pray. Amen.

July 16–22. **Patty Duncan** teaches fifth grade at Eugene Christian School, parents her teenage son, and spoils her two grandsons. She grew up in the Church of Christ in Cottage Grove, Oregon.

Coming Back to God

If . . . My people who are called by My name humble themselves and pray, and seek My face and turn from their wicked ways, then I will hear from heaven, will forgive their sin, and will heal their land" (2 Chronicles 7:14, *New American Standard Bible*).

Scripture: **2 Chronicles 7:11-16**
Song: **"Prayer Is the Soul's Sincere Desire"**

Judy Buck, a busy second-grade teacher, mentors young women in her church who want help. She studies with them through a Bible course that provides an understanding of the Lord's work of redemption. Her effort provides a foundation for Christian living for new converts or those returning to the church.

Sometimes Judy's students have moral issues; for example, some may be living with a boyfriend before marriage. "Some people think I shouldn't waste my time with those young ladies," Judy says. But she disagrees. More and more children and teenagers are growing up with no Christian training and don't know how to choose a godly lifestyle. Judy believes in loving them and helping them find their way back to God.

God promised the Israelites that if they changed their ways He'd forgive them and bring healing. He welcomes wanderers home. We can do the same in His name.

Father, help me embrace people with a warm welcome as they struggle to find their way to a living relationship with You. Thank You for welcoming me in just that way! I pray in the name of Jesus. Amen.

Catch Him, Lord!

The LORD said to him, "I have heard your prayer and your supplication, which you have made before Me" (1 Kings 9:3, *New American Standard Bible*).

Scripture: 1 Kings 9:1-9
Song: "Eternal Father, Strong to Save"

"My son, David, had gotten away with some things, like minor shoplifting," said my friend Kay, a single mom. "I could see a dangerous pattern developing, so I prayed for God to catch him if he got involved in anything that wasn't good for him. The next time, he was in handcuffs when I picked him up at the police station.

It seems David had gone joyriding with a friend who'd stolen a car. The police officer had no apparent reason to pull the boys over; nevertheless, he stopped them.

"I told David how I had prayed," said Kay. "He broke the law one more time, got caught again, and quit for good! David had a heavenly Father who knew everything he was doing and loved him enough to catch him!"

Kay had asked God to father her son, and God answered her prayers. Soon David was telling his friends he couldn't get away with anything. For me, the point is clear: as we watch teenagers testing their boundaries, we can pray for their heavenly Father's intervention in their lives. He does, indeed, hear our prayers.

Father, we who parent need Your help in extra measure during our kids' adolescence. Reveal Yourself to teens in a personal way, we pray, so they will choose to love You and live in Your blessing. In Jesus' name, amen.

It Never Entered My Mind

"They have built the high places of Baal to burn their sons in the fire as offerings to Baal —something I did not command or mention, nor did it enter my mind" (Jeremiah 19:5).

Scripture: **Jeremiah 19:1-6**
Song: **"Jesus Loves the Little Children"**

Since abortion became legal in the United States in 1973, approximately 40 million babies have died before birth. Worldwide, according to Planned Parenthood's research arm (the Guttmacher Institute), about 46 million babies were aborted in 1995, 26 million legally and 20 million illegally. The trend continues.

In Jeremiah's day, worshipers of idols burned their children in fire on public altars. Today the sacrifice of innocents occurs in private, in medical offices with doctors and nurses—who've been trained to heal and not harm—performing the deed. Even God's chosen people in Jeremiah's time sacrificed children to Baal, a god most closely resembling the love of money in modern times.

Sadly, today's women rarely abort their children for medical reasons—because of rape or incest or because their own health is in danger. Many are young or unmarried when becoming pregnant and often respond to pressure from others to just make their "problem" go away. It never entered God's mind that things should be as this.

God, for all who may regret terminating a pregnancy—assure them of Your abiding love and perfect forgiveness through Your Son. Comfort them all their days as You set them on the path of life. In Jesus' name, amen.

If You Choose to Break a Rule

"'Perhaps they will listen and everyone will turn from his evil way, that I may repent of the calamity which I am planning to do to them because of the evil of their deeds'" (Jeremiah 26:3, *New American Standard Bible*).

Scripture: **Jeremiah 26:1-6**
Song: **"The Law of God Is Good and Wise"**

In my fifth-grade classroom I post six basic rules, including "listening when others are talking" and "keeping your hands and feet to yourself." Next to the rules poster hangs another titled, "If You Choose to Break a Rule." It states the consequences of disobeying.

If students break rules, I write their names on the board as a warning and keep them inside from recess (five minutes for each mark I tally by their names after the warning). If the problem persists, or a student severely misbehaves—cheating or fighting—I call the parent later in the day. And in the case of a serious incident, I send the child to the principal immediately. Though I have it all planned out, I dislike enforcing rules and hate dealing with serious infractions.

Doesn't God feel the same way about us? He didn't want to bring disaster on the Israelites; He kept hoping they'd change their ways so He wouldn't have to discipline them. He provides boundaries for our good. Those boundaries discourage our straying from Him.

Lord, *it's hard to thank You for providing trouble when I go astray. But I know You're simply coaxing me back. Thank You, in Jesus' name. Amen.*

Rescued!

Thus says the LORD **of hosts, the God of Israel, "Amend your ways and your deeds, and I will let you dwell in this place"** (Jeremiah 7:3, *New American Standard Bible*).

Scripture: **Jeremiah 7:1-7**
Song: **"This World Is Not My Home"**

When I discovered slimy black mold growing on the walls of our water-heater closet, I feared the worst. I knew that our dentist's family had developed serious illnesses after exposure to a toxic black mold in their home. Testing confirmed my fears: stachybotrys, not the typical harmless black mold, contaminated our house also.

Overwhelmed, I sought advice from experts and followed their precautions. My son and I moved into an apartment, relieved to escape danger. We didn't mind the cramped quarters or close neighbors. In fact, it felt like a vacation because we were so thankful to God for rescuing us from illness. We lived there all summer while our manufactured home was demolished and replaced.

When God invited the Israelites to change their ways and dwell in the land with Him, He used a word meaning "to live in a temporary residence." I cherish owning my home, but when God moved us for a summer, I experienced His provision in a way I'll always remember.

O Lord of hosts, thank You for inviting me to live in Your ways, and dwell with You here on earth, while yearning for my permanent home in Heaven. Continue to prepare my heart for that glorious day! I pray this prayer in the name of Jesus, my merciful Savior and Lord. Amen.

Sick, or Getting Better?

"Will you steal, murder, . . . and offer sacrifices to Baal, and walk after other gods that you have not known, then come and stand before Me in this house?" (Jeremiah 7:9, 10 *New American Standard Bible*).

Scripture: **Jeremiah 7:8-15**
Song: **"Heart of Worship"**

My grown son, Amos, and I recently wondered aloud how Christians can live together out of wedlock and still come to church as if nothing were wrong. "They think God's cool with it," Amos said, and I sadly agreed. However, this popular picture of a permissive heavenly Father who smiles down at us without the hang-ups of old-fashioned morals hardly comes from the Bible!

We can hear the real God voicing real exasperation through Jeremiah. He cries out to His people who have lost their bearings in a corrupt culture, as so many have in our world today.

So what happens when the church gathers for worship? Are sinners present? Definitely. One hundred percent of the people in attendance fit that category. But working on issues differs from flaunting them. For example, our church offers loving support groups and classes for those battling addictions or struggling in other ways. Far from condoning the soul-sickness of sin, our churches can serve as hospitals for sinners who want to get well.

Father, You sent Your Son to come for sinners. Thank You for including me in that gracious rescue effort! In His name I pray. Amen.

Never Alone

The Lord upholds all those who fall and lifts up all who are bowed down (Psalm 145:14).

Scripture: **Psalm 145:13-21**
Song: **"Precious Lord, Take My Hand"**

The world watched, and the image remains imprinted on countless minds. Runner Derek Redmond had shattered Great Britain's 400-meter record but had missed the 1988 Olympics due to injury. Then, in 1992, he arrived in Barcelona ready to rock the world.

He didn't win the race, but what happened was much more memorable. Midway down his lane, Derek tore a hamstring muscle. He slowed, and then fell down. Tears streaming down his face, he struggled to his feet.

A commotion arose in the stands. A man fought past guards to get onto the track—Derek's father. "That's my son out there, and I'm going to help him," he said.

Jim Redmond put his arm around Derek's shoulders. "I'm here, son. We'll finish this together." Slowly, painfully, they walked 120 meters to the finish line while the crowd cheered.

That is the picture of our heavenly Father. When we fall, when we fail in our attempts to reach a goal, He lifts us up. Never, ever, do we run the race alone.

Father, thanks for lifting me back to my feet when I fall. Help me never be too ashamed to look to You for a new start. In Christ's name, amen.

July 23–29. **Darlene Franklin** lives with her mother in Denver, Colorado, where she discovered the greatest love of all—the God who loves "no matter what."

Man Hunt

"'Their leader will be one of their own; their ruler will arise from among them. I will bring him near and he will come close to me, for who is he who will devote himself to be close to me?'" declared the Lord (Jeremiah 30:21).

Scripture: **Jeremiah 30:18-22**
Song: **"Turn Your Eyes upon Jesus"**

The people of New Hampshire lost a beloved icon when the granite formation nicknamed "The Old Man of the Mountain" tumbled down in a rock slide in May 2003. The amazingly lifelike profile that graces their state quarter inspired one of my favorite stories, "The Great Stone Face" by Nathaniel Hawthorne.

In the story, the hero spends his life looking for a man who looks like the granite formation. He is sure that anyone with that majestic profile will match it in character. First one candidate, then another, disappoints. In the end, he discovers that he himself has the face that matches the mountain. After a lifetime of devotion, he resembles what he sought. Isn't this the idea in our Scripture today?

It happens that way in our spiritual growth. The more we seek the Lord and honor His character, the more we take on His qualities. It's the Spirit's work within us, moving us closer to that day when He will even "transform our lowly bodies so that they will be like his glorious body" (Philippians 3:21). What a complete work He does!

*Praise to You, **Father,** for making me into the likeness of Your dear Son! Yes, work mightily to conform me to His image. In His name, amen.*

Jump—for Rest

This is what the Lord says: "The people who survive the sword will find favor in the desert; I will come to give rest to Israel" (Jeremiah 31:2).

Scripture: **Jeremiah 31:1-9**
Song: **"My Faith Has Found a Resting Place"**

There comes a time for most of us when we feel as if we've jumped out of the frying pan into the fire. Like an ever-escalating novel, as soon as one disaster resolves, another appears. Have you been there recently?

Some years ago our landlady needed our apartment back, so we had to move. I looked for another apartment close to my place of employment but, for a long time, nothing worked out. I would have taken anything! But then, after making a list describing my *ideal* apartment—I found it! The biggest problem was that we'd now live farther away from my office than we'd been before.

That turned out to be just as well, though. A day after moving, I lost my job. I survived the sword of apartment hunting to end up in the desert of unemployment.

But that's where God gave me rest. He let me stay in the new apartment for five years before moving me to something even better. He led me to a new job and a new church, where great opportunities waited. If I had never jumped into the fire of the desert, I would never have experienced God's rest.

*When I wander in the desert, **God,** set up a campsite for me. Thank You for the kind of rest and peace only You can provide. In Jesus' name, amen.*

Baby Doll

"They will be like a well-watered garden, and they will sorrow no more" (Jeremiah 31:12).

Scripture: **Jeremiah 31:10-14**
Song: **"God, Who Touches Earth with Beauty"**

When the green thumbs were handed out, I must have been absent. My decidedly brown thumb has killed even the hardiest of plants. But when my daughter Jolene wanted to grow a nice houseplant in her apartment, a friend gave her a small botanical wonder that looked like a miniature palm tree. She called it Baby Doll and lavished love and care upon it.

The day came when Jolene had to leave her apartment for a few weeks, and she brought her precious plant to me. "Will you take care of Baby Doll for me?" she asked.

Chills ran up my spine as I envisioned the brown, shriveled stalks that would greet Jolene when she returned. Nevertheless, I put Baby Doll by my patio door and watered her once a week. She grew! Then she multiplied. Two miniature palm trees became four. Eventually, we added plants until half a dozen now crowd a small table, all of the leaves straining for the sun.

That's what God wants for us—lavish growth of our spirits. He lavishes love on us, calls us by a special name, waters us with the Living Word, and gives us everything we need to bear fruit in His kingdom.

Heavenly Father, *I am so thankful that You reproduce Your life in Your children. Help me grow and bear fruit for You. In Jesus' name, amen.*

This Computes!

"This is the covenant I will make with the house of Israel after that time," declares the Lord. "I will put my law in their minds and write it on their hearts. I will be their God, and they will be my people" (Jeremiah 31:33).

Scripture: **Jeremiah 31:33-37**
Song: **"The Law Commands and Makes Us Know"**

When I woke up this morning, I saw colored bugs going around in circles behind my closed eyelids. It was the pattern of a computer game I'd played before I went to bed. I often play it to relax at night. But apparently I play it too much, since the visual patterns were still implanted on my brain upon awaking.

Really, I'd rather have God's Word appear behind my eyelids when I awake in the morning. That would be wonderful, but what would it take?

I suppose I'd have to take seriously the GIGO principle that's so well-known among computer users: garbage in, garbage out. Whatever you feed into a computer, that is essentially what will come out, in spite of modifications; bad data always produces bad conclusions. Perhaps I could use the BIBO principle instead: Bible in, Bible out. The more I take in God's "data," the more His law will be written on my mind and flow out from my heart to others. That's a computation I can live with.

Lord, *I praise You for revealing yourself in the Bible. Let me so immerse myself in Your written Word that it's the first thing I see in the morning and the last thing I see at night. Through Christ the Living Word, amen.*

Putting Down Roots

"Build houses and settle down; plant gardens and eat what they produce" (Jeremiah 29:5).

Scripture: **Jeremiah 29:1-9**
Song: **"Brighten the Corner Where You Are"**

I grew up in Maine, the largest of the New England states, and it defined America for me. When I left for school in New Jersey and, later, Texas, I compared everything to Maine. Nothing measured up.

It took my college roommate to shake my thinking. "I try to find something good about every place where I live," she said.

Something good about the dry desert that was Texas? Surely she was joking. But I took her advice. I did enjoy the Fort Worth Zoo and then attended the Texas State Fair. When I moved to Arkansas, my children played in the Mississippi River. In Oklahoma, I learned more about our Native American heritage. In other words, wherever we moved became home. I learned to put down roots.

That was Jeremiah's advice to the Israelites, pining away for their homeland. "Build and plant, folks, because you're going to be here for a while!" Instead of pining for the past or dreaming of the future, suppose we get to work right where God has placed us today? Thankfully, wherever He is, there is peace and joy.

Gracious heavenly Father, I long to be Your servant—like the apostle Paul who was content in whatever state he found himself. Abiding in Your presence, I know it's possible. I pray in Jesus' holy name. Amen.

The Hiding God

"I will be found by you," declares the Lord, **"and will bring you back from captivity"** (Jeremiah 29:14).

Scripture: **Jeremiah 29:10-14**
Song: **"Open the Eyes of My Heart"**

Have you noticed there are times when God seems to play hide-and-seek? It happened for me when police arrested my teenage son for drug possession and he left home—for good. Hope deserted me. I had fought hard to make a good home for my children and now, *this!*

Where were God's promises? Where was God's love? Where was . . . God?

Looking back, I can now say: He was right there, waiting for me to seek Him. I found Him in a loving church family and amid a circle of marvelous, self-giving friends. His Holy Spirit carried my cries, which were too deep for words, straight to the Father's throne (see Romans 8:26).

God brought me back from that captivity of heart, slowly, over a period of years. My adult son is now a committed Christian soon to be married and no trace of his rebellious youth remains. We talk regularly.

It must be that when God seems to be hiding, He is doing extra teaching duty—diligently training us how to seek Him with all our hearts, the very best thing we could ever do with our lives.

Almighty God, when I can't find You as the Lord of the universe, let me seek You as my loving Father. In the name of Christ, amen.

Wait for God

The Lord longs to be gracious to you; he rises to show you compassion. For the Lord is a God of justice. Blessed are all who wait for him! (Isaiah 30:18).

Scripture: **Isaiah 30:15-19**
Song: **"Pass Me Not, O Gentle Savior"**

Tears clouded my vision as I stared at the results of the pregnancy test I'd just taken. This time I had been certain I was expecting, but I was wrong yet again. It was taking forever to start the family my husband and I so dearly wanted. Meanwhile, all around us, other couples were announcing their upcoming blessed events. I was genuinely happy for them, but I worried that we might never share in the great adventure of parenthood.

Several more months went by. Whenever a worry crept up on me, I turned it into a prayer. Then, finally, I saw that wonderful red line I'd been hoping to see on the test kit. A baby was on the way.

When our daughter, Honor, made her appearance, I knew that the wait had been well worth it. Only God could have given us such a gift. His graciousness overwhelmed me as I gazed into beautiful twinkling eyes. Never before had I considered the blessedness of waiting. Not until that very moment.

Lord, it's hard to wait when desires burn in my heart. Give me the courage to hold on, reminding me of the blessed rewards. In Jesus' name, amen.

July 30, 31. **Whitney Von Lake Hopler** has served as an editor for Crosswalk.com and for several newspapers and periodicals. She lives in Fairfax, Virginia.

Dismal Captivity

He was captured. He was taken to the king of Babylon at Riblah, where sentence was pronounced on him (2 Kings 25:6).

Scripture: **2 Kings 25:1, 2, 5-7**
Song: **"We'll Not Be Defeated"**

Just like Judah's King Zedekiah (whom the Bible says "did evil in the eyes of the Lord"), Saddam Hussein was captured after many in the free world condemned his deeds as Iraq's dictator. His sons were killed, and many of his soldiers scattered, just as things unfolded with Zedekiah.

Hussein had once reigned with great power, living in the splendor of luxurious palaces. But none of that could save him when it came time to reckon for his behavior. After U.S. forces invaded Iraq, Hussein was forced to hide in a filthy hole until they found him. He emerged shocked, broken, and defeated.

Those of us who follow Christ can find a cautionary example here. Are we caught up in our own ambitions? In His sacrifice on the cross, Christ has already achieved for us the ultimate accomplishment: complete spiritual freedom. No amount of power, money, or luxury can match that marvelous gift. To seek elsewhere for satisfaction is to live in dismal captivity.

Mighty God, thank You that You overcome evil with good. Let me not be found in any kind of opposition to You or Your will in the world. Deliver me from the captivity of self-centered ambitions. Through Christ, amen.

DEVOTIONS

*C*ome near to
God and He will
come near to you.

—James 4:8

AUGUST

Photo © Comstock

Gary Allen, Editor

© 2006 STANDARD PUBLISHING, 8121 Hamilton Avenue, Cincinnati, Ohio, 45231, a division
of STANDEX INTERNATIONAL Corporation. Topics based on the Home Daily Bible Readings,
International Sunday School Lessons. © 2003 by the Committee on the Uniform Series. Printed in the
U.S.A. All Scripture quotations, unless otherwise indicated, are taken from the HOLY BIBLE, NEW
INTERNATIONAL VERSION®. NIV®. Copyright © 1973, 1978, 1984 by International Bible Society.
Used by permission of Zondervan. All rights reserved. Where noted, Scripture quotations are from the
following, used with permission of the copyright holders, all rights reserved: *The New King James Version
(NKJV),* Copyright © 1982 by Thomas Nelson, Inc. *New American Standard Bible (NASB),* © The
Lockman Foundation, 1960, 1962, 1963, 1968, 1971, 1972, 1973, 1975, 1977, 1995.

Count on God's Love

The eyes of the LORD are on all those who fear him, on those whose hope is in his unfailing love (Psalm 33:18).

Scripture: **Psalm 33:12-22**
Song: **"He's in the Midst"**

I paced between rooms, anxiously wondering why my husband, Russ, was so late calling me from Beijing, China, where he was staying on a business trip. Finally the phone rang. "Hi, it's me," Russ said in a hollow voice that told me something was wrong. "I'd meant to call earlier, but I'm sick."

"Sick!" I exclaimed. That was just what I'd feared most about his travel to Asia. "I think I ate something bad today," he groaned.

"What do you . . . " I began, intending to ask him about his symptoms. "Oh, no—I'm dizzy," he interrupted. "I'm sorry, but I can't sit up anymore. Got to go. Call you later."

"Wait!" I pleaded. But I heard a click and then a dial tone. My husband was half a world away, and I had no way of getting to him—but I knew who could. So I prayed for God to help Russ (and He did). Then I went to bed with newfound peace in God's love, a love that never fails.

Father, in my fallen world, where worry can overwhelm me, remind me of Your magnificent power and constant goodness. In Jesus' name, amen.

August 1–5. **Whitney Von Lake Hopler** has served as an editor for several newspapers and periodicals. She lives in Fairfax, Virginia.

Offer What You've Received

If you, O LORD, kept a record of sins, O LORD, who could stand? (Psalm 130:3).

Scripture: **Psalm 130**
Song: **"Give Thanks to God the Lord"**

The moment Kathy's face appeared, my pulse began to race. About 10 years earlier she had stirred up trouble for me at the college campus newspaper where we'd both worked. A guy to whom she'd been attracted had asked me out instead. She had retaliated by lying to our editor-in-chief about my work in an attempt to get me fired. My job had been saved when the truth came out, but I was livid and managed to avoid her for the rest of college.

Now here Kathy was again—in church, of all places! She approached me and struck up a conversation about the heartache she'd endured over the past decade. Then she apologized for what she did to me in college . . . and asked me to forgive her.

My bitterness evaporated as God reminded me that I had made a few little mistakes of my own over the years! I was no less of a sinner and no more worthy than anyone else of God's marvelous gift of forgiveness through Christ. So I knew I should offer His beloved child Kathy nothing less than what I had so graciously received.

*Praise to You, **Lord of All**, for the gift of forgiveness that comes through Your Son's precious blood! Let me never take this gift for granted or devalue it in any way by refusing to forgive those who may hurt me. This I pray in the name of Him who died for me. Amen.*

Flying Joy

Because of the Lord's great love we are not consumed, for his compassions never fail (Lamentations 3:22).

Scripture: Lamentations 3:19-24
Song: "After the Rain"

A brownish gray flutter of movement caught my eye as I walked past a neighbor's green lawn. There in the grass was a young robin, struggling in vain to fly. Nearby lay a broken nest that had apparently fallen out of a tree during a fierce thunderstorm the night before.

The robin lifted its head and stared at me with beady eyes that seemed to plead for help. I hesitated as I gazed at the extent of its injuries, but I couldn't deny the sense of hope that pulled me toward it like a magnet. Since God had decided to let the bird survive the terrible storm, I dared to think His compassion in this new day could help it recover.

I called our county's animal control department, and an officer came out to scoop the robin into a cage. "This one has a chance to make it," he said. "We'll try to nurture it back to health." Because God had given me compassion for the robin, it might take flight once again.

And what a sense of joy took flight in me!

Dear God, thank You for the great love You have for everyone and everything in Your creation. Please help me to remember that every person I meet today is equally loved by You. And may I be an instrument of Your love to cause a seeking heart to turn toward You in response. Through the name of Jesus, amen.

Our Only Real Hope

The Lord is good to those whose hope is in him, to the one who seeks him (Lamentations 3:25).

Scripture: **Lamentations 3:25-33**
Song: **"Come Down, O Love Divine"**

From the time he was just a young teen, Willie Williams spent 40 years shuttling in and out of various prisons. Each time he was released, he vowed never to become incarcerated again. But his willpower alone wasn't enough to ensure that he'd emerge victorious from a life of crime.

Nor was it enough to help him break free of his addictions to heroin and alcohol. By the time Williams ended up in a Salvation Army alcohol rehabilitation center (where I interviewed him for a newspaper story), he had exhausted all means of trying to help himself.

He decided to turn to Christ and be baptized.

Then an amazing thing began to happen. Williams found he finally had the power he needed to let go of the anger and addictions that had imprisoned him for so long. He took a productive job that he thoroughly enjoyed and also reunited with several family members. Williams had sought Christ and placed his hope in the right place. The Lord was good to him.

O Lord, all too often I misplace my hope, trusting in my own feeble efforts to engineer my life. Thank You for bringing me to the point of letting go, of knowing that You alone are my only real hope—for this life and the next. In the name of the Father, the Son, and the Holy Spirit, I pray. Amen.

Believe the Upholder

You have seen, O Lord, the wrong done to me. Uphold my cause (Lamentations 3:59).

Scripture: **Lamentations 3:55-59**
Song: **"Held in His Mighty Arms"**

"Hey, look! It's the suitcase girl!" Jen snickered as I walked through our middle school's locker bay. I could feel the heat in my cheeks as they flushed red from embarrassment. Jen had taunted me for several months, targeting my book bag ("It's so big, it looks like a suitcase!"), my glasses ("Hey, four eyes!"), and my quiet nature ("Nobody can hear you! Speak up, baby!").

I had tried both avoiding her and confronting her, but neither approach had stopped her teasing. Finally, one night at home, I whispered a heartfelt prayer that God would change Jen's heart.

Shortly afterward, Jen walked right by me when she saw me in a hallway. I figured she just hadn't seen me, so I cringed the next time I encountered her and our eyes met. I waited for her to say something mean, but she didn't. In fact, she never teased me again.

Had God upheld my cause? I believe it to this day. And I will believe it in the days ahead, too, when justice seems as scarce as common kindness in my world.

O Father, help me remember that no injustice escapes Your notice. Your Son walked the earth and suffered taunting and the questioning of His motives. Uphold me by Your power when it happens to me. Thank You, Lord! In the precious name of Jesus I pray. Amen.

Someone Paid the Price

There is one God and one Mediator between God and men, the Man Christ Jesus, who gave Himself a ransom for all, to be testified in due time (1 Timothy 2:5, 6, *New King James Version*).

Scripture: 1 Timothy 2:1-6
Song: "I Will Sing of My Redeemer"

A workplace acquaintance was having a hard time understanding how Jesus could have paid the price for our sins. But then he related an episode that had just occurred with his new wife. "Things were going fine—until last night," he said. It seems he'd decided to go out with his work crew to celebrate a job well done. He arrived home an hour later than usual. "She just blew up at me," he said.

A little questioning on my part revealed that his wife had previously been married to an alcoholic. Clearly, she feared a repeat experience with her new husband.

"You're paying for that fellow's sins," I said. "He abused her, and now you can't do certain things without aggravating old wounds." I then spoke of how our sins have abused God's law and more than wounded the relationship between us; how Jesus stepped into our place as the perfect Son we could never be; how the Father could lavish His love upon us without violating His justice.

Father, without the mediation of the God-Man, Jesus, what hope would I have of Heaven? Praise You, through my Lord Christ, amen.

August 6–12. **Brad Leach** lives in Loveland, Colorado, and hopes to become a full-time freelance writer some day.

Hidden Dangers

I have kept the ways of the Lord, and have not wickedly departed from my God (Psalm 18:21, *New King James Version*).

Scripture: **Psalm 18:20-24**
Song: **"Rise Up, O Men of God!"**

The company I work for in water-starved Colorado has created a system of canals draining water from the mountains into many reservoirs. The water, as it flows along these concrete chutes, looks inviting to aquatic thrill-seekers. But it contains a hidden danger. The only way water can cross ravines, roads, or rivers is by pipe or tunnel. Either is deadly for someone swimming or riding an inner tube.

Warning signs appear throughout the canal systems. However, occasionally someone ignores the warnings, climbs over the gates, and faces his own demise. Those lucky few who survive usually explain, "I just couldn't imagine such danger existed!"

"The ways of the Lord" (v. 21) in our Scripture today refers to God's laws, and they operate like my company's warning signs. Danger lurks when we ignore them. David was tempted to kill King Saul and make himself king, but he chose to keep God's ways instead. Thus God not only made him king but blessed him with riches and honor.

Father in Heaven, give me the eyes of wisdom that I may read Your words and heed the hidden dangers of straying from Your side. How I long to acquire a taste for righteousness! Work in my heart for just such a purpose. I pray in the name of Jesus, my Savior and Lord. Amen.

It's Where You Finish

"When the righteous turns from his righteousness and commits iniquity, he shall die because of it. But when the wicked turns from his wickedness and does what is lawful and right, he shall live because of it. Yet you say, 'The way of the Lord is not fair'" (Ezekiel 33:18-20, *New King James Version*).

Scripture: **Ezekiel 33:12-20**
Song: **"At Calvary"**

Talking about his favorite film series, a friend told me he thought it unfair that at the end of the *Star Wars* saga, Anakin Skywalker was shown happy and restored, after all the evil he had done as Darth Vader. I pointed out that another character, the evil emperor, spends much time initially helping the good guys before his evil nature is revealed. Then he meets a less-than-pleasant end. "Was George Lucas being unfair here, as well?" I asked. My friend decided that "it's where you end up" that counts, not where you start from.

Please don't push this rather dubious analogy too far! However, I do see Ezekiel responding in similar fashion to the charge of God's seeming unfairness. Those who turn and end up doing right shall live; those who start well and then succumb to evil inherit a decidedly sad ending.

May none of us produce a "tearjerker" ending to the story of our days! No matter our situation now, it is never too late to accept the life He still offers.

Gracious and longsuffering Father, I too harbor a rebellious heart. Work Your will in me, and let me finish in faith. Through Christ, amen.

It's Not My Fault

"What do you mean when you use this proverb concerning the land of Israel, saying: "'The fathers have eaten sour grapes, and the children's teeth are set on edge'"? (Ezekiel 18:2, *New King James Version*).

Scripture: **Ezekiel 18:1-4**
Song: **"Kind and Merciful God"**

"It's my parents' fault." This is a common twenty-first-century complaint, but here we see the ancient Israelites voicing the same allegation.

Raised during the Depression, my parents constantly reminded me to eat everything you take and clean your plate. Apparently, every spoonful of spinach unconsumed meant another child in India going without (my offer to airmail the leftovers not withstanding).

On the other hand, one surefire attention-getter in my meat-and-potatoes family was to eat stupendous amounts of food. This solicited grins and responses such as, "You must have a hollow leg" or "He's a fine, growing boy." Eating became my reward, and by age 40-something, I was starting to resemble a small, third-world country.

I could blame my parents, right? But honestly, I'm the one who chooses to take every single bite. My confession and repentance, along with God's mercy, will reduce my problem. Blaming Mom and Dad will just set everyone's teeth on edge.

Lord, I know I can't transfer the blame for my poor choices. Help me grow more mature in accountability and responsibility. In Jesus' name, amen.

The Time Is Always Right

"If he has walked in My statutes and kept My judgments faithfully—he is just; he shall surely live!" says the Lord God (Ezekiel 18:9, *New King James Version*).

Scripture: **Ezekiel 18:5-9**
Song: **"Through the Love of God, Our Savior"**

When Ezekiel wrote these words to the Israelites, they faced a future of slavery. They were going to Babylon as a captive people to serve their new masters, and they wondered whether they really deserved this fate. God assured them that if they followed His ways, they would live, no matter what their forefathers had done.

Why? I believe one answer comes through in the words of Dr. Martin Luther King, Jr.: "The *time* is always right to *do* what is right." For Dr. King, the time to turn from racism and hatred was "now." The time to protest injustice was "now." The time for all humans to relate to each other according to character, not skin color, was "now." No excuse was acceptable, no delay in pursuit of righteousness tolerated.

God's statement in Ezekiel's book serves as a call to return to moral ways. Even when our desires often lead us into virtual slavery, it's not too late to turn around. In Ezekiel's day and in ours, the time is always right to walk in God's ways.

Father, without Your Son's gift of true freedom I would have remained enslaved to my own self-centeredness. Yet I pray for Your daily strength to walk close to You in the ways of righteousness. In Christ's name, amen.

Self-Destructing?

**"Do I have any pleasure at all that the wicked should die?"
says the Lord God, "and not that he should turn from his ways
and live?"** (Ezekiel 18:23, *New King James Version*).

Scripture: **Ezekiel 18:19-23**
Song: **"Almost Persuaded"**

Early in the twentieth century, a crime reporter traveled through the South on his way back to New York.
When his car broke down, he found himself stranded for
two days in a small rural town. Thinking of a possible
story, the man decided to visit the local courtrooms.

The morning offered only the usual, small-town
misdemeanor infractions of the law. But in the afternoon,
a young man came before the judge for sentencing. The
journalist sensed the tension in the judge's shaking voice
as he pronounced 22 years—the least he could render for
the crimes of armed robbery and deadly assault.

Interviewing the judge afterward, the journalist noted
the emotion with which sentence was issued and how
this man so differed from the jaded, big-city judges he'd
known. Then, with eyes moist, the judge confessed that
the young man was his son.

Like that judge, our God of infinite, holy character
must punish lawbreakers—a thing that surely breaks His
heart. As the prophet tells us, there is no pleasure for God
in seeing our self-destructiveness unfold before Him.

*Holy Lord, turn me from my ways today—the small and large decisions
that so often work to bring my downfall. In Jesus' name, amen.*

Why Die?

Rid yourselves of all the offenses you have committed, and get a new heart and a new spirit. Why will you die, O house of Israel? (Ezekiel 18:31).

Scripture: **Ezekiel 18:25-32**
Song: **"Breathe on Me, Breath of God"**

Imagine you've bought a fine, solid automobile. You finally feel secure on the roads, convinced you can go anywhere and handle anything. Soon afterward, you hear on the radio a recall notice for your car's year and model. The manufacturer says your car is dangerous, that many have already died. Fear creeps into your mind, and you notice an ominous shimmy in the front wheels. But the radio announcer states the manufacturer will correct the problem—free!

Relaxing, you admit you'll have to get that done some day, and you keep on driving. The highway vibrations get worse, and various parts start coming off, but you press on to greater speeds.

It's foolish to risk death when the fix is without charge. But our unredeemed human natures are those flawed vehicles, destined to maim and kill us. We need a fix and, thanks to Christ, it's free, "in order that the righteous requirements of the law might be fully met in us, who do not live according to the sinful nature but according to the Spirit" (Romans 8:4).

Lord, create in me a new and vibrant heart, one willing to yield every beat to the glory of Christ and His kingdom, in whose name I pray. Amen.

Come as You Are

Draw near to God and He will draw near to you (James 4:8, *New American Standard Bible*).

Scripture: **James 4:6-10**
Song: **"Just as I Am"**

Joy beamed from Chuck's eyes when he shared the story of his conversion to Christianity. He testified to an encounter with Jesus while sitting on his mother's gravestone in a dark cemetery. That night he gave his life to the Lord. All I could think was, "Is this the real thing?"

Yet he and his wife were off drugs. They toted their Bibles everywhere and told everyone about Jesus. Their rusted-out VW™ bus—with "Jesus Saves" painted on all sides in primary colors—sat in the church parking lot on a regular basis.

I thought back to my own respectable church background and my try-hard-to-be-like-Jesus brand of Christianity. In frustration I cried out one morning, "I *can't* be like Jesus! God, if You are there and want me, I give myself to You." Chuck and I both lacked Bible knowledge, but Christ graciously received us when we admitted our need and surrendered ourselves to baptism. No matter what we look like, or what our prayers sound like, He always responds to a heart hungry to know Him.

Dear Father, thank You for receiving me when I stumbled toward You with confused theology and desperate prayers. In Jesus' name, amen.

August 13–19. **Sandy Ewing,** mother of 5, grandmother of 13, is a writer and speaker. With her minister husband she's led Christian seminars in several nations.

Rescue Operation

The LORD is compassionate and gracious, slow to anger and abounding in lovingkindness (Psalm 103:8, *New American Standard Bible*).

Scripture: **Psalm 103:8-18**
Song: **"Lo, a Loving Friend Is Waiting"**

I studied the helicopter in the summer sky. In Rocky Mountain National Park, helicopters mean only one thing. "Somebody must be in trouble," I called to my neighbor.

"Park ranger missing," she replied. "Three days now."

The knowledge of someone lost, perhaps injured and helpless, hovered in my mind all day. News broadcasters reported that the young man's friends rushed to join the searchers. When temperatures dropped toward evening, and rain fell, my concern deepened. At daybreak, the helicopter was joined by four others, and the ground crew swelled to 250 people. Five days later, a saddened hiker stumbled upon a broken body at the foot of a cliff.

In the midst of prayers for the ranger, I thought of our own lostness, our own need to be rescued. I recalled that Jesus left His home in Heaven to come to earth and die for our sins. By doing so He restored us to a relationship with His Father. I asked myself: Am I so filled with God's compassion that I will give of myself in some way this day to search out a lost seeker?

Father, open my eyes for opportunities to search and rescue on behalf of those for whom Jesus died. I pray in His precious name. Amen.

Sing Yourself Strong

"Behold, God is my salvation, I will trust and not be afraid; for the LORD God is my strength and song, and He has become my salvation" (Isaiah 12:2, *New American Standard Bible*).

Scripture: **Isaiah 12**
Song: **"I Will Bless the Lord at All Times"**

I glanced at my watch and let out a huge sigh. In 30 minutes, a group of ladies would fill the room and raise their eager faces to me, their Bible study teacher. Waves of worry over a family situation lapped at the shores of my mind. All my faith seemed sucked out to sea. How will I be able to teach today?

I slumped into a chair and flipped open my notebook to the lesson notes for the day, entitled, "Our spiritual blessings in Christ." I read each point aloud and soaked in the promises: love, grace, mercy, supply for every need. Within minutes, thanksgiving and joy began to wash away my dismal outlook. I continued reciting the list, this time in an impromptu song—my own musical creation.

By the time the ladies arrived, I was pounding out my song on the piano—and taught it to them too! "The Happy Song" we named it, with good-natured laughter. My little ditty won't be playing on a radio station near you anytime soon. But the whole episode reminded afresh that God's supply of strength is greater than anything I will face in this life.

Dear Lord, I choose today to declare: You are my strength and song. Fill me today with the joy only You can give. Through my Lord Christ, amen.

Listen Up!

"The L**ORD**** Almighty says: 'Turn from your evil ways and your evil practices.' But they would not listen or pay attention to me, declares the L****ORD****"** (Zechariah 1:4).

Scripture: **Zechariah 1:1-6**
Song: **"Listen to the Blessed Invitation"**

One of the pleasures we looked forward to after a year teaching English in China was a reunion with our old dog, Woody. After collecting him from the friends who'd cared for him, we headed for our new home eight hundred miles away.

We were happily reunited, but at an overnight stop I made a frightening discovery about our beloved pet. On an early morning walk in a nearby park, I watched Woody head straight for a street choked with rush-hour traffic.

I called, I shouted, and then I screamed. He couldn't hear! With Woody only yards from the street, in desperation I clapped my hands. The sharp sound caught his attention, and he stopped a foot from the curb. He looked back at me, puzzled, but safe. Does he have a hearing problem—or just not *want* to hear?

My hope is that Woody will learn to listen a little better. And that is my desire for my own spiritual growth. "Be still, and know that I am God" says the Lord (Psalm 46:10). Can I sit still for a moment today? Can I stop the constant mental chatter and just listen for Him?

O God, Your Word reminds me how dangerous it is to ignore You. May I set my heart to listen and obey You today. In Jesus' name, amen.

God's Fierce Love

"They made their hearts like flint so that they could not hear the law and the words which the Lord of hosts had sent by His Spirit through the former prophets; therefore great wrath came from the Lord of hosts" (Zechariah 7:12, *New American Standard Bible*).

Scripture: **Zechariah 7:8-14**
Song: **"Spirit of the Living God"**

The idea thrilled me. How many times can I run into the middle of the street before the bus passes my house? What a challenge for a 5-year-old! I zoomed out and back. Twice. Three times. One more time?

A hand gripped my arm so hard I winced. My mother's face was a storm of anger. I had to run to keep up with her quick steps as she marched me into the house, sat down on the hall bench, swung me over her lap, and gave me a swat. I was too startled to cry. When she pulled me upright again, I saw tears in her eyes.

"Sandra, whatever were you *thinking?* You could have been killed." She clutched me in a fierce embrace and wept. Years later, when I struggled to understand how a God of love could also demonstrate great wrath against self-destructive sinners, I remembered my mother's tear-stained eyes.

Almighty God and Father, *Thank You that Your love won't let go of me even when I make bad choices. I yield my will afresh to You, asking that You renew a right spirit in me and give me joy and peace in Your service. I pray this prayer in the name of Jesus, my merciful Savior and Lord. Amen.*

Restored

"'They will be My people and I will be their God in truth and righteousness'" (Zechariah 8:8, *New American Standard Bible*).

Scripture: **Zechariah 8:1-8**
Song: **"We've a Story to Tell to the Nations"**

Before my husband accepted a troubled ministry in another state, we knew about the congregational splits, the confused identity, and the dismissal of two previous ministers. But nothing matched the judgment made by a new acquaintance soon after our arrival when he asked, "Well folks, what brings you to this area?" When we told him, his smile disappeared as if we'd flipped a switch. "That church has wrecked many friendships," he said.

Later, I laid our challenge before the Lord in prayer. I felt that, somehow, He would remove the reproach from this assembly of downcast believers, that He would cleanse and lead us on a wholesome path in the future.

Little by little, God worked in our midst. Prayers of commitment followed times of repentance. When we left 14 years later with joy in our hearts, the promise of Zechariah had become a living reality in that place.

The experience left me with a deeper confidence in God and a greater appreciation of His sovereignty in all things—especially in the hearts of His people.

Lord of the church, *thank You for caring so diligently for the whole body of Your people, giving it the gifts it needs to function in peace and fruitfulness. Continue to build my community of faith in the graces of love and mutual encouragement, for the sake of Jesus, in whom I pray. Amen.*

Transformed Attitudes

"'Let none of you devise evil in your heart against another, and do not love perjury; for all these are what I hate,' declares the LORD" (Zechariah 8:17, *New American Standard Bible*).

Scripture: **Zechariah 8:14-17, 20-23**
Song: **"O to Be Like Thee!"**

"Sandra, don't use the word 'hate'," said Mom. "You may say, 'I dislike' or 'I strongly dislike.' But you may not say 'hate'."

I glared at the untouched, dull-green mound on the china plate in front of me on the dining table. "But I don't strongly dislike spinach," I protested. "I *hate* it." Just the thought of the long, dangly stems trailing down my throat made me gag. Yet my mother's will prevailed, and the word was purged from my vocabulary. I had to gulp down the horrid vegetable.

What a shock, years later, to find the banned *H* word in the Bible! I discovered God doesn't just strongly dislike certain things, He *hates* them—and says so. The list I compiled from my study on the subject included warnings about our attitudes and behaviors toward others.

I decided that if God hates something, maybe I should as well. And whatever God loves, I'd better love too. Seldom could I win an argument with my mother. I figure I can't win one with God either.

Dear Lord, conform my viewpoints to Yours. May I never be a hateful person, but do help me love what You love and hate what You hate. In the name of Jesus, my Lord and Savior, I pray. Amen.

With Promise

The LORD redeems his servants; no one will be condemned who takes refuge in him (Psalm 34:22).

Scripture: **Psalm 34:11-22**
Song: **"Redeemed, Restored, Forgiven"**

My parents gave me a new Bible for my 16th birthday. The pages are filled with notes from hometown sermons, National Youth Conference meetings, and Bible college seminars. There are favorite verses highlighted and some letter markings at many verses—*DC* written beside some, and *P* next to others.

You see, I was fascinated when our minister pointed out that every direct command *(DC)* is followed by a promise *(P)*. He challenged us in our Bible reading to note direct commands and then look for their promises.

As a parent, I tend to use this pattern with my children—"Brush your teeth . . . and you won't get cavities." "Do your chores . . . and we'll go to the park." As you read the Scripture selections for this week, I challenge you to look for the *DCs* and their *Ps*. Think about God's reason for giving the command; then claim His promise. In other words, mark up your Bible. It's OK. I promise.

Dear Father in Heaven, *thank You for giving me clear direction in Your holy Word. Help me to see Your plan and cherish Your promises as I read. I pray in Jesus' holy name. Amen.*

August 20–26. **Guyla Greenly** lives with her two children in Casper, Wyoming. She is an avid scrapbooker and addicted to TV decorating shows.

Choose Your Building Materials

If any man builds on this foundation using gold, silver, costly stones, wood, hay or straw, his work will be shown for what it is (1 Corinthians 3:12, 13).

Scripture: **1 Corinthians 3:10-15**
Song: **"The Solid Rock"**

Several years ago we set a manufactured home on a foundation in the middle of an alfalfa field. I live in windy Wyoming, and this house is solid. When the wind blows our gas grill off the deck, I don't hear or feel a thing inside the house—not even the grill crashing into my son's rock garden. My home is built tight and solid, but one strike of the match, and I'd be left with nothing but the foundation once again.

Eight months after moving into the house, I went through a divorce, and my world blazed with pain, down to its foundation. If that foundation had not been Jesus Christ, and a support system of awesome family and friends, I don't know how I would have survived.

And a refining fire it was! With God's leading, I am rebuilding upon the solid-rock foundation of Jesus. As I labor in reconstruction, I'm trying to choose quality building materials—a firm knowledge of God's Word, a daily dependence upon His Spirit, a regular participation in worship and fellowship.

O Father, sustain me through the refining fires! Help me to make wise choices when building upon the foundation of Jesus Christ my Savior. In the name of the Father, the Son, and the Holy Spirit, I pray. Amen.

Who

Judge nothing before the appointed time; wait till the Lord comes. He will bring to light what is hidden in darkness and will expose the motives of men's hearts. At that time each will receive his praise from God (1 Corinthians 4:5).

Scripture: **1 Corinthians 4:1-5**
Song: **"They That Overcome"**

Something about her caught my eye, and I watched her during the speaker's testimony. She sat with arms folded across her chest, chin up, and lips drawn down in a scowl. "There's no way this speaker is getting through to her," I thought. As I watched her armor-like demeanor, I began to pick apart the words of the speaker and mentally list what he was doing wrong in trying to reach this woman.

I later found out the woman had made a decision to follow Christ that night—so much for my ability to interpret body language! This experience taught me a real-life lesson on the old cliché, "You can't judge a book by its cover." I had jumped to a conclusion about this woman's faithfulness. My impulses were critical, while hers were accepting. If God had revealed our inner worlds to that group of women, I would have been humiliated.

It's so easy to become self-righteous, to judge the actions of others without knowing anything about them. It's not so easy to let God be the judge—but I'm trying.

Lord and Judge of all, reveal to me my deepest secrets and private motives. Show me where You would have me change and how You would have me treat others. In the precious name of Jesus I pray. Amen.

Still Another . . .

"'Ever since the time of your forefathers you have turned away from my decrees and have not kept them. Return to me, and I will return to you,' says the LORD Almighty" (Malachi 3:7).

Scripture: **Malachi 2:17–3:7**
Song: **"Ancient of Days"**

I am totally amazed by the patience of God. After centuries of human rebellion, He continues to offer reconciliation with humanity. In the days of Noah, God promised never to destroy humankind with a flood again. He doesn't change, but after 40 years of listening to the Israelites bicker and complain in their wilderness wanderings, I would have sent a few scary thunderstorms, at least! My attitude would be, "Sure, I said I wouldn't destroy you, but I'm God; I can do whatever I want."

Good thing I'm not God, right?

The Lord not only has integrity, He *is* integrity. By His very nature God is all good and pure. He cannot go back on a promise because that wouldn't be consistent with His eternal being and character. I find comfort in that.

We humans are quite fickle, though. Even today, just like those wandering Israelites, I tend to gripe about every little inconvenience. But He doesn't change. He stands steadily by, giving me one more chance . . . then another . . . and another . . .

Lord Almighty, thank You for being a God of second chances–and more! Help me to appreciate Your gracious love now so I'll be prepared to spend eternity in praise of it. In the name of my Savior, Jesus Christ, amen.

Excited to Bless

"Bring the whole tithe into the storehouse, that there may be food in my house. Test me in this," says the LORD Almighty, "and see if I will not throw open the floodgates of heaven and pour out so much blessing that you will not have room enough for it" (Malachi 3:10).

Scripture: **Malachi 3:8-12**
Song: **"Give of Your Best to the Master"**

Every Christmas, Dad would choose a special gift for each of my sisters and me, and then hide the packages somewhere in the house. He could hardly stand it while we opened our other presents. "Hurry up!" he'd urge. "Open those presents. I'm hungry." Of course, he didn't really want to eat breakfast; he wanted us to find his hidden gifts. He was as excited to see us hunt for our gifts as we were to find them! He'd give us hints and tell us whether we were "hot" or "cold."

God tells us over and over again in Scripture that if we trust Him and give all of ourselves to Him and His ways, He will bless us. In today's verse He says, in effect, "Try it! Let me prove it to you!" Basically, He's so excited about the many gifts He has in store for us that He's urging us to hurry up. Just as my earthly father was excited to bestow gifts upon me, my heavenly Father wishes to heap His blessings upon all of us who look for Him.

Dear God, thank You for Your many blessings, which are gifts of Your grace. Help me give my tithes and offerings with a cheerful heart, knowing that all I have has come from Your hand. Through Christ I pray. Amen.

Never Wrong to Do Right

"You have said, 'It is futile to serve God. What did we gain by carrying out his requirements and going about like mourners before the LORD Almighty?'" (Malachi 3:14).

Scripture: **Malachi 3:13-18**
Song: **"Search Me and Know Me"**

I followed the formula. I took a vow of purity, prayed for my future spouse, attended Bible college, met him at church, participated in premarital counseling, and had a church wedding.

It didn't work. A giant scarlet *D* is emblazoned across my chest. I did everything I thought I was supposed to do to ensure 'til-death-do-us-part marital success, but I still ended up divorced. What difference did it all make?

At one point in my complaining, a friend said, "It's never wrong to do right." Not exactly the pity-party favor I had in mind! I wanted to feel sorry for myself and blame God. After all, I'd held up my end of the bargain, so why hadn't He? But the Lord spoke to me through those words. *Why* was I doing right anyway? Was it for my own benefit? Or was it to honor a holy God?

It all comes down to either an eternal or temporal perspective, doesn't it? If I'm looking at the temporal, then maybe there really is no point, especially when I sense no personal gain. But if I look at the eternal, then it truly is never wrong—and hardly futile!—to do right.

My God and Father, today keep my eyes focused on Your kingdom, that I may live to please You above all others. Thank You, in Jesus' name. Amen.

Joyful Abandon

"For you who revere my name, the sun of righteousness will rise with healing in its wings. And you will go out and leap like calves released from the stall" (Malachi 4:2).

Scripture: **Malachi 4:1-6**
Song: **"You Are My King"**

My life is a series of deadlines—newsletters to print, bills to pay, articles to write. As each due date looms, it weighs heavier upon me. But as I approach a project's completion, I begin to feel a little giddy. Once I finally finish the work, and mark it off my list, I feel like running through a cheesy movie montage. You know the ones—beautiful girl in a gauzy, flowing dress runs down a gentle hill in a slightly out-of-focus meadow. She glides through the wild flowers with her arms upraised on each side, her long, golden curls blowing in the breeze. An overly sentimental song plays while the beautiful girl frolics and dances.

OK, maybe I get a little carried away, but haven't you ever thrown your arms up and spun around in the sunshine—at least once in your lifetime? Do you ever have this feeling bubbling up inside—and you just have to do something with joyful abandon?

That's the joy of the Lord, friend. Let it out; leap in the sunshine of God's goodness. Bring a smile to His face.

God, awaken my heart to Your goodness on this day, whether the sun shines or not. Help me to know without doubt the difference between happiness in my circumstances and joy in Your arms. Through Christ, amen.

From Honor to Glory

You made him a little lower than the heavenly beings and crowned him with honor and glory (Psalm 8:5).

Scripture: **Psalm 8**
Song: **"To God Be the Glory"**

Our antique dining room chair seats needed new rush webbing. We searched in vain for an artisan to do the work. Following a friend's advice, my husband removed the chair seats, and we took them to a man she suggested. As we viewed his workshop, he told his story.

"We lived in upstate New York, and my mother was a member of a co-op of skilled workers," he said. "When she died, two chairs were waiting to be finished. I learned to do this work so her responsibility would be fulfilled."

He replaced the rush in my chairs. Then, years later, I read of his death and wrote a note to his widow. I told her how his dedication had touched me, and how his talent had endured to bring honor to his family.

We are made in the image of God, and, as such, we excel in honor and glory among God's creatures. As creatures, we inherit these enduring qualities. Yet He calls us to greater glory—to honor Him by returning to Him through His Son, Jesus, that we might also know the eternal glory of Heaven.

*I am Your handiwork, **O God.** In every instance of resourcefulness and skill, help me see Your hand at work. Through Christ I pray. Amen.*

August 27–31. **Cos Barnes** is a freelance writer who lives in southern Pines, North Carolina. An avid hand bell-ringer, she has three children, seven grandchildren.

Night and Day

God saw that the light was good, and he separated the light from the darkness (Genesis 1:4).

Scripture: **Genesis 1:1-5**
Song: **"Heavenly Sunshine"**

It's 2:00 AM, and I yearn for daylight. Troubled by woes, I cannot sleep. I keep thinking about my friend, who, after suffering two strokes, is contemplating a move to a nursing facility. And I have recently cried with a college classmate dying of cancer.

As I lie here, all of life's disappointments, failures, and heartaches march by in review: the unfinished manuscript in my filing cabinet, loneliness caused by the distance separating me from my family, concern for those in my neighborhood who are displaced, frightened, homeless. Heavy-hearted, I examine unfulfilled dreams, things left undone, old nagging doubts.

Sleep won't come, so I rise and do menial chores. Attempting to read, I watch the words fly from the page with neither understanding nor entertainment.

Is this what is meant by "the dark night of the soul?" I wonder as I continue tormenting myself, probing the past, questioning the present. Why do these unhealthy thoughts steal through my sleeplessness?

Then I remember age-old wisdom: "It is always darkest before the dawn." The light is on its way.

*Thank You, **God,** for each new day. And thank You so much that You are always good, whether I'm in sunlight or darkness. In Jesus' name, amen.*

What Technique!

God called the expanse "sky." And there was evening and there was morning—the second day (Genesis 1:8).

Scripture: **Genesis 1:6-8**
Song: **"Some Golden Daybreak"**

Genesis reveals the creation of the universe. As the supreme being, God speaks and the design of the world bursts out of nothingness into being. In these verses the expanse or firmament is divided and the sky is made.

I recently viewed the work of a young artist and asked him how he depicted clouds so realistically. He explained his technique: painting the undertones below the clouds with a chopstick.

God also had a technique.

When our children were young, their dad would take them camping overnight in the backyard. Lying on their backs they explored the heavens, repeating after their mentor the names and positions of the constellations. Inevitably, it would rain, and they would scamper into the house in the wee hours. They were wet but exhilarated from this nighttime learning experience.

As the children grew older, they camped out with the Scouts, and deepened their appreciation for the stars and their relationships to the overall pattern of the heavens. They studied the constellations and acknowledged God's handiwork, His most brilliant, incomparable technique.

"For the beauty of the earth," **O God,** *"for the glory of the skies," I give You thanks. In the precious name of Jesus I pray. Amen.*

Winds and Waves Obey

God called the dry ground "land," and the gathered waters he called "seas" (Genesis 1:10).

Scripture: **Genesis 1:9-13**
Song: **"Peace! Be Still!"**

During the autumn of 2005 our country was plagued with hurricanes. We saw the devastation caused by *Katrina, Wilma,* and *Rita,* among others. Large areas were evacuated due to severe flooding, mud slides, and the washing away of entire communities.

Dams and rivers overflowed. Homes, churches, and schools were destroyed. People waited in line for hours to collect jugs of water, ice, and gas. Stores sold out of generators, chain saws, water, and propane fuel. In the midst of this horrendous cataclysm, many wondered: How could God let this happen?

God was in control at creation and He is still in charge of our universe today. Yet He does allow things to occur in our world—at least for a while. This is a time in which He calls all people to repentance and belief in Christ.

The good times and bad can point us to God. In fact, sometimes only the worst of times are able to turn human hearts from their own self-reliance to see and revere the mighty King of the universe. Thankfully, His power to save us knows no limit.

My heavenly Father, teach me to look to You not only in the good times but also when I face the worst crises. You are always there for me! I pray through my deliverer, Jesus, Your Son. Amen.

Dark Park

God made two great lights—the greater light to govern the day and the lesser light to govern the night. He also made the stars (Genesis 1:16).

Scripture: **Genesis 1:14-19**
Song: **"Dark Is the Night"**

In my county, a section has recently been designated Dark Park. By nature it has the clearest, darkest night skies on the Eeastern seaboard between Maine and the Florida keys. Because of its rural location, it attracts astronomers, photographers, scientists, and ordinary stargazers who love studying the heavens. These gatherings are called star parties, and participants thoroughly enjoy them, sharing their knowledge and findings.

A new form of family fun, star parties were formerly limited to serious astronomy students because telescopes were expensive and required much technical skill to build. Now, however, they are relatively inexpensive; even binoculars are much improved from yesteryears.

Without light pollution, viewers may bask in the celestial wonders of God's heavens. These luminaries are God's way of indicating times and seasons to humankind. And star parties show me that—at least occasionally—we try to use that time wisely.

Your majesty and Your might, **Dear Father,** *I acknowledge. As I go about my routine today, give me pause to look up and recall Your vast creation. Then help me recall the closeness of Your Spirit dwelling within me. In the name of Jesus, Lord and Savior of all, I pray. Amen.*

DEVOTIONS

O LORD, our Lord, how majestic is your name in all the earth!

—Psalm 8:1

SEPTEMBER

Photo © istock

Gary Allen, Editor

© 2007 STANDARD PUBLISHING, 8121 Hamilton Avenue, Cincinnati, Ohio, 45231, a division of STANDEX INTERNATIONAL Corporation. Topics based on the Home Daily Bible Readings, International Sunday School Lessons. © 2003 by the Committee on the Uniform Series. Printed in the U.S.A. All Scripture quotations, unless otherwise indicated, are taken from the HOLY BIBLE, NEW INTERNATIONAL VERSION®. NIV®. Copyright © 1973, 1978, 1984 by International Bible Society. Used by permission of Zondervan. All rights reserved. Where noted, Scripture quotations are from the following, used with permission of the copyright holders. *The Living Bible (TLB),* © 1971 by Tyndale House Publishers, Wheaton, IL. *New American Standard Bible (NASB),* © The Lockman Foundation, 1960, 1962, 1963, 1968, 1971, 1972, 1973, 1975, 1977, 1995.

Powerful Reminder

God blessed them and said, "Be fruitful and increase in number and fill the water in the seas, and let the birds increase on the earth" (Genesis 1:22).

Scripture: **Genesis 1:20-23**
Song: **"His Eye Is on the Sparrow"**

"Mom, guess what?" my daughter said when I answered the telephone. Not waiting for a reply, she rushed on, "Today I saw a baby being born."

Sharing my daughter's excitement, I felt goose pimples rising on my arms and legs. My daughter, a third-year nursing student, was learning rapidly.

"It was a perfect baby girl," she continued. "And the parents were so thrilled."

"You have seen God's greatest miracle," I said. "Many people never do. And you assisted in that miracle."

I read more in my daughter's words than the reassurance that she would make a fine nurse; I witnessed the enduring power of God's command to be fruitful on the earth. For at no time are we more aware of the call upon our lives to acknowledge our creaturehood—and to lift thankful hearts to our creator—than at the birth of a child.

Creator of All, thank You for filling the earth with all good things for my enjoyment. Keep me mindful this day of my origin in You and my constant need to depend on Your grace and care. In Jesus' name, amen.

September 1–2. **Cos Barnes,** a freelance writer living in Southern Pines, North Carolina, has three children, seven grandchildren, and is an avid handbell ringer.

What a Heritage!

God made the wild animals according to their kinds, the livestock according to their kinds, and all the creatures that move along the ground according to their kinds. And God saw that it was good (Genesis 1:25).

Scripture: **Genesis: 1:24, 25**
Song: **"Praise God, from Whom All Blessings Flow"**

The first chapter of Genesis has been called a doxology—a hymn of praise to God as creator. In these two verses the repeated phrase "their kinds," is especially meaningful to me these days, as I have been diligently pursuing my genealogy. I recently met a long-lost cousin, and he shared with me some papers written by a kindred ancestor who was a book publisher in seventeenth-century London.

Holding those precious documents, I was overcome with emotion. As I studied the archaic English, the logo of his print business, and saw the pictures of his shop in St. Paul's Square, I gasped, "I feel a connection to this forebearer! All my life I have loved pretty stationery, ink, newsprint—anything to do with the printed word. Now I know why—it's in my blood!"

Similarly, the accounts of Genesis portray an entire family's character by detailing its origins. When we see God in those pages, we see our holy heritage, all that we are meant to be in Him and in His Son.

My Father, You created me to bring You glory in all I do and say. Work in me today a little more of Your matchless character! Through Christ, amen.

Gazing in Love

Lift your eyes and look to the heavens: Who created all these? He who brings out the starry host one by one, and calls them each by name (Isaiah 40:26).

Scripture: **Isaiah 40:25-31**
Song: **"The Wonder of It All"**

As a child I loved stargazing. I lived in a small Oregon town with few streetlights to blur my view of the heavens. My whole family would stretch out on the grass and admire the night's brilliant display.

Dad pointed out the constellations and tried to teach me their names. I only mastered locating the Big Dipper and the Little Dipper. I quickly recognized the North Star being at the end of the Little Dipper's handle, and I later learned that some 88 constellations could be recognized. (Never by me, however.)

Today's Scripture not only tells us that God created the sun, moon, and stars, He also named each one of them. Each is in its place, fulfilling the purpose for which it was designed—bringing light to the world. None are missing.

The God who named the stars also knows us by name. Therefore let us never forget: we are constantly in His loving gaze, through the day and also through the night.

Lord, help me trust Your love and concern for me in a deeper way. Every time I enjoy Your star-spangled sky, let me lift up the eyes of my heart to Your kind gaze. Thank You, in Jesus' name. Amen.

September 3–9. **Pat S. Johnson,** a speaker and freelance writer, served for 20 years as a missionary in the Middle East. She now lives in Temple City, California.

Looking Like God

God created man in his own image . . . male and female he created them (Genesis 1:27).

Scripture: **Genesis 1:26, 27**
Song: **"O to Be Like Thee!"**

While growing up I was perplexed by the idea of being made in God's image. I just didn't look like the illustrations of God in my Sunday school papers! That full-bearded man with the piercing blue eyes and authoritative posture was not me.

Later, of course, I realized that being made in God's image had little to do with my physical attributes. I came to understand my *personhood* as a reflection of God's own nature; I too was a being with intellect, emotions, and will. And my actions were to reflect God's character too. But I would never look like Him.

My initial interpretation of God-like living included never disappointing God in any action or attitude. Therefore, I often felt my self-serving responses to life's irritations and disappointments demonstrated spiritual weakness. As I yearned to develop the attributes of God in my own character, I grew into a transformed understanding of what it means to live as one made in His image. It's about allowing God free reign in my life, to guide and direct me in His ways. Only then can I truly reflect His image to those I meet each day.

Dear Heavenly Father, help me respond to Your Spirit's leading in my life so I can truly mirror You in my world. In Jesus' name, amen.

Every Good Landscape

God saw all that he had made, and it was very good (Genesis 1:31).

Scripture: **Genesis 1:28-31**
Song: **"For the Beauty of the Earth"**

In my 34 years as a missionary, I was blessed to live in different parts of the world. My first assignment was Lebanon—often called the "Switzerland of the Middle East." Its snow-capped mountains, bubbling springs, tide-licked coastline, and fertile gardens reflected creation's beauty in every season.

Our move to Jordan brought a dramatic change to the landscape. Because of the meager yearly rainfall, rolling, rock-strewn hills with little vegetation covered most of the country. The sun's rays reflecting off dust-filled air produced sunsets which were winners on a regular basis. My time in Papua, New Guinea, introduced me to the world of the jungle. There tropical fruits abounded: pineapples, mangoes, bananas, passion fruit, and guavas. It was easy to revel in the land's lush abundance.

In every land where I've lived, I learned to appreciate the beauty of God's earth. When He made this world, He proclaimed it good. We too—if we keep our eyes open to the miracle of life in all its variety—will see the good hand of God in every landscape to which He leads us.

Lord, *I have seen Your world, and it is good. Help me to be a responsible steward and caretaker as I partake of its bounty and enjoy its beauty. In the name of Jesus, my Savior, I pray. Amen.*

Rules or Rest?

God blessed the seventh day and made it holy (Genesis 2:3).

Scripture: Genesis 2:1-3
Song: "Brethren, We Have Met to Worship"

I grew up in a rather strict and conservative religious family. Our Christian lifestyle was controlled by a long list of "don't!" rules. Some of these rules centered on keeping Sunday holy. In my home, for example, we were forbidden to read the Sunday newspaper. It never made sense to me that we could listen to the Sunday news on the radio or watch a news program on television; we just dare not touch that newspaper!

After my husband and I married we developed our own Sunday schedule. It included a Bible study class as well as worship services. We'd sing in the choir, help in the nursery, and bring food for potlucks. (And I must confess, we'd read the Sunday comics in the afternoon.)

When our children were old enough, we began teaching them to give thanks at mealtime and to join in family devotions before bedtime. We also taught them the importance of setting aside Sunday to focus on God. Our family's routine included Sunday school class and morning and evening church services. My point is simple: focusing on worship—going beyond rules—made Sunday holy to us, and still does today.

God, I am thankful that You rested on the seventh day of creation and called us to emulate Your example. May my Sunday activities reflect just that desire—to rest, not just from work but in You. Through Christ, amen.

Let's Go Outside

The heavens declare the glory of God . . . Their voice goes out into all the earth (Psalm 19:1, 4).

Scripture: **Psalm 19:1-6**
Song: **"This Is My Father's World"**

I am the oldest of six children. You'd think it would take a mighty big voice to call all us into supper when we were kids. But Mom's soft, husky tone was designed for polite conversation, not yelling. Nevertheless, she knew exactly how to get our attention—she whistled! It didn't matter whether we were in our own backyard, at the neighbor's house, or at the park, we immediately responded to her one-of-a-kind trill.

Our heavenly Father uses more than words to get our attention. For example, the beauty of the heavens speak for Him, as the psalmist so eloquently proclaims. It's as if a voice from the Lord calls to us, amazing us with a cycle of light and dark, thrilling us in a celestial revelation of His power and glory. God's majesty is declared in the blazing sun by day, the soft light of a changing moon by night, and in the myriad stars lighting up the universe from beyond time.

I've decided to go outside this very night and admire God's handiwork. I want to revel in His marvelous creation, feel His presence and power. Won't you join me?

Father in Heaven, thank You for Your beautiful creation. Best of all, thank You for letting me hear Your voice through it. In the name of Jesus, Lord and Savior of all, I pray. Amen.

Reflect His Compassion

The LORD is compassionate and gracious, slow to anger, abounding in love (Psalm 103:8).

Scripture: **Psalm 103:1-14**
Song: **"The Love of God"**

The psalmist tells us that God abounds in love. And because we are to reflect God's image in our world, we also have the great privilege of abounding in love. But how do we do it?

It's easy to love the lovable—those gracious people who say "Please" and "Thank you" and live up to our expectations. It's the *others,* though—the folks who fall into the category of unappreciative or selfish or malicious—that give us our love-challenge. However, choosing whom *to* love and whom *not* to love isn't an option. The very idea of "abounding" precludes that kind of choice.

We are to love whoever comes our way, constantly enlarging our circle of care and concern. That way, our love reaches out to an ever-growing number of people with the kind of compassion and grace we ourselves have received.

Not easy! It requires asking God for a fresh supply of love for each day. Only then do we find the fruit of love ripening and cheering the people in our lives. And what a joyful way to live!

Gracious God, how great is Your goodness to me over the years! Help me reach out to those in need around me as one who, like them, was rescued by Your compassion through no merit of my own. Through Christ, amen.

Crowning of a King

The LORD has established his throne in heaven, and his kingdom rules over all (Psalm 103:19).

Scripture: **Psalm 103:15-22**
Song: **"The Lord Jehovah Reigns"**

It's a big day for a country when it crowns a new king. Pomp and circumstance rule. Parade routes are marked and security measures checked. Streets are swept, tree branches trimmed, and curbs refreshed with new coats of color. It's a public holiday in celebration of the occasion, and leaders from neighboring countries make it a point to attend. At least that's what happened at the 1999 coronation of his majesty, King Abdullah II of the Hashemite Kingdom of Jordan.

I was there, watching the school children excitedly pressing against each other on the curbs, chanting "Long live King Abdullah!" The enthusiastic crowds lining the parade route held bobbing balloons and billowing banners. A formation of fighter planes streaked through the sky above, their roar mingled with the shouts of the crowd. It was a day for the history books.

However, the reign of all earthly kings will end one day. All pomp and glory will pale in the splendor of His Majesty, king of the universe!

*Your reign, **my Heavenly King,** is eternal and all-encompassing. Therefore, let me acknowledge Your undisputed rule within my heart in this quiet moment. In the name of the Father, the Son, and the Holy Spirit, I pray. Amen.*

He's There!

Listen to me, all who hope for deliverance, who seek the Lord! Consider the quarry from which you were mined, the rock from which you were cut! (Isaiah 51:1, *The Living Bible*).

Scripture: **Isaiah 51:1-5**
Song: **"The Rock That Is Higher Than I"**

Northwest of Thermopolis, Wyoming, on State Highway 120, a series of rock formations thrusts out alongside the road. A few miles down that road, these same formations, buried several thousand feet below the surface produce hydrocarbons—one of earth's most important natural resources because of the energy produced when burnt.

We sometimes forget that our Lord is like these rock formations. He can be buried far below the surface of our consciousness, but He also rises to the surface of our lives in our actions and words. He provides the foundation for our production of fruit in His kingdom.

In Isaiah, the Lord reminded the Israelites that they were cut from His quarry and He alone could deliver them. May we too always remember that God is our rock—the rock of all ages—dwelling within us by His Spirit. In every fearful circumstance we can call upon Him for help and deliverance.

Lord, when I'm blinded by the day-to-day problems of my world, open my eyes to Your abiding presence through Your loving Word. I pray through my deliverer, the Lord Jesus Christ. Amen.

September 10–16. **Kristi Stingley**, a retired engineer and lawyer, now dedicates her time to writing Christian novels and inspirational nonfiction books.

Lord of the Stars

He took him outside and said, "Now look toward the heavens, and count the stars, if you are able to count them." And He said to him, "So shall your descendants be" (Genesis 15:5, *New American Standard Bible*).

Scripture: **Genesis 15:1-6**
Song: **"Blessed Assurance"**

When did you last look into the heavens and marvel at the number of stars? I would do this often as a child, but *counting* the stars never entered my mind. Who could count that high?

I imagine God taking Abraham outside on one of those clear, moonless nights that always invite a meditative upward gaze. He pointed to the sky and told His servant to . . . count. I might have said under my breath, "Are you kidding?"

But the Lord delivered on His promise to Abraham, as the apostle Paul confirmed centuries later: "Be sure that it is those who are of faith that are sons of Abraham," (Galatians 3:7, *NASB*). What a vast family God has given this one who believed such an awesome promise as he stood under a cloudless night sky! All through the ages, from his day to ours, Abraham's sons and daughters have been lifting their praise to the Lord of the stars.

Dear Father in Heaven, just as I can't count the stars in the sky, I can't count all the ways You touch and bless my life. Make me ever grateful for Your many blessings and show me Your will in all I will say and do this day. In the name of Jesus, my Lord and Savior, I pray. Amen.

Now We Live in Gratitude

God said to Abraham, "As for Sarai your wife, you shall not call her name Sarai, but Sarah shall be her name" (Genesis 17:15, *New American Standard Bible*).

Scripture: **Genesis 17:15-22**
Song: **"A Child of the King"**

Have you ever wished you could be someone different? Would you like to change your name and start over again? Many European immigrants desiring a new life in America change their names, hoping to assimilate into society with more ease.

The Lord provided Abram and his wife with new names but for a different reason. Abram became *Abraham,* and Sarai become *Sarah,* in order to signify their new roles in God's world-saving plan. They would become the father and mother of many nations, and the great, great . . . great grandparents of the One in whom the Lord God would establish His new covenant—Jesus Christ.

We are a part of it all! The Lord gives us new names when we enter the waters of baptism. We're no longer just John or Jane Doe in some no-name family. We are God's adopted sons and daughters, chosen ones, the recipients of eternal life (see Ephesians 1:5). From now on the life of gratitude is the only life for us.

Dear Lord, thank You for making me new in Your name, for giving me a new identity—one that glorifies Your precious name. Keep working in me, transforming me into the likeness of Your Son, Jesus, until I see Him face-to-face. I pray these things in His precious name. Amen.

Bow to Him

[Abraham] said, "My lord, if now I have found favor in your sight, please do not pass your servant by" (Genesis 18:3, *New American Standard Bible*).

Scripture: **Genesis 18:1-8**
Song: **"All Creatures of Our God and King"**

The stewardship ministry team in our congregation recently produced a play titled, *Come to the Castle*. In it, crowds gather to hear the announcement of the king's return. On his journey to the castle, a sty warden ("pig boy" to most) encounters many who shy away from him due to his distinct odor, while others treat him with respect and kindness. In the end it is revealed that the sty warden is the king himself!

In our Scripture today, three men visit Abraham. Unlike those in our stewardship play, Abraham instantly recognizes his king. He bows down at the visitors' feet and asks them not to pass him by but to let him provide for their refreshment.

It makes me consider: What do I do when the Lord calls me? Do I let Him pass by because I just don't recognize Him? Or do I immediately know His voice and bow down in service?

Lord of my life, all glory and praise to Your holy name! Give me an open heart that is ready to hear and receive Your guidance. And when You call, may I, like Abraham, recognize Your presence and answer Your call with all that You have given me—with my time, my abilities, and my money. In the name of Your Son, my Savior, I pray. Amen.

Surpassing Greatness

"Is anything too difficult for the LORD?" (Genesis 18:14, *New American Standard Bible*).

Scripture: **Genesis 18:9-15**
Song: **"He Will Make a Way"**

I have friends whose daughter was in a car accident. At the hospital, after being told their daughter was brain dead, they were asked to donate her organs. What a request! Could you do it?

What is the most difficult thing you have been asked to do? In our Scripture, God tells Abraham and Sarah that at their advanced age they would become parents. They couldn't believe it. Sarah laughed, thinking it sounded ridiculous. But God responded, "Is anything too difficult for the Lord?"

Sometimes we ask ourselves: can God really help with this mess I'm in? As the Lord reminds Abraham and Sarah—and reminds us too—nothing falls beyond the bounds of His abilities. He remains eternally omnipotent and omniscient—all-powerful and all-knowing.

Whatever your struggle today, whether big or small, simple or complex, let the one who can handle anything handle it for you. In so doing, you honor Him, glorify His name, and witness to His surpassing greatness.

Lord, You can do anything; nothing is too large or too small, too simple or complex for Your loving attention. Help me to remember that whatever my struggle, You can help me overcome and be victorious. For Your name's sake, I pray. Amen.

Joy with Me!

Sarah said, "God has made laughter for me; everyone who hears will laugh with me" (Genesis 21:6, *New American Standard Bible*).

Scripture: **Genesis 21:1-8**
Song: **"Down in My Heart"**

I have two sisters. As children, sometimes while playing or joking around, we would break out in uncontrollable laughter. Our dad said, "Who gave you the giggle gas?" This, of course, made us laugh even harder.

Sarah laughed at God when He told her she would bear a child, but it was a somewhat sarcastic laugh. After bearing the promised child, Sarah's laughter turned to a bubbling joyfulness—an infectious kind of laughter like the kind my sisters and I shared.

In fact laughter can be catching. Often people walking in on the end of a joke will start to chuckle, even though they don't know exactly why. Isn't it interesting that God made laughter with such a contagious quality?

He's not our giggle-gas, though. For even when we can't laugh, when joking is clearly inappropriate, when we're immersed in serious pain or heartache, He is the source of a deep-down joy that remains through it all. That joy, of course, goes beyond humor to form a solid basis for all our fellowship and worship.

Lord, help me always remember that You are my source of joy. When I rely on circumstances for happiness, keep me ever mindful that You alone bring true happiness to my life by Your abiding presence. In Jesus' name. Amen.

Step Out in Faith

Abraham trusted God, and when God told him to leave home and go far away to another land which he promised to give him, Abraham obeyed. Away he went, not even knowing where he was going (Hebrews 11:8, *The Living Bible*).

Scripture: **Hebrews 11:8-12**
Song: **"Faith of Our Fathers"**

Have you noticed that faith can lead us to do many things we might not otherwise do?

I ventured over 700 miles away from my hometown in Nebraska to attend college in New Mexico. I believed I would get the education I needed to propel me into a successful and prosperous career as an engineer. My faith wasn't unrequited.

Abraham believed God when He said He would give him a new home, even though Abrham had never seen the place. Abraham also believed God when He said Abraham would be the father of many nations. Through Abraham's obedience, we have an example of how we can demonstrate our faith in the Lord.

Never fear or be ashamed to show your Christian faith because it isn't the popular thing to do. By expressing faith openly, we glorify the Lord (and might just make "faithing it" a little more popular).

Almighty Lord, make my faith as strong and reliable as Abraham's. Help me never fear or be ashamed to show those around me that I am a Christian and that You are my Savior. And when I hear Your call to go, let my feet be swift to answer! In the precious name of Jesus, I pray. Amen.

Everybody Else's Fault

Then Sarai said to Abram, "You are responsible for the wrong I am suffering. I put my servant in your arms, and now that she knows she is pregnant, she despises me" (Genesis 16:5).

Scripture: **Genesis 16:1-6**
Song: **"My Tribute"**

Confronted by my manager about a late project, I was ready with excuses. "It was the customers! They didn't know what they wanted and didn't support me. And those people working with me! They didn't do their share, so I had to do both my job and theirs. And, besides, you're always giving me too much to do!" I could go on, but I think you get the general idea. . . .

Notice that everybody else was to blame except me. Even if those other people shared in the blame, I refused to take my share. I was "victimized" by them instead of owning up to my own failings. I was living the old adage, "To err is human; to blame it on others is even more human."

Even though Sarai allowed Hagar to be with Abram, she still blamed him for the problems that followed. There was enough blame for everybody, but she refused to take her share. But then, I thoroughly understand how that could happen.

Dear God, *help me to take responsibility for what I have done instead of blaming others. Through Christ I pray. Amen.*

September 17–23. **Terry Magee** is a writer living in Pennsylvania, where he serves his church while attending school. He is married and has two grown children.

We Are Not Alone

The angel of the LORD said to her: "You are now with child and you will have a son. You shall call him Ishmael for the LORD has heard of your misery" (Genesis 16:11).

Scripture: **Genesis 16:7-16**
Song: **"Praise to the Lord, The Almighty"**

The television show *Hee Haw* featured a recurring song that recounted the cast members' dreadful state of life, filled with gloom, despair, and agony. They were poking fun at misery, but it can be easy for any of us to wallow in a woe is me attitude during tough times Especially when we feel that nobody notices or cares—or even that God has turned His back on us.

Yet a common experience of those who seek God with fervent hearts is that they will, at some point, enter what's known as the dark night of the soul. God may indeed feel absent at those times, but our feelings don't give us the true picture. For Christ has promised to be with us always, even when we don't feel Him. And the indwelling Holy Spirit intercedes for us, even when prayerful words won't come to our lips.

All of this to say: Just as the Lord heard Hagar, he constantly beholds us and hears our own hearts. He hears and cares whether we're experiencing joy or misery, gloom or gladness. That we grow to be more like His Son is what matters most to Him.

Dear God, thank You for never abandoning me! Help me enjoy your presence even now. Thank You, in Jesus' name. Amen.

Lasting Inheritance

"Get rid of that slave woman and her son, for that slave woman's son will never share in the inheritance with my son Isaac" (Genesis 21:10).

Scripture: **Genesis 21:9-13**
Song: **"One Pure and Holy Passion"**

Dying childless, the old woman left a sizeable estate. Her surviving family members eagerly awaited the reading of the will, expecting everything to be divided among them.

Not so! Shock preceded anger as they all discovered she'd left everything to one relative. Angry accusations flew, followed by silence, as family members refused to speak to one another. Years later, the rift remains.

Sarai refused Ishmael a share in the inheritance she felt belonged solely to Isaac. She saw that anything given to Ishmael would diminish Isaac's portion.

Many families are permanently broken by money or inheritance struggles. However, we have an inheritance that is limitless in Christ. What we have received from Him can flow out in boundless grace among countless peoples. And since there is more than enough for all, how important that we share it every day of our lives!

Dear God, help me remember today that everything in my earthly life is limited and temporary. Anything I acquire here I will soon leave behind. Therefore, let me live with a view to what is most important: pleasing You in word and deed, living by Your Spirit each moment. Help me do it! I pray this prayer in the name of Jesus, my merciful Savior and Lord. Amen.

Doing Compassion

She went off and sat down nearby, about a bowshot away, for she thought, "I cannot watch the boy die" (Genesis 21:16).

Scripture: **Genesis 21:14-16**
Song: **"Comfort, Comfort Ye My People"**

According to news reports, the family was enjoying a bike ride along a tour road in the Florida Everglades when disaster struck. Their 6-year-old son fell off his bike and landed in an alligator's nest. The mother alligator, reacting to an apparent attack on her offspring, clamped onto the boy. The boy's mother, seeing her son in the alligator's jaws, rushed to his defense, beating the alligator with her bare hands to save her child. Thankfully, everyone survived this rare alligator attack.

Compassion for our young is built into us by God. We show it by risking our lives when they are attacked or by simply being in misery as Hagar was. She felt helpless to stop her son's suffering, yet she did stay nearby to watch over him.

Every parent knows this protective instinct. However, all of us, whether we have children or not, are surrounded by the young, defenseless, or suffering. Hagar knew of no response but to feel compassion. May we ourselves go even further—and *do* compassion.

Dear Father, Your Son always had time to put His compassion into action. Give me the discernment to see those suffering around me. But also help me put my feelings of compassion into action. Help me reach out in the most practical forms of help. In Jesus' name I pray. Amen.

Seeing or Just Looking?

Then God opened her eyes and she saw a well of water (Genesis 21:19).

Scripture: **Genesis 21:17-19**
Song: **"See, Jesus, Thy Disciples See"**

"Where are the car keys?" I asked my wife as I was rushing to leave for an appointment.

"On the dresser," she replied from the next room.

I searched again, including the drawers. "I still can't find them!" I called impatiently. "Are you sure they're here?" She came into the room and, pointing to the dresser, said, "Open your eyes; they're right in front of you!" Just like magic, those keys had appeared on the dresser!

Except that it wasn't magic, was it? I was *looking* without *seeing*.

Of course, it's all too easy to go through life missing the obvious—that God is constantly with us, that people around us long for kind words, that our neighbor might need a little help.

The well didn't magically appear for Hagar; it had been there all along. She just needed God to open her eyes, to show her the source of her survival. What kinds of opportunities and blessings would you like Him to show you this week?

Dear God, thank You for seeing and knowing everything. It is too easy for me to miss what should be obvious. Open my eyes and help me to see everything around me with Your eyes, both opportunities to serve and special blessings from You. In the name of Your Son, I pray. Amen.

Everyday Presence

God was with the boy as he grew up. He lived in the desert (Genesis 21:20).

Scripture: **Genesis 21:20, 21**
Song: **"Lead Us On"**

The golfer had been given a remarkable gift. When his ball was on the green, an imaginary line appeared only to him, a line he could follow to hit his ball in the hole. He was able to use this wonderful gift to join the professional golf tour and fulfill his life's ambition.

I sometimes dream of having some remarkable gift—especially if I could know that it came directly from God's hand.

The Bible speaks of God being with Ishmael as Ishmael grew up, yet it doesn't relate any miraculous examples of God's grace during this time. No doubt God's goodness was unfolding, though, in the mundane, normal activities of his life.

We look for God in miraculous events. But isn't He more commonly present in the ordinary ones? God is just as powerful when working in subtle, almost hidden ways as when He works in dramatic and miraculous ways. In the most ordinary of our daily activities, we can find the Lord of our lives.

Lord of my every moment, thank You for being with me amid all the routines of my life. Help me enjoy this fellowship with You throughout the day as I learn to pray always. In the name of the Father, the Son, and the Holy Spirit, I pray. Amen.

Proud Legacy—or Not?

His descendants settled in the area from Havilah to Shur, near the border of Egypt, as you go toward Asshur. And they lived in hostility toward all their brothers (Genesis 25:18).

Scripture: **Genesis 25:12-18**
Song: **"Let Everything That Has Breath"**

I constantly struggled with the heavy traffic and aggressive driving behavior while living in New Jersey. And I often responded by blasting my horn and yelling unkind things at other drivers. I was both surprised and humbled one day when my 2-year-old son, upon hearing a car horn in the distance, yelled "You turkey!"

Children watch us all the time and pick up our behaviors—good and bad. I couldn't pick and choose when my son watched me. I couldn't stop and say, "Don't do what I'm doing, because it's wrong." No, children are like sponges, soaking in everything around them.

Ishamel was born and raised in strife. And he passed that strife on to his children, who lived in hostility with those around them.

We're building a legacy each and every day of our lives. The question is, would it make us proud?

Dear Lord, help me to be aware that I am not alone, that my actions affect and influence those around me. Let me continue to reflect Your love and grace with everyone I know, so that I might build a legacy that brings honor to my family and glory to Your name. Especially keep me mindful of the little ones looking on, learning from me how to be. I pray this prayer in the name of Jesus, the one who died for my sins. Amen.

Can You Loosen Up?

"The LORD . . . will send his angel before you so that you can get a wife for my son from there" (Genesis 24:7).

Scripture: **Genesis 24:1-9**
Song: **"I Will Serve Thee"**

When I was a girl, one of my greatest joys was roller-skating. Gliding across the rink made me feel so light and graceful.

But initially learning how to skate had been another matter. My legs were rigid, and my knees were constantly locked tight for fear of falling. I thought that if I could just control my legs and knees, I'd get the hang of it. But then my sister told me to "just let go" and loosen up. When I did, I relaxed—and finally knew the joy of moving across the ice with a free spirit.

Life is like that. We have family or work problems, and our first inclination is to try to seize control of the situation and fix things. We lock our jaws and rigidly "clamp down." Like Abraham's servant, we want to cover all our bases, so we develop a contingency plan.

God's way, though, is to invite us to relax and let Him work out the details. We are simply called to trust and obey Him. When we do that, our walk of faith becomes as graceful as a skater floating across the rink.

Father, I know You are fully capable of guiding me without my constant suggestions. Help me trust You more fully! Through Christ, amen.

September 24–30. **Lisa Konzen** is an administrative assistant for United Way in Janesville, Wisconsin. She also writes health articles for her local newspaper.

All About Attitude

After she had given him a drink, she said, "I'll draw water for your camels too, until they have finished drinking" (Genesis 24:19).

Scripture: **Genesis 24:10-21**
Song: **"The Servant"**

Like most people, I'm not a fan of household chores. But they've become a little easier for me since I learned that I could do them in two different ways. The first way was to view every task as a drudgery; just get them done and move on.

The other way? I found I could offer every mundane chore as an act of service in thanksgiving to God. For instance, as I took up that attitude, washing dishes became more than a cleaning duty. It was now a loving act of caring for the family God had given me.

It's all in the attitude, isn't it? It seems to me that Rebekah invested her chores with meaning too. When Abraham's servant asked her for a sip of water from her jar, she didn't just give it to him. She went beyond what was asked of her and watered the camels too. Her willingness to be kind and generous won the approval of the servant. And her gracious spirit also prepared her for her role as Isaac's wife.

Small things done with love can make wondrous changes in our lives. Just ask Rebekah.

Loving Father, remind me that You care more about the quality of my heart than the length of my good works list. Through Christ I pray. Amen.

Driving Directions

"As for me, the LORD has led me on the journey to the house of my master's relatives" (Genesis 24:27).

Scripture: **Genesis 24:22-27**
Song: **"Follow On"**

When my sister moved into her new home on the other side of town, I had to call her for detailed directions to her house. She told me all the turns to make and even gave me landmarks to observe so I'd be sure of traveling in the right direction.

When we set out on a journey to an unfamiliar destination, it helps to consult a road map. Or do as I did, and call ahead for directions. Without instructions, the journey can be frustrating or even frightening, and we're likely to get lost.

Abraham's servant knew how to find the wife God intended for Isaac. Why? Because he knew he wasn't traveling blindly. God directed him each step of the way, and he was able to find Rebekah without any trouble.

We too have a road map to follow on the Christian journey. God's Word shows us the way, pointing out the turns we must take and the landmarks that will indicate whether we're headed in the right direction. We don't have to go it alone.

Dear Father in Heaven, You have given me the great privilege of knowing You through Your revealed Word. Help me to be faithful in my Bible reading and devotional times, so I'll be able to follow wherever You lead. In the name of Your Son, my Savior, I pray. Amen.

All That Glitters

As soon as he had seen the nose ring, and the bracelets on his sister's arms . . . he went out to the man and found him standing by the camels near the spring. "Come, you who are blessed by the Lord," he said (Genesis 24:30, 31).

Scripture: **Genesis 24:28-32**
Song: **"Little Is Much When God Is in It"**

Movie stars are rich, so they must be doing something right. Correct? Maybe if we could look more like them or buy the products they endorse, we could get in on the blessings they have. Right?

Rebekah's brother Laban also judged by appearances. When he saw the expensive jewelry, he was impressed. If Abraham is rich, he thought, maybe I can get in on that blessing too.

But all that glitters is not always gold. A person's net worth has nothing to do with his or her relationship with God. Although it's true that Abraham was wealthy and that he was a righteous person, his righteousness certainly didn't make God bless him. God blessed him with wealth and righteousness because He chose to do so.

Abraham couldn't earn God's blessings, and neither can we. Affluence isn't necessarily a sign of God's influence in a person's life. In fact, faithful service done in gratitude shines brighter than all the gold in the world.

Giver of all good gifts, I thank You for the greatest gift of all—Your Son Jesus Christ. May I adorn myself with His grace today, the one who loved me enough to die for me. In His name I pray. Amen.

Friend for the Journey

"The LORD, before whom I have walked, will send his angel with you and make your journey a success, so that you can get a wife for my son from my own clan and from my father's family" (Genesis 24:40).

Scripture: **Genesis 24:33-41**
Song: **"Traveling Home"**

My sister is a nervous highway driver, so when she had to travel the 30-mile journey from her home to an appointment with a lawyer, she asked me to accompany her. Somehow, just having me nearby made her calmer, and she actually enjoyed the trip.

What are some of the frightening things you face in life? Isn't it always better to have a friend with you?

A companion may not actually protect us, but having him or her with us calms our fears and helps us face our challenges with greater courage and perhaps even humor.

We can be faithful friends to those around us who face challenges in their walks of faith. Just being there, encouraging and loving them, can help make their journey successful. The same Lord who sent His angel as a companion to Abraham's servant also sends us as messengers to those around us, calling us to convey His peace, hope, and love.

Father, thank You for the people in my life who have held my hand along the way. Help me, in return, to offer my own hand in friendship to fellow travelers on their way home to You. In Christ's holy name I pray. Amen.

Wonderful Counselor

Laban and Bethuel answered, "This is from the LORD; we can say nothing to you one way or the other" (Genesis 24:50).

Scripture: **Genesis 24:42-51**
Song: **"Open My Eyes That I May See"**

Have you ever struggled to discern God's will for you? It would be nice if God would send down a giant neon sign flashing, "Here I am, and here's what I want you to do." But God doesn't usually work that way. So what are we to do?

I find an important clue in today's Scripture passage. Laban and Bethuel listened carefully to what Abraham's servant told them. They had a tough decision to make about Rebekah's future, but they were able to make it easily because they knew God had arranged it all. They knew Abraham's servant was obeying the Lord, and that was enough for them.

When we face our own important decisions, we can be certain that God has given us many faithful counselors to help point the way. Our families, ministers, and other church members will often provide helpful wisdom. But the most important and authoritative guide of all is the Holy Spirit, who speaks to us in Scripture and in our hearts. When we study the Word and listen to His leading, we will know the next step to take.

Lord, I face so many choices every day. Help me find direction in Your Word and by being very attentive to Your still voice within. In the name of the Father, the Son, and the Holy Spirit, I pray. Amen.

Love Through the Generations

The LORD is good and his love endures forever; his faithfulness continues through all generations (Psalm 100:5).

Scripture: **Psalm 100**
Song: **"Great Is Thy Faithfulness"**

My father is 84 years old and quite frail. During his most recent hospitalization, he had some trouble with memory, so the doctors frequently asked him questions like "Where are you now?" and "Who are these people in the room with you?" Often it would be my sisters and I, and then my dad would tell the doctors about his seven children and how proud he was of them. He couldn't remember much else, but he knew his legacy of love lived on in us.

God's love is alive and well in us too. God has always loved, and He always will love. That constancy has not wavered throughout history. From Adam to Abraham, from Moses to David, from the birth of Christ to His future glorious appearing, God's love is eternal.

And just as my dad's love lives on in his children, so too God's love is lived out in the daily lives of His children. Whenever we help our neighbor, we allow God's love to be shared in our generation and in the generations to come.

God of eternity, Your great love causes me to sing Your praises and to offer my whole life as a witness to You. Help me this day to be faithful in serving You as You have always been faithful in loving me. I pray this prayer in the name of Jesus, my Savior and Lord. Amen.

My Prayer Notes

_____

_____

_____

_____

_____

_____

_____

_____

_____

_____

_____

_____

_____

_____

_____

_____

_____

_____

_____

_____

DEVOTIONS

*L*et the hearts
of those who
seek the LORD
rejoice.

—Psalm 105:3

OCTOBER

Photo © Jupiterimages

Gary Allen, Editor

Give Him the Glory

According as it is written, He that glorieth, let him glory in the Lord (1 Corinthians 1:31, *King James Version*).

Scripture: **1 Corinthians 1:26-31**
Song: **"To God Be the Glory"**

On April 29, 1962, President John F. Kennedy made the following comment at a dinner honoring the Nobel Prize winners of the Western Hemisphere: "I think this is the most extraordinary collection of talent, of human knowledge, that has ever been gathered together at the White House—with the possible exception of when Thomas Jefferson dined alone." That witty remark gave perspective to those specially chosen honorees. They were among the world's best and brightest, but the brilliant impact of one man—Jefferson—gave them all a nation that could appreciate and appropriate what they had done.

Paul told the Corinthian believers they'd been specially chosen by the Lord. However, for most of them, at least in the world's eyes, their main distinction was their seeming *lack* of any distinction! But God used the ordinary to do the extraordinary. And, as usual, the Lord deserves all the credit for developing lesser abilities in humble circumstances. When we gather for worship, it is not to congratulate ourselves but to give Christ the glory.

Dear Savior, thank You for Your special calling and using me beyond what was even thought possible. In Jesus' name, amen.

October 1–7. **Richard Robinson** is a minister in Denver, Colorado, and Bible teacher on The Holy Ground Radio Broadcast, aired daily throughout the state.

Guided, Gracious, Grand Life

Laban and Bethuel answered and said, The thing proceedeth from the LORD: we cannot speak unto thee bad or good (Genesis 24:50, *King James Version*).

Scripture: **Genesis 24:50-61**
Song: **"The Guiding Hand"**

The beautiful story of Abraham's servant finding a wife for Isaac presents three striking features: First, we see how this faithful servant was guided by God. As Rebekah's family heard how God precisely answered the servant's prayer, they knew that the events had been issued from the Lord. Like the servant, we should say to all would-be helpers in the drama of God's will, "Hinder me not, seeing the LORD hath prospered my way" (v. 56, *KJV*).

Second, we see how gracious all the parties were in their interactions with each other. Obviously, the right attitude always helps.

Third, notice the grand undertones of this whole story. We sense it from the servant's spontaneous worship, from Rebekah's sweet surrender, even from Laban and Bethuel's reluctant blessing, saying, "Thou art our sister; be thou the mother of thousands of millions" (v. 60, *KJV*). Like them, we all need expanded views of God's will and work. Are we indeed caught up in something bigger than ourselves?

Dear Lord, *help me to walk by faith and experience Your guidance, graciously doing Your will in Your grand plan for my life. I pray this prayer in the name of Jesus, my wonderful Savior and Lord. Amen.*

A Sigh of Relief

Isaac . . . took Rebekah, and she became his wife; and he loved her: and Isaac was comforted after his mother's death (Genesis 24:67, *King James Version*).

Scripture: **Genesis 24:62-67**
Song: **"O Perfect Love"**

Picture Isaac seeing the camel caravan off in the distance. In anticipation, he went to meet the traveling party. Rebekah saw him walking toward them, inquired of the servant, and was told that it was his master—and her new husband! Upon meeting, Isaac was told the whole amazing story of God's guidance. With appropriate tenderness, Isaac took his new bride into his mother's tent to consummate their marriage.

The void in the patriarch's heart after his mother's death was finally filled by the love and comfort that Rebekah extended to Isaac. Only the right woman matched to the right man could produce this right result—and at just the right time!

God brought Isaac and Rebekah together across a vast space, closing the distance at the appointed time. As Proverbs 18:22 says, "Whoso findeth a wife findeth a good thing, and obtaineth favour of the LORD" *(KJV)*. That kind of favor always ends, as it did for Isaac, with a sweet sigh of relief.

God, thank You for the way You bring others into my life, especially when that special someone is sent to bring comfort. Through Christ, I pray. Amen.

A Shining Moment

Isaac entreated the LORD for his wife . . . and the LORD was entreated of him, and Rebekah his wife conceived (Genesis 25:21, *King James Version*).

Scripture: **Genesis 25:19-23**
Song: **"I Must Tell Jesus"**

Theodore Roosevelt delivered a speech on April 10, 1899, titled "The Strenuous Life" and made this observation: "If we are to be a really great people, we must strive in good faith to play a great part in the world. We cannot avoid meeting great issues. All that we can determine for ourselves is whether we shall meet them well or ill."

These words describe Isaac's situation in today's Scripture. Isaac had now reached a comfortable stage in his life, a peaceful and predictable time. But his wife's barrenness was a growing concern to both of them. This led the easy-going, calm-natured patriarch to "entreat the LORD for his wife" (v. 21, *KJV*). The word "entreat" conveys the idea of pleading, and this prayer was so intense and persuasive that God granted his request. Soon after, the happy couple was expecting.

As Roosevelt pointed out, there is no avoiding "great issues," even in the most secure, well-to-do homes. But we can meet them as Isaac did—by rising to the occasion with our finest prayers. It was Isaac's shining moment.

Father God, in my prayers give me the perseverance and urgency of an Isaac. Let me learn for myself what it means to entreat the Lord with an open and sincere heart. Thank You, in Jesus' name. Amen.

Destiny of Two Boys

The boys grew: and Esau was a cunning hunter, a man of the field; and Jacob was a plain man, dwelling in tents (Genesis 25:27, *King James Version*).

Scripture: **Genesis 25:24-28**
Song: **"Children of the Heavenly Father"**

After Rebekah gave birth to twin boys, the prophecy given earlier began to be fulfilled (see v. 23, *KJV*). Two nations developed, as opposite as the boys themselves. Esau became an avid outdoorsman with a taste for adventure, tending toward the worldly and secular.

Jacob preferred the domestic circle over the great outdoors. He was less active but just as ambitious, using his mind more than his muscle. Jacob also possessed the raw materials of spiritual leadership and became God's chosen patriarch-in-the-making.

These two boys remind all parents that a child's destiny begins . . . in childhood. Several people have been credited with saying, "Give me a child for the first seven years, and you may do what you like with him afterwards." It's true! Young children respond to training—of any kind, from any person, whether good or bad. Thankfully, good parenting still shapes the child who shapes the future. Yet, as Isaac and Rebekah demonstrate, only when parents work together will the future of children be bright.

Dear Lord, may all those with children depend on Your wisdom and grace, remembering that the future of many lives is at stake. In the holy name of Jesus, my Lord and Savior, I pray. Amen.

Birthright at a Bargain

Jacob said, Swear to me this day; and he sware unto him: and he sold his birthright unto Jacob (Genesis 25:33, *King James Version*).

Scripture: **Genesis 25:29-34**
Song: "Falter Not"

Compared to the secretive, scheming Jacob, Esau seemed like an open book, freely sharing what was on his mind. When he came in from the field, tired and hungry, Jacob was ready for him. With the delicious aroma of a fresh pot of stew hitting his nostrils, Esau immediately wanted some. Jacob simply said to his brother, "Sell me this day thy birthright" (v. 31, *KJV*).

Esau reacted impulsively with no thought of the consequences and swiftly agreed to the deal. He sold his birthright, ate the stew, and went his way. The Bible puts the whole transaction in its true light: Esau *despised* his birthright, something of precious, inestimable value.

Like Esau, we all have a birthright, those special privileges granted only to children of God. Praying, teaching, counseling, leading, serving, giving—these all tap into our spiritual inheritance. But if we give in to our fleshly appetites, we are prodigal children squandering our birthright. Jacob drove a hard bargain that day, which Esau later regretted. May we never sell our birthright at any price!

Heavenly Father, keep me from foolish, impulsive, and short-sighted compromises that defraud me of spiritual blessings. I pray, amen.

He Got What He Wanted

When Esau heard the words of his father, he cried with a great and exceeding bitter cry, and said unto his father, Bless me, even me also, O my father. And he said, Thy brother came with subtility, and hath taken away thy blessing (Genesis 27:34, 35, *King James Version*).

Scripture: **Genesis 27:30-40**
Song: **"Take the World, but Give Me Jesus"**

Intense human emotion drips from this story. Esau finally arrived to receive his father's highest blessing, reserved for the firstborn—only to discover that Jacob had gotten there first! Yes, the schemer had already tricked his father into giving him the birthright. Esau begged his father to bless him anyway, which he did, but not with the great patriarchal blessing.

As it turned out, Esau ended up getting exactly what he wanted. He valued worldly success and material things, so his father blessed him with "the fatness of the earth, and of the dew of heaven from above" (v. 39, *KJV*). God gave him his heart's real desire, but at the awful price of constant striving and a forfeited birthright (v. 40, *KJV*).

It makes me realize that I ought to be very careful what I ask for. I just might get it!

Blessed Father, it is so tempting to choose immediate gratification over the promise of future rewards. But remind me, Lord, that Your promise is sure and unfailing. So cleanse my heart from inordinate affections here on earth, the love of the world and the lusts of the flesh. Instead, let me desire only Your will and glory for as long as I live. In Jesus' name, amen.

Say, Can You Sing?

Sing to him, sing praise to him; tell of all his wonderful acts (Psalm 105:2).

Scripture: **Psalm 105:1-6**
Song: **"O Worship the King"**

Recently, our school district hosted a motivational seminar for a few hundred teachers. At one point our energetic speaker instructed us, "Raise your hand if you can sing." Perhaps 20 hands braved an answer. Amazing! Only that many people regard themselves as singers?

I considered my classroom of 6-year olds. All sing. All paint. All write. In fact, they regard themselves as experts at everything.

How could a singing child mature into an adult incapable of carrying a tune in a bucket? Perhaps mind-set is the answer. Some of us adopt the notion we're inept because we're not the best in the field. However, the Lord never asks us to sing to Him only if we're trained vocalists or if our albums top the charts.

We bless God when we offer melodies from a grateful heart. Today's passage details several of God's attributes worthy of including in a song of worship. We may not be experts in all things, but we've been given so much. A song of gratitude waits to praise Him. Who will sing it?

Lord, *thank You for the goodness You've brought to my life. I want to praise You with heartfelt words, whether spoken or sung. In Jesus' name, amen.*

October 8–14. **Vicki Hodges** teaches first grade and writes from her home in the Colorado Rockies.

Imagination Express

"To you I will give the land of Canaan as the portion you will inherit" (Psalm 105:11).

Scripture: **Psalm 105:7-11**
Song: **"Holy, Holy, Holy"**

A few weeks ago a friend asked, "What is the best thing you can imagine?" A lifetime supply of chocolate, of course! Maybe I should have answered visits with loved ones, or traveling to all the places on *my list*, or always being in sound health. Pause a few moments to explore your own response.

Someone has rightly noted that our most important thoughts are those of God and Heaven. Today's Bible passage overflows with significant descriptions of God. He is: the Lord our God, just, faithful, a promise keeper, and our benefactor. Just as God promised Abraham's descendants the land of Canaan as their inheritance, all followers of Jesus are promised Heaven as an inheritance by their faithful, promising Lord of all.

In his letter to the Ephesians, Paul proclaims that God "is able to do immeasurably more than all we ask or imagine (3:20). That includes taking us to Heaven, of course. Thoughts of Heaven always stretch my mind, but God isn't interested in just confirming my finite thoughts. He continually exceeds my imagination, for Heaven is far better than the best we can envision.

Lord, You are not limited even by my highest thoughts. I am so eager to experience the best You can create. Praise to You in Christ's name! Amen.

Glowing in Grace

Esau held a grudge against Jacob because of the blessing his father had given him. He said to himself, "The days of mourning for my father are near; then I will kill my brother Jacob" (Genesis 27:41).

Scripture: **Genesis 27:41-45**
Song: **"And Can It Be That I Should Gain?"**

Fire needs four ingredients: oxygen, fuel, a heat source, and a chemical reaction. When one of those is missing, flames can't exist. This year at my workplace, some drastic policy changes have produced relational wildfires. Staff tempers grew short, attitudes flared, and production plummeted. And I'm sorry to say, my own bad attitude has contributed to the blaze.

Esau kindled a personal wildfire. Disappointment, anger, and hatred—all natural emotions—fueled his desire to kill his brother. This unchecked seething caused him to become disordered, virtually psychopathic. Twisted thoughts of Jacob's demise consoled Esau, though he could have chosen to enjoy God's goodness instead.

Esau's experience teaches me much. Just as God would have delighted to show grace to Esau, He would also be pleased to shower my life with grace. The climate at work would likely be improved if I would set aside my seemingly justified reactions and choose to let Christ transform my attitudes.

Lord, help me surrender my frustration and anger to You today. By Your example and indwelling Spirit, put out these fires! In Jesus' name, amen.

Never Give a Good Gift

Rebekah said to Isaac, "I'm disgusted with living because of these Hittite women. If Jacob takes a wife from among the women of this land, from Hittite women like these, my life will not be worth living" (Genesis 27:46).

Scripture: **Genesis 27:46–28:5**
Song: **"The Gifts of Love"**

The skillet sizzled with melted butter and fresh fish. I considered the size of this gift. Our friend drove several miles and spent a couple of hours to catch his legal limit of salmon. When he arrived at our house, the fish were cleaned, skinned, filleted, and packaged. He could have handed over a dripping stringer of slimy fish for us to prepare, but he chose to give a *better* gift.

Rebekah was a giver of good gifts. When she learned of Esau's plot to kill Jacob, she insisted her husband send Jacob away. Of course, she diluted the truth by saying she didn't want Jacob marrying a Canaanite. Even though this plan spared Jacob from certain death, Rebekah's means were deceitful. She endowed Jacob with a good gift: the gift of life. However, she could have afforded a better gift: the gift of honesty.

When deciding between a good and better gift, which will we choose? Do we donate the worn-out or the new? Do we prefer the best for ourselves or give it away?

Father, *Thank You for giving Your best gift, Your Son, Jesus, at great sacrifice. My tendency is to give when it's convenient and doesn't cost too much. By Your power, help me to follow Your example. Through Christ, amen.*

Motives and Actions

Esau then realized how displeasing the Canaanite women were to his father Isaac (Genesis 28:8).

Scripture: **Genesis 28:6-9**
Song: **"Fairest Lord Jesus"**

Josh was a boy in one of my elementary classes years ago. He tripped over his untied shoes, had a runny nose and mussed hair. Kids frequently tattled on his abrasive behavior, and he rarely completed class assignments. When his single mom, mired in a custody battle, asked me to write a letter indicating her positive influence on his grades, cleanliness, and behavior, I told her the evidence wouldn't allow me to accommodate the request.

The next day a clean Josh brought me a bouquet of shriveled aspen leaves. The following day he slipped me a purple-crayoned drawing of two stick people holding hands. Now when turning in his homework, he says, "I love you. You're my favorite teacher." (If he'd fork over some chocolate I might cut a deal!)

What motivated Josh to change? Perhaps it was the same thing that urged Esau to shift gears. He realized what it would take to please his parent.

While we likely don't approve of either rationale, both guys made decisions for positive change. Sometimes it takes time for a noble motivation to catch up with our actions. And vice versa.

Lord, do Your work in my heart, for You know my own actions are often driven by selfishness more than virtue. In Your holy name, I pray. Amen.

The Best Calling Plan

He was afraid and said, "How awesome is this place! This is none other than the house of God; this is the gate of heaven" (Genesis 28:17).

Scripture: **Genesis 28:10-17**
Song: **"Be Thou My Vision"**

Both our daughters worked abroad during the summer, but geography hardly separated us. While we missed them greatly, phone calls and e-mails helped us stay in touch. We shared news and expressions of love. Though we were physically apart, we remained connected.

When Jacob left home he spent a night in what seemed an arbitrary location. He settled in for the night, sleeping on a rock pillow, dreaming of angels ascending and descending from a stairway bridging earth and Heaven. From above the top step, God spoke to Jacob, establishing His identity and reassuring Jacob that He would be *his* God, as well as being the God of Abraham and Isaac. Imagine Jacob's surprise at finding God in such a random place!

Where do we expect to find God? He is a thought away. Prayer, instant communication between earth and Heaven, is our great privilege. And Jesus, our resident intercessor, bridges both realms as He constantly talks with the Father on our behalf (see Romans 8:34).

Lord, thank You for Your constant presence. You always listen to me and speak wisdom. Teach me to explore Your mind until I come into agreement with Your heart. Through Christ, my Lord, I pray. Amen.

Memory Rocks!

Early the next morning Jacob took the stone he had placed under his head and set it up as a pillar and poured oil on top of it (Genesis 28:18).

Scripture: **Genesis 28:18-22**
Song: **"Come, Thou Fount"**

When our family vacations, we generally collect a rock to remind us of the trip, and a section of our front yard is designated for those special souvenirs. We have jade, quartz, petrified wood, copper-streaked stones, a desert rose, agate, rose quartz, lava, sandstone, flint, and a kidney-shaped stone. Each rock holds a special memory, except for the kidney. None of us remembers where we got it.

I think Jacob would have liked our rock garden. After his amazing dream of angels and God's conversation with him, Jacob called that area "God's house" (v. 22). He promptly erected a small memorial from the stone pillow he had used the night before and anointed the top of it with oil. This memory-rock served to commemorate God's promise to bless and multiply Jacob's descendants. It was also a reminder of the vow Jacob made to God.

Any significant encounter with the Lord is cause for celebration, isn't it? Whether we anoint our own memory-rock by journaling, or just by telling family and friends, the remembrance is an important faith-builder.

Heavenly Father, You are my rock and my salvation. May You always be my best memory, as well! In the precious name of Jesus, I pray. Amen.

Finally, Breathing!

He will cover you with His pinions, and under His wings you may seek refuge; His faithfulness is a shield and bulwark (Psalm 91:4, *New American Standard Bible*).

Scripture: **Psalm 91**
Song: **"Under His Wings"**

Growing up as a member of a large family that normally rode Greyhound busses for extended trips, I surprised no one when I fell wildly in love with flying at a young age. I equated safety with those huge wings and always looked forward to any flight. However, by the time September 2001 arrived, I'd taken too many business trips to retain my childhood wonder at flying.

About a week after September 11, while flying from the southwest back eastward, I realized I'd unconsciously held my breath ever since the fall of the Twin Towers. Sheepishly, I admitted to a friend my reluctance to board a plane ever again. She advised, "Read Psalm 91. It's one of my favorites."

Reading that psalm flooded me with the image of our powerful God enfolding me within huge, divine, omnipotent wings. I read those blessed, lyric lines, wept . . . and finally exhaled.

O God, forgive me for sometimes losing sight of how grand You are. You are always there with Your loving arms and omnipotent care. All glory to You, in the name of the Father, the Son, and the Holy Spirit. Amen.

October 15–21. **Phillis Harris Brooks** is an experienced devotional writer who enjoys the aspens of Colorado with her husband and son.

If Nothing Else

It came about, when Jacob saw Rachel the daughter of Laban his mother's brother, and the sheep of Laban his mother's brother, that Jacob went up, and rolled the stone from the mouth of the well, and watered the flock of Laban his mother's brother (Genesis 29:10, *New American Standard Bible*).

Scripture: **Genesis 29:1-12**
Song: **"Take Time to Be Holy"**

Imagine a kiss causing death. A news story told of a teenage girl with extreme allergies. One of those allergies involved a reaction to peanut oil. She died after kissing her boyfriend, who had eaten a peanut butter sandwich.

Love requires mindfulness, if nothing else. What does mindfulness look like? In the case of Jacob, it could involve rolling a stone away from a well for his cousin Rachel. Yet, in his case, mindfulness may have taken a backseat to pride. Jacob probably longed to favorably impress his attractive cousin. Perhaps current day mindfulness, for us, might entail investing the necessary time to better appreciate a close friend.

I know that such mindfulness can draw me into closer fellowship with God, as well. If I embrace Him as the lover of my soul, then my soul needs to strive to mirror that which would please my love. And how do I begin to know what would please God? By not being afraid to spend time alone with Him and His Word.

Lord, help me set my mind on You today. Even if I can only spare five minutes, let those moments be genuine and precious. In Jesus' name, amen.

No-Boundary Loving?

Jacob served seven years for Rachel and they seemed to him but a few days because of his love for her (Genesis 29:20, *New American Standard Bible*).

Scripture: **Genesis 29:13-20**
Song: **"Love Lifted Me"**

Our family learned a lot about the heaviness of time this previous year. As though under siege, we catapulted from one challenge to another. A favorite aunt died. After 19 years, a brother questioned his marriage. Spring found me recovering from a quadruple bypass surgery, only to have another blockage surface in my leg. And diagnosed with breast cancer early in the year, a younger sister then confronted brain cancer 11 months later.

The disappointments and heartaches of the year reduced time's speed to the slowness of a dance in quicksand. Against such a backdrop, it isn't at all difficult to understand how Jacob's seven year labor of love, heightened by anticipation, would assume the sensation of warp speed for him. Joy and anticipation can color an attitude so that no sacrifice looms too great.

I wonder if it's possible to live for God in the same manner. In this day and age, with its encouragement to set boundaries, that might constitute a pretty scary thought —loving God without any boundaries!

*No matter what the cost, **Lord,** whether health, time, or family, I give my days and years to You. They were never mine anyway; I have always belonged to You. In Christ's holy name, I pray. Amen.*

Entitlements

It came about in the morning that, behold, it was Leah! And he said to Laban, "What is this you have done to me? Was it not for Rachel that I served with you? Why then have you deceived me?" (Genesis 29:25, *New American Standard Bible*).

Scripture: **Genesis 29:21-25a**
Song: **"Have Thine Own Way, Lord"**

How often we've heard the outraged accusation "That's not *fair!*" No matter our age, we all have a keen sense of what constitutes fair play. Don't kick a person when she's down. Share, and share alike.

Many of us appreciate the concept of Camelot, with its Knights of the Round Table to enforce the concept might doesn't make right. Our expectation is that, having agreed to certain terms, the other parties will do the right thing to fulfill their obligations as well.

We really should be grateful, though, that God isn't quite the stickler for rules we sometimes tend to be. God sees each of us believers as His beloved adopted children. He overlooks our tantrums in the midst of adversity, cradles each sobbing child until he's comforted enough to run, play, and . . . throw tantrums again.

Sounds quite a bit like parenting, doesn't it? Yes, we all know how much fairness a good daddy expects to receive.

Father in Heaven, regardless of the experiences I may have had as a child, inspire me to approach You as the loving parent I've desired. I ask this in the name of Your Son, Jesus the Christ. Amen.

Wrong Direction?

But Laban said, "It is not the practice in our place, to marry off the younger before the first-born" (Genesis 29:26, *New American Standard Bible*).

Scripture: **Genesis 29:25b-30**
Song: **"Pure Within"**

One of my coworkers lives for competition. If I'm not careful, I'll occasionally fall into the trap of trying to out-shine her. Of course, once I enter into that game, then we fuel each other's egos. The result: the project doesn't turn out quite as well, requires more time, and leaves me with a general sense of dissatisfaction.

I'm pretty sure my disquiet has more to do with my behavior than with the results of my performance. Why? Because I know that I know better. My allowing others to goad me into purely selfish behavior says much more about me than about them.

God deliberately equipped us with consciences to act as moral compasses. Perhaps Laban misplaced his compass! Otherwise, he'd have fulfilled his promise to Jacob, rather than continuing this sad competition for his daughters. In fact, as soon as any of us begin to suspect that we've started in the wrong direction, we can immediately stop and ask God's assistance to regain our ethical bearings.

Lord, *You know how quickly I falter, so remind me that when I stumble, You remain at my side to catch me. In the holy name of Jesus, my Lord and Savior, I pray. Amen.*

Just Thank Him

She conceived again and bore a son and said, "This time I will praise the LORD." Therefore she named him Judah. Then she stopped bearing (Genesis 29:35, *New American Standard Bible*).

Scripture: **Genesis 29:31-35**
Song: **"Now Thank We All Our God"**

One Christmas when I was 10-years-old, after I'd prayed for a great toy, someone gave me a pair of what had to be the ugliest shoes in the world. Candy-apple red, complete with bone-crushing pointed toes. They looked as though they'd escaped the set of *The Wizard of Oz*. Because of their glitter, passersby found it difficult, if not impossible, to rip their gazes from them.

How I hated those shoes! Yet my mother eventually demanded to know when I intended to write the thank you note for them. I looked at her in astonishment. Why in the world would I thank someone for giving me something so impractical and embarrassing?

Naturally, my mother's outlook differed significantly. "You needed shoes," she said. "And we don't tell God how to answer our prayers. We just thank Him." It took some time before I could take up her outlook as my own. But as Leah must have discovered so long ago, I too have begun to realize that "No" also represents a divine response. Ingratitude only serves to chill my relationship with the one who always answers my prayers.

Giver of every good thing, help me never discard Your greater gifts for the easier way. In the name of Christ, I pray. Amen.

Missing the Alarm?

Then God remembered Rachel, and God gave heed to her and opened her womb (Genesis 30:22, *New American Standard Bible*).

Scripture: **Genesis 30:22-24; 35:16-21**
Song: **"Brighten the Corner Where You Are"**

None of us read the signals my sister's body had sent. Her brow would pucker and she'd admit to one of us, "I don't remember how to get there." We chalked it up to her busy lifestyle or her habit of overextending herself. Thoroughly organized, she made it a point to have her doctor's office conveniently located up the street from where she worked.

One day while at work, she confessed to one of her coworkers, "I don't feel well. I should go to the doctor, but I can't remember where his office is." The alarms had finally transformed into loud warning gongs for our family; she had brain cancer.

There's a sense in which God sends us alarms regularly—those inner longings or feelings of uneasiness—may be God tugging at our sleeves. God's persistence in getting our attention is His way of reminding us that He has not moved but we may have wandered from Him. It is the wandering that leads to our forgetfulness about His constant, abiding presence, no matter our situations.

Light of the world, *when I wander from You, my world becomes a darker place. Remind me that Your brightness is ever near, and I need only turn homeward to feel the warmth of Your presence. In Jesus' name, amen.*

Why Worry?

"Save me, I pray, from the hand of my brother Esau, for I am afraid he will come and attack me, and also the mothers with their children" (Genesis 32:11).

Scripture: **Genesis 32:3-12**
Song: **"A Prayer for God's Blessing"**

In October of 1942, Eddie Rickenbacker was forced to crash land his B-17 bomber into the Pacific Ocean. He and his crew were out of radio range, so prospects for rescue were dim. After eight days of floating in a small raft, the crew members had run out of rations and were growing hungry. That morning, after their daily devotional time, Rickenbacker leaned his head back and pulled his hat over his eyes. A seagull landed on his head. Rickenbacker caught it, and the crew ate it while using the bird's intestines for bait to catch fish with hooks provided in their survival kits.

A seagull 900 miles from land? Rickenbacker had a simple explanation for their deliverance: "We prayed."

Fearful circumstances often drive us to our knees, don't they? Jacob feared his brother was seeking vengeance, and so we read "Then Jacob prayed" (vv. 9-12).

Any trouble worth worrying about is worth praying about. And once we've prayed about it, why worry?

Dear Lord, *strengthen my faith that I might always recognize Your presence in my most fearful times. In Christ's holy name, I pray. Amen.*

October 22–28. **Dan Nicksich** is a minister who writes articles and devotionals from his home in Somerset, Pennsylvania.

Time to Reconcile

"You are to say, 'They belong to your servant Jacob. They are a gift sent to my lord Esau, and he is coming behind us'" (Genesis 32:18).

Scripture: **Genesis 32:13-21**
Song: **"Brothers, Joining Hand to Hand"**

I need to get even with my brother. First, he drove a rental truck 500 miles to help pack and move our household goods. Now he hosts family gatherings and opens his swimming pool to us on hot summer days. I really do need to get even with him.

Of course, it wasn't always this way. As a younger brother, I constantly felt I was being abused and harassed by him during our childhood years. Getting even (in a different way) seemed to be a constant, consuming passion. How a little maturity changes such perspectives!

One of the saddest funerals I ever conducted was that of a young man whose brothers and sisters experienced a kind of reunion because of his tragic death. "He'll never know how he got us all together for the first time in years," one sister told me through her tears. How sad it is when we carry such harsh feelings toward others without making an effort to reconcile before death.

Jacob had once outrageously cheated his brother. He'd been a wily deceiver. Now he sought reconciliation. Good for him!

Dear Lord, *if there is someone with whom I have had a falling out, grant me the wisdom and courage to seek reconciliation. In Jesus' name, amen.*

Expecting the Worst?

Esau ran to meet Jacob and embraced him; he threw his arms around his neck and kissed him. And they wept (Genesis 33:4).

Scripture: **Genesis 33:1-4**
Song: **"Count Your Blessings"**

When I entered the hospital room, the elderly couple sat side by side on the bed, holding hands and crying. They had just received good news, no sign of his suspected cancer. They were both in their 80s.

Jacob was expecting the worst. He put his wives and their children in the back of his procession to give them a better chance of escape. His beloved Rachel and favorite son, Joseph, were bringing up the rear—the safest place, should violence erupt.

What joy Jacob must have felt as his brother ran to meet him and overwhelmed him with an affectionate embrace and kiss! Jesus would paint a similar picture in a parable involving reunion between a father and his wayward son (see Luke 15:11-32).

The Bible says that God can bring good from evil (see Genesis 50:20). He has a way of extending His blessings, even when we expect the worst: a clean bill of health despite the gloomy prognosis, peace and love where once bitterness ruled.

Dear Heavenly Father, sometimes I expect the worst and then experience Your wonderful blessings instead. Help me to trust You always, even when the days seem darkest. I pray in the name of Jesus my Savior. Amen.

The Other Side of Giving

"Please accept the present that was brought to you, for God has been gracious to me and I have all I need." And because Jacob insisted, Esau accepted it (Genesis 33:11).

Scripture: **Genesis 33:5-11**
Song: **"Give of Your Best to the Master"**

The church wanted to provide Thanksgiving dinners to some of their senior members, and everything was now in place—volunteers to cook meals, others to deliver them. But then they hit a snag. Many of the intended recipients refused the offer; a few even appeared offended.

While the church often teaches on giving, it may be that we also need to instruct our people in the art of receiving. One cannot give what another refuses to receive. A gracious acceptance completes the exercise of gift-giving.

Jacob insisted, Esau accepted. Most people I know are accustomed to being the giver: the caregiver, the gift giver, the willing helper in a time of need. Once the roles are reversed, they struggle to receive. But God says there will be times when those with plenty must supply the needs of others so that, in turn, the roles may be reversed in due season.

Perhaps this is a time of plenty for you, and you are helping provide for others. But are you also willing to be the needful one at times? How else would it be possible ever to experience love, grace, and caring?

*Humble me, **Lord,** that my pride might not hinder the gifts of those who seek only to give of their best to You. Thank You, in Jesus' name. Amen.*

Seeking Favor

"Just let me find favor in the eyes of my lord" (Genesis 33:15).

Scripture: **Genesis 33:12-15**
Song: **"Blest Be the Tie That Binds"**

Ben Franklin once felt that a certain individual seemed to harbor ill feelings toward him, though he could think of no offense or disagreement that had arisen between them. He thought it might have been some perceived, but unintended, slight, or simply a personality clash.

Franklin sent word to the other man, asking whether he could borrow a certain book from his personal library. The book was promptly sent, and thereafter relations between the two were cordial. Franklin's wise approach was to create a situation wherein he was indebted to his potential adversary. He treated the other man as a person of value and worth, and so attained his favor.

Jesus said that even when we are the offended party, we need to take the initiative and seek reconciliation. Of course, this runs contrary to human nature. Shouldn't the offending party bear the burden? But those who simply seek the favor of another will find a way to forgive and move forward.

Esau and Jacob were once again going their separate ways. Once they had departed in anger. Now they departed in peace.

Lord, may it be that my departure from others would always be in peace. May the regret I feel always be that of the pain of separation and never the pain of unresolved differences. In Jesus' name I pray. Amen.

Not Really Foolish

There he set up an altar and called it El Elohe Israel (Genesis 33:20).

Scripture: **Genesis 33:16-20**
Song: **"Freely, Freely"**

I once read a delightful story called "The Foolish Offering." Whenever confronted with an unexpected expense or potential time of financial hardship, this couple would make what they dubbed their foolish offering. They made a special offering, beyond their weekly gift to their church, some mission, or other worthy cause. They gave in faith, anticipating that God would provide for them in their time of need.

I heard of a church once that operated on the same principle. Whenever things were tightest financially, one of their elders was sure to say, "Time to give more to missions."

It's appropriate that Jacob's journey, including his time of reconciliation with his brother, ends in worship. God's actions on our behalf should bring corresponding acts of praise, thanksgiving, and worship. Some are so confident that they respond to God *in anticipation of blessings yet to come.* How fitting that we not forget God once we've actually reaped His favor!

Lord, I know that You give all good things at just the right time. Help me give praise and thanks to You whenever You have blessed me. But help me also to give in faith beforehand, anticipating Your sure blessings in Christ. In His precious name I pray. Amen.

Precious Oil!

How good and pleasant it is when brothers live together in unity! (Psalm 133:1).

Scripture: **Psalm 133**
Song: **"Together, Lord, We Come to Thee"**

We purchase perfume by fractions of an ounce. Yet a woman once poured a whole pint of expensive perfume on Jesus, an amount worth more than a year's wages. Some proclaimed this a waste, but Jesus praised her generous act of devotion (see Mark 14:3-9).

It's difficult to relate to the picture of precious oil running down over Aaron's head to the extent that his beard and even the collar of his robes are drenched. Yet the point that comes through is awesome: there are times for a bit of extravagance in our worship of God.

What inspires the outpouring of God's blessings like so much precious oil? Simply this—brothers living together in unity (v. 1). Yet the Bible abounds with brothers who experienced disunity—Cain and Abel, Esau and Jacob, Joseph and his brothers, and the sons of David. You could probably pencil in a few names yourself. You may even know a few examples of brothers or sisters in your own extended family who never seem to reconcile. Thus the precious oil of God's blessing is withheld.

Dear Lord, thank You for the blessings that appear in my world. But wherever there has been injury or disunity, make me an instrument of peace that others would come to know the abundant outpouring of Your blessings. In the name of the Father, the Son, and the Holy Spirit, I pray. Amen.

Child in His Old Age

Israel loved Joseph more than any of his other sons, because he had been born to him in his old age; . . . When his brothers saw that their father loved him more than any of them, they hated him (Genesis 37:3, 4).

Scripture: **Genesis 37:1-4**
Song: **"God Moves in a Mysterious Way"**

After his wife died, Hank remarried to a woman almost 25 years younger than he. When their son, Sam, was born, the 50-year-old father doted on the boy. He bought him lots of toys, played with him in the park after work, and took him fishing on the weekends.

But what about Hank's older children? They became jealous of little Sam. Their dad hadn't bought them lots of fancy toys. Nor had he spent as much time with them.

Joseph's brothers were jealous of him too. Their hatred must have hurt. But both boys, Joseph and Sam, were loved deeply by their fathers. Little Sam, like Joseph, could not know what the future held for him, but he knew he could always depend on the love of his father. In the same way, we are loved by our heavenly Father. We can't know what the future holds, but His unchanging love keeps us secure.

Dear Heavenly Father, *I know You hold the future in Your hands. I ask that You help me expect and accept, as Your plan, those difficult circumstances that come into my life. In Jesus' name, amen.*

October 29–31. **Dell Smith-Klein** shares Bible truths in the form of stories that touch the hearts of hearers. She lives in the Weaver Mountains of Arizona.

Scorned by His Brothers

His brothers were jealous of him, but his father kept the matter in mind (Genesis 37:11).

Scripture: **Genesis 37:5-11**
Song: **"Love Is the Theme"**

Joseph had another dream and felt compelled to share it with his family. His brothers could have begun praising God for revealing something very important to the boy; instead, they succumbed to envy and hatred. And as time went by, they began to scheme against young Joseph.

As I pondered this Bible story, I came up with this scenario: What if someone at church volunteered to be in charge of the children's choir, even though I have always been the choir director? Would I respond with joy that God is working through this person?

In Joseph's case, God was preparing him for leadership long before the need appeared. Joseph didn't know that, nor did his brothers. All they had was Joseph's strange dream about the sun, moon, and stars bowing before him.

It would be hard to figure out the truth if that was all we had to go on—a little brother's dream. After thinking about that children's choir volunteer, I had to ask, "Am I a dreamer like Joseph or a schemer like his brothers?"

Dear God, thank You for guiding me, even when I don't understand the meaning of the difficult events in my life. With all my heart I lean on You and believe that You have my best interest in mind each step of the way. I pray this prayer in the name of Jesus, my Savior and Lord. Amen.

Helped to Glory

A man found him wandering around in the fields and asked him, "What are you looking for?" He replied, "I'm looking for my brothers. Can you tell me where they are grazing their flocks?" (Genesis 37:15, 16).

Scripture: **Genesis 37:12-17**
Song: **"All the Way My Savior Leads Me"**

Stories abound of people who've been helped by an unknown stranger. Some have claimed that the benevolent visitor was an angel, but most of the time the helper is just a good-hearted soul willing to lend a hand in difficult times.

One summer, my husband was driving about 50 miles from home when he saw an older couple parked at the side of the road. He stopped to help and found two very weary 80-year-olds. My husband tried a simple fix on their car, but the couple only drove a few miles before it broke down again. This time, my husband drove all the way home, got the part they needed, and drove back to replace it for them. He wasn't an angel; just a stranger who felt led by God to help.

Joseph knew where his brothers were to be camped, but when he got there, they were gone. A kind stranger directed him to their new location—and to Joseph's rather painful immediate future. But the unfolding of his entire life was in God's hands. And what eventual glory!

Father, I don't know the motives of others, but I know that I can trust You to bring about what is best in my life. I thank You in Jesus' name. Amen.

DEVOTIONS

May all
who seek you
rejoice and be
glad in you;
. . . "Let God be
exalted!"

—Psalm 70:4

NOVEMBER

Photo © istock

Gary Allen, Editor

Where Will You Serve?

When Reuben heard this, he tried to rescue him from their hands. "Let's not take his life," he said (Genesis 37:21).

Scripture: **Genesis 37:18-24**
Song: **"Servant of God, Well Done!"**

I once had a friend, raised in a minister's home, who sensed from an early age that his gifts for leadership and teaching ought to be used in the church as well. Instead he went into sales.

For years nothing seemed to work out for him in the business world. When he was in his 50s, he realized that he had tried to thwart an essential calling on his life. After a long session on his knees, he signed up for Bible school. Within a few years he became the minister of a church in a small town where he was truly needed.

Joseph's brothers were so consumed with hatred that they didn't take time to think about what they were planning. They saw Joseph coming and let their anger get the best of them.

They couldn't, of course, thwart God's work in Joseph's life. Nor can His plans for us be thwarted as we seek His guidance day by day. Our part is to assess the spiritual gifts we've been given and then put them to use in His kingdom. The Spirit will lead us to just the right place.

Lord, help me to know myself well enough to know where and how I can serve You best. Then lead me there! In Jesus' name, amen.

November 1–4. **Dell Smith-Klein** shares Bible truths in the form of stories that touch the hearts of hearers. She lives in the Weaver Mountains of Arizona.

Painfully, Gloriously Awesome

When the Midianite merchants came by, his brothers pulled Joseph up out of the cistern and sold him for twenty shekels of silver (Genesis 37:28).

Scripture: **Genesis 37:25-28**
Song: **"Where He Leads Me"**

When I was about 8 years old, my cousins shut me in the tack house at my family's ranch. They thought it was pretty funny. There I stood, locked in with dusty saddles, bridles, saddle soap, and curry combs. But surely, my cousins would come back for me soon!

It wasn't funny for me. My heart pounded, and my legs shook as I hollered for them to let me out.

Joseph must have felt like that. I imagine he sat on the musty-smelling floor of that dry well waiting in fear, maybe calling out from time to time. Surely his crazy brothers would come back and lift him out.

I was only locked in the tack house a short time before my teasing cousins pulled the door open, but Joseph's story ended differently. When his brothers finally hauled him out of the pit, he realized their scheme included a business transaction. He watched Midianite merchants count 20 shekels of silver into his brothers' eager palms. What an awesome thing to witness! And even more awesome: though he didn't know at the time, it was all in God's plan.

__Lord,__ sometimes I feel as if I've landed in a pit of despair. It's not very comfortable there. Help me to a deeper trust today, in Jesus' name. Amen.

A Father's Grief

All his sons and daughters came to comfort him, but he refused to be comforted. "No," he said, "in mourning will I go down to the grave to my son." So his father wept for him (Genesis 37:35).

Scripture: **Genesis 37:29-36**
Song: **"The Grave Itself a Garden Is"**

In October 2005, the body of a World War II airman was found in a glacier at Kings Canyon National Park. He was apparently part of a crew that crashed in those mountains 63 years earlier. The airman's family knew his plane had gone down, but searchers had never recovered his body. Thus, a family spokesperson said the family's grief had had no ending—until now.

After Joseph's brothers sold him to a traveling band of traders heading toward Egypt, they lied to their father, saying a wild animal had killed his favorite son. Their father's grief was so deep he couldn't be comforted—even when surrounded by all his other children. Never again to look upon, or hold, his child was beyond this father's capacity to bear.

Yet, God's purpose was unfolding. There would come a day in the lives of Joseph's brothers when they would be grateful Joseph hadn't died in that pit. In the meantime, they watched their father mourn the death of a son who was just as alive as you or me.

God, sometimes my grief is so deep! But thanks for walking with me through it. In You I find comfort and peace. In Jesus' name, amen.

Look and See!

You are my help and my deliverer; O Lord, do not delay (Psalm 70:5).

Scripture: **Psalm 70**
Song: **"Deliverance Will Come"**

Even though his angry brothers tried to destroy Joseph and God's plan, they couldn't do it. And when Reuben tried to rescue Joseph, he couldn't do that either. God had it in control. Every step of the way, from the time of his youth, God's hand was upon Joseph, directing and delivering.

Once when my children were small, we camped in the forest together. At dusk we took a little walk, and I became so interested in showing the children the moss on the rocks and the minnows in the stream that I failed to keep an eye on the setting sun. At dark we were still some distance from our campsite.

It was a moonless night, and we couldn't see the path. My heart pounded as I walked along carrying the 3-year-old and leading the 5-year-old. Then another camper, flashlight in hand, stepped up beside us. He shined his light on our path and walked with us all the way to our campsite. I was so grateful!

Even when we can't recognize God's direction, it's there. He shines His light on our dark pathway and delivers us. When we look, will we truly see?

Lord God, I praise You as I think how You have, time and time again, led me through dangerous situations. Glory to You, through Christ! Amen.

One Path to Success

The LORD was with Joseph, so he became a successful man (Genesis 39:2, *New American Standard Bible*).

Scripture: **Genesis 39:1-6a**
Song: **"Spend One Hour with Jesus"**

Remember the story of King Midas, who requested that everything he touched would become gold? He soon discovered the gift was actually a curse—when his beloved daughter turned to solid gold at his touch! We could say that Joseph had a kind of midas touch. His benefactor was God, and the gift wasn't a curse at all.

The prophet Jeremiah penned the words revealing God's wonderful touch upon His people: He knows His plans for us, plans to prosper us, to give us hope and a future (see Jeremiah 29:11).

God certainly knew what He had planned for Joseph from the beginning. And while it may not have seemed a blessing to be sold by his brothers into slavery—going from the pampered son of a wealthy rancher to a slave doing menial tasks—God had a purpose in it all.

We know the story of Joseph's success and his eventual rulership in Egypt. The thing we must never forget, though, is this: Joseph had nothing to do with his success other than being a willing, obedient servant of God.

Lord, *help me see that even in the most difficult circumstances, You have my good in mind. I pray through my deliverer, Jesus. Amen.*

November 5–11. **Marjorie Vawter**, of Westminster, Colorado, loves to write and has authored several published devotionals and book reviews.

Plan Ahead!

"How then could I do such a wicked thing and sin against God?" (Genesis 39:9).

Scripture: **Genesis 39:6b-10**
Song: **"Thy Word Have I Hid in My Heart"**

As a teacher in a Christian high school, I enjoyed the frequent opportunity to sit under wonderful, godly preaching in our twice-weekly chapel services. Many of the preachers taught our young people the importance of being morally pure. The best piece of advice I heard came from our youth minister: "In order to stand firm in temptation, make the decision to please God *long before* the temptation comes."

Joseph recognized that the temptation he faced would, in reality, lead to a sin against God. God had blessed Joseph with such great stewardship responsibility that Potiphar had no idea what he owned; it was all trusted to Joseph's wise management. The only thing or person Potiphar withheld from Joseph was . . . Mrs. Potiphar! Sadly, Mrs. Potiphar was obsessed with Joseph's good looks.

But isn't all sin ultimately an affront to God? Spurning His wonderful blessings, we choose immediate gratification over long-term peace. But knowing how this grieves God's heart, we can determine far ahead of time our plan of escape.

Father God, help me determine ahead of time to stand firm on the principles of Your Word when I face temptation. In Jesus' name, amen.

Try a Footrace!

He left his garment in her hand and fled (Genesis 39:12, *New American Standard Bible*).

Scripture: **Genesis 39:11-20**
Song: **"Yield Not to Temptation"**

In general the Bible tells us to stand firm and resist our temptations. However in certain sudden, sticky situations, its best just to . . . *run!*

Literally. Like Joseph did.

In the New Testament, Paul encouraged Timothy to flee the lusts of youth and chase after godly virtues, such as righteousness, faith, love, and peace (see 2 Timothy 2:22).

Joseph did just that, leaving his garment in Mrs. Potiphar's hand. He may not have anticipated her anger when she didn't get what she wanted. And he may not have expected to end up in prison. But Joseph did the right thing.

Writer Jerry Bridges, in *The Pursuit of Holiness,* tells us that John's view of holiness (not sinning) was different from his own goal of (not sinning *very much*). It would be like a soldier going into battle with the aim of not getting hit *very much.* If merely this is our aim in life, we can be sure the darts of temptation will hit us over and over again. A good old-fashioned footrace has much better chance of success.

Lord, no matter how hot the battle, keep me close to You in pursuing holiness. When it's time to run, help me do it. Through Christ I pray. Amen.

Waiting for Refining

Two years later, Pharaoh dreamed that he was standing on the bank of the Nile River (Genesis 41:1, *New Living Translation*).

Scripture: **Genesis 41:1-8**
Song: **"How Firm a Foundation"**

Have you noticed how difficult it is to wait on God? Yet God uses those times of waiting to mold and refine us, preparing us to accomplish His plans in our lives. When Habakkuk wondered how long it would be before God fulfilled His promises of deliverance to Israel, God answered: "These things I plan won't happen right away. Slowly, steadily, surely, the time approaches. . . . If it seems slow, wait patiently, for it will surely take place. It will not be delayed" (Habakkuk 2:3, *NLT*).

We don't know much about Joseph's wait in prison other than that he interpreted the dreams for Pharaoh's chief cup-bearer and baker. We don't even know how long his imprisonment lasted. But it was another two years before God was ready to release him and exalt him to the No. 2 position in the land of Egypt.

God used the time well, however: He prepared Joseph for the tasks ahead, even though the waiting must have been hard for the young man. Perhaps Job said it best amid all his patient sufferings: "He knows where I am going. And when he has tested me like gold in a fire, he will pronounce me innocent" (Job 23:10, *NLT*).

Lord, help me each day to wait patiently for you to mold me into a vessel fit for the work You've placed at hand. In Jesus' name, amen.

Can You Focus Like This?

"Now as for the repeating of the dream to Pharaoh twice, it means that the matter is determined by God, and God will quickly bring it about" (Genesis 41:32, *New American Standard Bible*).

Scripture: **Genesis 41:25-36**
Song: **"If You Will Only Let God Guide You"**

What is our usual first reaction when we've been wronged? For me, as soon as I get a chance, I go into defense mode. "This isn't fair! Justice should be done. My rights have been violated."

I'm impressed that Joseph didn't say any of these things when he came before Pharaoh. He didn't talk about being imprisoned on trumped-up charges. He didn't confront the cupbearer for forgetting him those two long years. Instead he focused on Pharaoh's request and kept his eyes on God. Three times in this passage Joseph tells Pharaoh that God sent the dream because God was ready to work in Egypt and the surrounding lands.

Joseph also refused to take credit for his ability to interpret dreams, again pointing his hearers to the sovereign God. Then he followed the dream's interpretation with words of counsel, not realizing God was going to use him to fulfill the plan of action he suggested. If I could keep everything focused on God like that, I know my life would bring greater glory to Him. How is it with you?

Father, Your Son, Jesus, suffered every injustice as my perfect high priest. Let me focus on honoring Him today as I pray in His name. Amen.

Finally, Justice!

Pharaoh said, "Since God has revealed the meaning of the dreams to you, you are the wisest man in the land! I hereby appoint you to direct this project" (Genesis 41:39, 40, *New Living Translation*).

Scripture: **Genesis 41:37-45**
Song: **"God Is So Good"**

Have you ever wondered how Joseph felt when Pharaoh spoke these words? In a single day, Joseph went from being a prisoner to the taking on the second highest position in the land of Egypt—from the chains of imprisonment to the soft raiment and jewels of royalty.

While Joseph's thoughts and words about it aren't recorded, we can know that he recognized God's hand in all of this. Years earlier he'd dreamed about holding this rulership above his family. And Jacob had rebuked him for his pride.

Yet now God fulfilled the dream. After all the years of testing, learning, and waiting, Joseph was ready for the job God had for him. I'm quite sure that God's ultimate justice helped him forget all the cruel injustices done to him. And we can do the same—but with some difficulty. For, as William Penn once said: "Justice is the insurance which we have on our lives and property. Obedience is the premium which we pay for it."

God, You indeed are good! You bring us out of the fire and exalt us above our enemies—in this life or in the next. You work all things together for good to those who love You. For this I praise You, in Christ's name. Amen.

Tested Character

Until the time came to fulfill his word, the LORD **tested Joseph's character** (Psalm 105:19, *New Living Translation*).

Scripture: **Psalm 105:16-22**
Song: **"Rejoice in the Lord Always"**

The writer of Hebrews tells us that Jesus learned obedience. How? Through suffering (see 5:8). Think of it—the perfect Son of God had to *learn* obedience.

Joseph was a teenager when his brothers sold him into slavery. But even that initial trial resulted in his being an honored servant to Potiphar, captain of Pharaoh's guard. But to truly test his character, God allowed Joseph to be imprisoned on a charge of rape. We're told that he was in fetters that bruised his feet and bound him around his neck. His entire being—body, soul, and spirit—was tested by those chains and the years he was in prison.

Even after the chains were removed, Joseph must have borne the marks of those fetters. Through all of this, Joseph's character was refined. I believe God allowed him the dream of ruling over his parents and brothers to sustain him in his darkest hours. Even Joseph's own testimony to his brothers spoke of understanding that God's way, though hard, is always best: "As far as I am concerned, God turned into good what you meant for evil" (Genesis 50:20, *NLT*).

Lord, help me remember that what seems bad to me, whatever is unfair in my life, whatever chains bind me—these things are opportunities to recall Your presence and draw on Your strength. Through Christ, amen.

Listening, Then Loving

I will listen to what God the LORD will say; he promises peace to his people (Psalm 85:8).

Scripture: **Psalm 85**
Song: **"Lord, Speak to Me"**

I turned off the TV news with a sigh. It was bad news again. Besides another devastating earthquake, I'd watched reports of disturbing crimes committed against innocent children. I couldn't stand to know anymore. I picked up my Bible and began to read. A hundred years ago it took a lot longer for such news to reach us. But in our instant media society, it is hard to avoid contact with the pain of others. How do we deal with all this suffering in the world?

The psalmist helps me here. If I focus on listening to the Lord, I will find personal peace. It is an act of the will to stop and listen to Him.

As we open to His inner peace, we will be strengthened to reach out to others with the first small steps of compassion. We can't save the whole world at once, but we can offer a cup of cold water to the one suffering next door. That is my prayer this day—that I will listen to the Lord and then reach out with the power of His peace.

Lord, I thank You that You desire to speak to me—even more than I want to listen. Help me to hear Your voice in the many ways You communicate with me every day. Then move me into loving service in Jesus' name. Amen.

November 12–18. **Janet Bair** is a freelance writer and a children's librarian. She lives in Ansonia, Connecticut, with her husband and two daughters.

Remember Me?

Although Joseph recognized his brothers, they did not recognize him (Genesis 42:8).

Scripture: **Genesis 42:1-20**
Song: **"Face to Face with Christ, My Savior"**

Has anyone ever come up to you and exclaimed, "Hi, remember me? I almost didn't recognize you." And as he or she talks on and on . . . you are still wondering who, exactly, *is* this person?

Sometimes we recognize that sudden stranger, and sometimes, like Joseph's brothers, we don't. The person's looks may have changed significantly over the years. Simply growing up changes peoples faces.

Joseph was 17 years old when his brothers sold him into slavery, and about 25 years had passed before they met again. Pharaoh had given him robes of fine linen and put a gold chain about his neck. At age 42, Joseph not only looked different but he was in a totally unexpected place when his brothers saw him again.

While we may have the same problem of recognizing people we knew long ago, there is one person we should always be able to recognize—Jesus. Someday when we see Him face-to-face in Heaven, we will know Him by His love for us. We will recognize His character. We will see the marks on His hands and feet. We will remember all He has done for us, and we will be eternally thankful.

Lord, as I learn more about You every day, help me to learn more of You in this wonderful relationship. In Your precious name I pray. Amen.

Don't Delay!

As it is, if we had not delayed, we could have gone and returned twice (Genesis 43:10).

Scripture: **Genesis 43:1-15**
Song: **"The Savior Is Waiting"**

Carol frowned as she looked at her long To Do list. She couldn't put off doing those chores any longer—the phone calls to make, a costume to alter, grocery shopping to do, and a huge yard of leaves to rake before it rained.

Procrastination! We're all guilty at times.

Joseph's brothers delayed going back to Egypt after their first visit during the famine. Even though Simeon was waiting in prison, they ate all of the grain before they went back. Judah finally reminded his father that they could have already gone—and come back twice—in the time it was taking Jacob to make a decision!

Sometimes I too hesitate to get moving. When the Lord prompts me to do something, it's usually pretty clear. God's still, small voice may nudge me to go and talk to a lonely neighbor or give some money to a struggling college student I know. It may be a small or a big thing. It may not make sense at the time. But the Lord has His own purposes and plans. And I long to be a part of the solution rather than a cause of delay.

Lord God in Heaven, help me with my procrastinating tendencies. I know that if I follow Your leading, the plans You have for Your kingdom will be accomplished in my small part of the world. Thank You for using me today. In the name of the Father, the Son, and the Holy Spirit, amen.

Don't Finish This

Deeply moved at the sight of his brother, Joseph hurried out and looked for a place to weep. He went into his private room and wept there (Genesis 43:30).

Scripture: **Genesis 43:16-34**
Song: **"Father, Make Us Loving"**

Have you ever been to a large family reunion with relatives you haven't seen in a long time? At such times, we wonder why we waited so long to get together.

Sometimes you want to cry for joy at seeing everyone again. The great Joseph wept when he saw his beloved brother Benjamin. In spite of the fact that his brothers had sold him into slavery, he was overcome with emotion upon seeing his family reunited again. Now Joseph was a tough man, ruling over thousands in Egypt, but he had a tender heart for his family.

God calls all of His people to have caring, reconciling hearts. As Hebrews 12:14 tells us: "Make every effort to live in peace with all men." Family reunions offer us the opportunity to resolve conflicts as we reconnect. God gives us these special times of great food and conversation to catch up on news but also to show how we can pray for one another and build one another up. As humorist Don Marquis once quipped: "I would rather start a family than finish one."

Lord, *thank You for the families and friends that You have placed with me. Help me to be a good listener and to see their true needs, praying for them with discernment. In Your name I pray. Amen.*

Another Test

Put my cup, the silver one, in the mouth of the youngest one's sack, along with the silver for his grain (Genesis 44:2).

Scripture: **Genesis 44:1-13**
Song: **"Wonderful Grace of Jesus"**

In a sermon one Sunday, Chrissy heard the story of how Joseph forgave his brothers. The closing prayer included an invitation to forgive any family member who had caused hurt. Later that day, Chrissy's forgiveness capability was tested. Another family member yelled and berated her at a party. Surprisingly, Chrissy was able to keep quiet and walk away. Later she realized the power of God had been at work in her life. For it is incredibly difficult to forgive while the sting of hurt or embarrassment still simmers in our hearts.

There are many tests in the Christian life, though most aren't as elaborate or as planned as Joseph's. When he had his own silver cup put in Benjamin's sack, he wanted to see whether his brothers really had changed. Would they abandon Benjamin as they had heartlessly left Joseph himself so long ago?

God will test our faithfulness too. But not for the purpose of failing us. Rather He will confirm and strengthen our faith through each trial. As Job proclaimed: "When he has tested me, I will come forth as gold" (Job 23:10).

Lord, let forgiveness always be on my heart and lips. And thank You for growing me toward maturity, even through the tough times. In the holy name of Jesus, my Lord and Savior, I pray. Amen.

Launched Back to Joy

Judah replied. "What can we say? How can we prove our innocence? God has uncovered your servants' guilt" (Genesis 44:16).

Scripture: **Genesis 44:14-34**
Song: **"My Sins Are Blotted Out, I Know!"**

"Did you finish your dinner?" Mom would ask as she was busy cleaning up. *Well* . . . I used to sneak those hated lima beans to our cat under the table. And my little brother would hide his unwanted food in a napkin and then throw it out. Funny how, so many years later, I can remember doing a little thing like that. I am sure I told my mother "Oh yes, I ate it all."

Secret sins stick with us, big or small.

Joseph's brothers had a secret sin that loomed large before them. When they met Joseph again 25 years later, and things weren't going well for them, their consciences quickly prodded them. They felt uncovered, soul-naked in their guilt.

Unconfessed sin can plague us like that. And it's a good thing it does! Then we can take it as a gracious call to open our hearts to God, to let Him know the hurts, the desires, the alienation that drove us to some sad form of self-destructiveness. There, at His feet, we obtain sweet mercy—and the courage to launch into life again with joy.

Heavenly Father, how I wish to serve You in all purity and perfection! But when I fail, help me run to You with unguarded heart to receive Your forgiveness. I pray through my deliverer, Jesus. Amen.

A Reconciliation Model

It was not you who sent me here, but God. He made me father to Pharaoh, lord of his entire household and ruler of all Egypt (Genesis 45:8).

Scripture: **Genesis 45:1-15**
Song: **"Others, Lord"**

Cindy sat down with her preschool class and began to color with the children. As soon as she started coloring her picture, two of the kids began watching her intently. They used the same colors she used and copied her picture—even down to the blue and green stripes she added on the boy's shirt.

Cindy was stunned to see how quickly they wanted to emulate her every move. She thought, "What else do the children copy?" She was humbled to find herself such a powerful public role model!

Children model adults as if it were second nature; they do need patterns to follow as they grow up. Joseph's forgiveness of his brothers—and their final reconciliation—is a good family model for any of us to copy. No matter how serious the offense, family members can work towards reconciliation. And it will benefit all concerned. As someone once put it: "When chickens quit quarrelling over their food they often find there is enough for all of them."

Lord, *thank You for Joseph's model of reconciliation. In my family where there are hurts, help us to take them to the cross where all is forgiven. In the name of the Father, the Son, and the Holy Spirit, I pray. Amen.*

Big Promises

"Never mind about your belongings, because the best of all Egypt will be yours" (Genesis 45:20).

Scripture: **Genesis 45:16-20**
Song: **"Standing on the Promises"**

God makes great big promises. Read the New Testament and see: We are promised fire that burns hot. We are promised wind that blows strong and light like that of a city set on a hill. God adds to those promises the startling radiance of a marriage banquet.

Pharaoh promised Joseph's family land in Egypt. It was a promise that eased an old past and pointed to a new future; a promise they could trust, invest their lives in, and look forward to. It was a promise they knew would come true. But Pharaoh promised even more: the most excellent land in Egypt.

God's promises are true and they are tremendous. Read the New Testament. It is the fatted calf and the best robe. It is abundant grace and unspeakable joy. It is a pearl of great price and a great, big box full of treasure. God's promises are true. They are also excessive, extravagant, and exceedingly abundant.

Dear God, thank You for wrapping Your strong arms around me, pouring out Your great love into my life, and lifting me up to the highest mountain of gift and blessing. Thank You for wide doors through which to pass and large rooms in which to stand. In the name of Christ, I pray. Amen.

November 19–25. **Phillip H. Barnhart**, writer of 14 books, retired in 2002 after 45 years in ministry. He lives on Perdido Bay, Florida, with his wife, Sharon.

Our God Speaks

God spoke to Israel in a vision at night and said, "Jacob! Jacob!" (Genesis 46:2).

Scripture: **Genesis 46:1-4**
Song: **"Speak to My Soul"**

It is no problem for God to speak to us. We are made in God's image, so God communicating with us is not unlike us communicating with one another. As God spoke to Jacob on his way to Egypt for a family reunion, He also speaks to us in all sorts of circumstances.

Besides the obvious—Bible meditation and prayer—we hear from God in the when and where and what of how things go in life. A road taken here, a page turned there, and we look back to see God's voiceprint all over our decisions and choices.

God is keen on self-revelation, isn't He? He likes to make himself known to us. It gives Him joy to plop down in our lives in ways we are foolish to deny. I've noticed that He occasionally likes to send a friend my way with a word for me that could have only come from Him. He likes to stir up a favorite emotion and speak to me from the wind that blows in the heart of my feelings. The point is, no venue is out of bounds for the voice of God.

My Father in Heaven, You are knowable to me. Every day, any place, I can hear from You. I am glad You aren't secretive about yourself! Of all the things You reveal, the most important are the incomparable aspects of Your character. And since You never quit speaking, may I never stop listening. In the name of Your Son, my Savior, I pray. Amen.

What a Hug!

Joseph got in his chariot and went to meet his father. When they met, Joseph hugged his father around the neck and cried for a long time (Genesis 46:29, *Contemporary English Version*).

Scripture: **Genesis 46:28-34**
Song: **"God Be with You Till We Meet Again"**

Joey was 13-months-old when his estranged father kidnapped him and took him to a faraway state to live. Years later as Joey visited an Internet chat room, a couple became curious about him. Joey's story sounded like another they'd heard. The couple contacted the police and, not long afterward, the FBI showed up on Joey's doorstep to tell him his mother had been searching for him for the past 14 years. Just before Christmas of that year, Joey and his mother were joyfully reunited.

In our Bible passage, Jacob is on his way to Egypt to be reunited with his son Joseph. It is a glorious journey as every step he puts down on the road leaves a footprint of joyful anticipation. He can't wait to see his boy again. Upon approaching Joseph, he throws his arms wide open, runs with abandon toward his son, and puts a hug on Joseph that will not let go. There is shouting, crying, dancing. There is the immeasurable joy of reunion.

I like to imagine how it will be when we, His long lost brothers and sisters, finally see Jesus face-to-face. What will that hug be like?

Dear God, no matter how far I roam, I will come home to You. Thank You for Your ready arms of welcome. In Jesus' name, amen.

Family Time

Joseph also provided his father and his brothers and all his father's household with food, according to the number of their children (Genesis 47:12).

Scripture: **Genesis 47:7-12**
Song: **"The Family of God"**

Little Mikey asked his mother, "Where was I born?" The answer came, "In Michigan." Another question had queued up behind the first one. "Where was sister born?" So Mom replied, "She was born in Wisconsin."

Little Mikey was not through. "How about you and Daddy?" Mikey's mother accommodated her son. "I was born in Georgia, and your dad was born in Oregon." Mikey thought about all of that information for a minute and then said, "Isn't it great we could all get together?"

After years of separation, Joseph gets together with his father and brothers. They are reunited and Joseph takes advantage of the reunion to give his family everything they need. His generosity celebrates his love for each and all of them. It is family time in Egypt, and like the best of family time everywhere, love communicates and joy dominates. No matter what the future holds, it's OK because the caring family is together. Each member rests in a haven of safety and security. Everyone knows this is where they belong, and these are the people they can count on. There's no time like family time.

*Thank You, **Dear Father,** for giving me a place in Your family. In this family, I am Yours and You are mine. Through Christ the Lord, amen.*

Going Home

"When I rest with my fathers, carry me out of Egypt and bury me where they are buried" (Genesis 47:30).

Scripture: **Genesis 47:27-31**
Song: **"On Jordan's Stormy Banks I Stand"**

I have decided what I want engraved on my tombstone. Put my name, year of birth and death, and then put, "To Be Continued."

When I die I will pass across the threshold of death into the storehouse of life forever. My sequence begun in the heart of God continues in the presence of God. I pray for the kingdom to come and I come to the kingdom.

When Jacob dies he wants to go home, to end up in his homeland, not in a foreign land. Joseph promises his father he will go home, just as God promises us that we will go home.

Yes, we will go home where the light never fails because the sun never sets. We will go home where the little chords we hear on earth become full-scale symphonies of beauty and majesty. We will go home where our speculations and intimations become absolute certainties. Heaven is the destination, the completion of a journey, the fulfillment of a promise. Heaven is home.

O Lord, You are God of earth and Heaven. You are God of beginnings, endings, and continuings. You are God of yesterday, today, and tomorrow. You are the God who comes and never leaves. You are God who always finishes Your sentences with the exclamation point of forever! In the holy name of Jesus, my Lord and Savior, I pray. Amen.

Bountiful Blessings

Jacob told him that in the future the people of Israel would ask God's blessings on one another by saying, "I pray for God to bless you as much as he blessed Ephraim and Manasseh" (Genesis 48:20, *Contemporary English Version*).

Scripture: **Genesis 48:8-21**
Song: **"There Shall Be Showers of Blessing"**

Every time someone tells me I'm lucky about something, I say, "Not lucky—*blessed*." I consider any so-called good fortune to originate in the heart of God's love for me. All the goodness of my life has its source in God's grace, and that grace shows up in full benevolent apparel at the beginning of each day. Each day that I wake up is a beautiful day, and I am blessed in it.

Jacob blessed Ephraim and Manasseh in such a way that people talked about it for generations. Similarly, God blesses me with the gift of life that opens my mouth in celebration and praise. That gift of good life takes many shapes, has many embodiments, and soaks itself into me everywhere.

There have been many times in my life when I have been pretty much blessed off my rocker! Times when I drink out of my saucer because my cup has overflowed. Times when I sit at God's table and am filled with God's blessings—but still He says to me, "Here, have another one."

Dear God, *each and every blessing You pour out to me in grace and love, I give back to You in thanksgiving and praise. In Jesus' name, amen.*

Tell It All

I will exalt you, my God the King; I will praise your name for ever and ever (Psalm 145:1).

Scripture: **Psalm 145:1-13a**
Song: **"Praise Him! Praise Him!"**

I cannot offer enough praises to God. I get paper and pencil to itemize the blessings for which I praise Him, but I run out of paper and my pencil wears down to a tiny nub. The most prevalent position for my arms and hands on any given day is a vertical one. They are lifted up, as my heart is elevated in appreciation for what God does and who God is. I am forever a psalmist, raising my praise to God.

Yes, the hard times come too. But let us be faithful in our adoration—not spasmodic and intermittent, but steady and consistent—showing up every day to praise God who gives us what we have and makes us who we are. Why not be exuberant in our adoration!

I've begun to see there is no better use of my vocal chords than utilizing them to express my thankfulness to God. Therefore, I want to be prolific in my adoration, go on a rampage of praise every now and then, and mention everything great and small that comes to mind. Yes, in the next few moments, I'm going to tell it all to God.

Dear God, I am far more concerned about what You do for me than I am about what I can do for You. I realize how You bless me. I see how You guide me. I know how You make me more able than I am. How I thank You, in the name of Jesus, my Savior and Lord. Amen.

Compliment Him

Say to God, "How awesome are your deeds! So great is your power that your enemies cringe before you" (Psalm 66:3).

Scripture: **Psalm 66:1-4**
Song: **"Praise the Lord, for He Is Good"**

"See, I told you. Things never work out for me." Linda used those words often, to the extent that they gradually became an overused phrase, a cliché that her friends tuned out. Soon people quit listening altogether. Sadly, they no longer heard Linda's cries for help.

Linda had experienced many disappointments. Because of this, she focused on her problems, undesirable circumstances, and past failures—most of them not her fault. Yet her perceptions often made bad situations even worse.

Then one day Linda met a Christian woman named Sandy. Sandy listened past the clichés and heard the cry of Linda's heart. Sandy suggested that Linda change the way she prayed. Instead of complaining to God, compliment Him. Her outlook on life changed dramatically. It didn't take long for her friends to notice the improvement.

God is a patient listener. He hears us when we talk about our problems, bemoan our circumstances, or complain about all the evil in the world. Even so, God surely enjoys our praises too!

Dear Lord, I am so thankful that You listen to my hurts and concerns. Help me to lift up my praises this day as well. Through Christ, amen.

November 26–30. Charles E. Harrel has been a minister for more than 30 years. He currently directs His Place Outreach in Portland, Oregon.

All That He Commanded

Both of them were upright in the sight of God, observing all the Lord's commandments and regulations blamelessly (Luke 1:6).

Scripture: **Luke 1:5-7**
Song: **"Go Forth at Christ's Command"**

As a 10-year-old, I visited my Uncle Mel and Aunt Millie one summer. Since Mel was a preacher, I knew that meant going to church. Not exactly my idea of a vacation, rating only slightly higher than going to the dentist. On Sunday morning, I put on my coat and tie. "Why are you wearing that stuff?" my uncle asked. "You better change into some blue jeans and grab a cowboy hat—you might need them later." Now he had my attention.

My aunt and uncle were a dedicated couple who obeyed God in all things. They sponsored a youth outreach with riding horses on Sunday afternoons. They also hosted a carnival on the church grounds every summer. Some members thought they were foolish; others left the church. The complaining stopped, however, when revival spread to the surrounding churches and nearby cities.

Following God and living uprightly has benefits. Elizabeth and Zechariah conceived a child of promise. For Mel and Millie, God granted what they wanted most: salvation for their young nephew and revival for their city.

Precious Lord, teach me to live my life in obedience to Your will. Even when Your ways seem unconventional to some, may I always follow the path You have marked out for me. In Jesus' name I pray. Amen.

Your Prayers Are Heard

The angel said to him: "Do not be afraid, Zechariah; your prayer has been heard. Your wife Elizabeth will bear you a son, and you are to give him the name John" (Luke 1:13).

Scripture: **Luke 1:8-13**
Song: **"The God of Salvation Hears"**

Laura wanted another child. She and her husband were happy with their two girls; still, she dreamed of having one more. God heard the cry of her heart. Although she was nearing the age when most women stop having children, she felt she had God's assurance to proceed. It even seemed that God gave her a name—a boy's name.

When she told her husband, Charles, he was less than sympathetic. "Are you sure? How do you know God wants us to have another child? What about hospital costs?" Charles had many concerns. However, when Laura mentioned that God had given her a name, he settled down and listened. She explained that God wanted this baby to have a special heritage and a name that pointed back to the Redeemer. With fears alleviated, they put their faith and love to work. Nine months later, little Christopher came into the world.

Sometimes it seems as if God forgets us, even ignores our prayers. But that is never the case. He listens to our every word. Even our thoughts are known to Him. Zechariah's prayers reached Heaven, and so do ours.

Dear God, teach me to trust You in all things. Whenever doubts arise, remind me that You always hear my prayers. In Jesus' name, amen.

Forerunners Still Needed

He will go on before the Lord, in the spirit and power of Elijah, to turn the hearts of the fathers to their children and the disobedient to the wisdom of the righteous—to make ready a people prepared for the Lord (Luke 1:17).

Scripture: **Luke 1:14-17**
Song: **"I'll Go Where You Want Me to Go"**

Johann Gutenberg designed a printing press with replaceable wooden or metal letters. His press furthered the gospel message by printing Gutenberg Bibles, the first books published in volume. In 1803, Lewis and Clark led an expedition across a newly acquired land, most of it unexplored; their efforts paved the way for a great westward expansion in America. The Wright brothers and their Wright Flyer became the first heavier-than-air machine to achieve controlled flight with a pilot aboard; their design opened wide the doors to modern aviation.

All these people, and countless others like them, were forerunners. They blazed new trails or repaired old ones, setting the stage for those who followed them. And thus was John the Baptist. His messages turned the hearts of many people back to God and prepared them for the arrival of Jesus the very Son of God.

God still uses forerunners today. They preach a common message: Get ready; Jesus is coming back.

God and Father of My Lord Jesus Christ, *I may not have the notoriety as others, but I can still reach out to my neighbors and befriend them. Help me do it with all graciousness for Your glory. In Jesus' name, amen.*

Age Doesn't Matter

Zechariah asked the angel, "How can I be sure of this? I am an old man and my wife is well along in years" (Luke 1:18).

Scripture: **Luke 1:18-23**
Song: **"After the Mist and Shadow"**

I never knew her first name. Everyone at church simply called her Lady J. Her husband had passed away years before, and her grown children lived out of town, wrapped up in their own lives. Although Lady J stayed busy, loneliness filled her days. What she missed most was being a mother.

One Sunday after church, the minister asked asked her to teach a class for young married couples. With his offer came the opportunity to be a "mother" again! God used Lady J in the senior years of her life. She wasn't given just one child to raise like Zechariah and Elizabeth; she was given many. Her nurturing and parental guidance inspired the class to serve Christ. In fact, most of her students became ministers, including me.

Zechariah thought he was too old for a blessing, but age doesn't determine our eligibility. The call of God doesn't depend on age either. The Lord can fill the barren places in our lives with a wave of His hand. If He wants to bless you, just believe and never ask why.

Lord God, Your promises are sure words that never fail. They do not weaken with age, nor do they expire with time. Throughout the ages, Your promises have blessed so many—eternal testimony to Your awesome lovingkindness. Thank You, in the precious name of Jesus. Amen.

My Prayer Notes

DEVOTIONS

***P*raise be to God, who has not rejected my prayer.**

—Psalm 66:20

DECEMBER

Photo © istock

Gary Allen, Editor

Pondering God's Purpose

After this his wife Elizabeth became pregnant and for five months remained in seclusion (Luke 1:24).

Scripture: **Luke 1:24, 25**
Song: **"Alone with God"**

I needed a break—or at least a short sabbatical. Maybe our church building project had affected me more than I realized. Although I enjoyed being a minister, my heart was somewhere else these days. My interests were changing. After decades of ministry, did God have other plans for me? Why would God ask me to start writing now?

I needed time to mull things over. I remembered that the apostle Paul sought solitude after his conversion experience on the Damascus Road. He allowed time for God's message to saturate his heart (see Galatians 1:16-18). Moses spent time on Mount Sinai. Elijah rested by a brook. Jesus himself sought out the quietness of the wilderness. In seclusion, they all communed with the Father. Similarly, Elizabeth remained by herself to reflect on the favor of God.

We today also need time alone with God. Thankfully, He draws us to "isolated places" in our lives that we might simply wait on Him. In the quiet, we can ponder His goodness and learn more of His purposes.

Draw me away, **O Lord,** *to that secret place of prayer. Help me listen closely for Your still, small voice. In Christ Jesus, I pray. Amen.*

December 1, 2. **Charles E. Harrel** has been a minister for more than 30 years. He currently directs His Place Outreach in Portland, Oregon.

Just Tell It

Come and listen, all you who fear God; let me tell you what he has done for me (Psalm 66:16).

Scripture: **Psalm 66:16-20**
Song: **"I Love to Tell the Story"**

The gold-plated fish hook on the man's shirt collar grabbed my attention. It reminded me of my dad; he often pinned his favorite fishing fly or lure on his hat. After I'd snuck several glances, the man walked over and introduced himself. Our conversation soon turned to fishing.

I discovered this gold hook was John's favorite one; he had caught more fish with it than any other. He told me that he once hooked a 200-pounder with it!

John always kept his favorite hook handy in case he saw a fish. In fact, he said, he had one on the line now (and he started to tug on his collar as if a fish were nibbling). That's when I realized John had been fishing for me. With his hook set, John told me the story of his own experience of being caught—by the greatest fisherman of all.

Our witness matters. People may dismiss our doctrine, or disagree with our beliefs, but they cannot deny what God has done in our lives. If we'll just tell them how God has graciously reached into our hearts, we can let Him take care of the rest.

Father, I know we all have different stories. Some have experienced Your healing, others a wonderful answer to prayer. But all of us have known Your unconditional favor through Christ's work of atonement. Help me to tell of Your great goodness in my life. In Jesus' name, amen.

Trusting for Each Step

Blessed is the man who makes the LORD his trust, who does not look to the proud, to those who turn aside to false gods (Psalm 40:4).

Scripture: **Psalm 40:1-5**
Song: **"I Could Not Do Without Thee"**

As I read Psalm 40 for my morning devotions, the fourth verse really seemed to stand out. I realized how often I am tempted to trust in people or things more than the Lord. Why? For one thing, we're constantly bombarded by media messages calling us to find our security elsewhere—with all kinds of appealing false gods.

And those gods come in many forms, don't they? Yet science and technology can't solve all of our problems. And mere possessions won't deliver a solid and settled joy. Even modern medicine—a great boon to civilization—can subtly pull us away from ultimate trust in God for our well-being. As educator Harold W. Dodds once said: "The way to be safe is never to be secure. . . . Each one of us requires the spur of insecurity to force us to do our best." Perhaps that is why God calls us to walk by faith and not by sight, one step at a time.

Dear Lord, I live in a world filled with so much that is questionable—or downright evil. Help me resist the allure of finite pleasures and trust You, instead, for every good thing. In the holy name of Jesus, my Lord and Savior, I pray. Amen.

December 3–9. **Gerry Kershner** writes from his home in Lancaster County, Pennsylvania. In addition to devotionals, he writes poetry and magazine articles.

Troubled by Good News?

Mary was greatly troubled at his words and wondered what kind of greeting this might be (Luke 1:29).

Scripture: **Luke 1:26-29**
Song: **"Joy to the World"**

Mary later exhibited tremendous joy and faith concerning this miraculous event. But why was she initially so troubled at Gabriel's words, wondering "what kind of greeting this might be"? This sudden introduction was a great surprise, of course—even a bit shocking. And no doubt Mary needed time to adjust to her new role.

We too may initially react to good news with a troubled spirit. In a wonderful 1983 film about redemption, *Tender Mercies,* the main character (played by Robert Duvall) is baptized and changed forever. But he later says to the lady who brought him into the church: "I prayed last night to know: *Why? . . .* I don't know why I wandered to this part of Texas, and you took me in, pitied me, and helped me to straighten out. . . . Why did that happen? You see, I don't trust happiness. I never did and never will."

We may not be able to explain (or fully trust) the sudden goodness of God in our lives, for sometimes that grace enters in almost shocking ways. We are right to be troubled—at least for awhile—until our consternation turns to unspeakable joy.

Dear Father, during this season when we celebrate the birth of Your Son, I am overwhelmed with Your sudden entrance into this world. Help me to accept Your many good gifts with joy. In Jesus' name, amen.

Let the Kingdom Show Through!

He will reign over the house of Jacob forever; his kingdom will never end (Luke 1:33).

Scripture: **Luke 1:30-33**
Song: **"There's a Song in the Air"**

Like many other Christians, I'm distressed by the crass commercialism and secular activities associated with Christmas in our culture. Every year we seem to experience less of the true meaning of Christ's incarnation.

As I read Luke 1:33 I wonder what the angel Gabriel means when he says that Jesus' kingdom will never end. Then I'm reminded that (at least for now) Jesus' realm is not a political, earthly kingdom. He refused political rule during His time on earth. No, Jesus reigns forever in the hearts of His followers, a kingdom that will never end.

As followers of Jesus we can share His love, His joy, and His peace with others during the Christmas season and throughout the year. We can do this no matter how others celebrate. In this way we can be a part of maintaining Jesus' kingdom and even helping spread it in our neighborhoods and throughout the world. As Jesus himself said, "The kingdom of God is within you" (Luke 17:21). But will we let His reign in our hearts be visible in the most practical and loving forms of outreach?

Lord, help me to keep my eyes, mind, and heart on You, continually reminding me that Your Kingdom is within me. And do move me to share Your love, Your joy, and Your peace with others during this Christmas season. In the name of Jesus, who came as Lord and Savior of all, I pray. Amen.

Back to Basics

The holy one to be born will be called the Son of God
(Luke 1:35).

Scripture: **Luke 1:34, 35**
Song: **"Silent Night"**

For many of us, the Christmas season is harried and hurried. We have gifts to make or buy, boxes to wrap, cards to address and send, parties to plan, food to buy and prepare, and church activities to fit into our busy schedules. Most of these activities are good, but I'm thinking of "going back to the basics."

I'm starting with the basic question, "What is Christmas all about?" In today's verse the angel tells Mary that the child to be born will be called the Son of God. In that brief announcement we can see that Christmas is really the most important event in the history of the world. God came to the world as a flesh-and-blood human being!

In light of this amazing truth, all of our Christmas activities take on new meaning. The gifts, cards, food, parties, and church activities now all become our part of celebrating the radical entrance of the Son of God. What a birthday this is—calling us to slow down, to contemplate its miraculous unfolding, to make room for many silent nights of praise.

Dear Father in Heaven, I come to You during this harried and hurried season, asking You to help me get back to the basics. Keep me focused on the great miracle of Your Son coming in person to love Your world. And help me love Him with all my heart in return. In His name, I pray. Amen.

Mary, the Lord's Servant

"I am the Lord's servant," Mary answered. "May it be to me as you have said" (Luke 1:38).

Scripture: **Luke 1:36-38**
Song: **"Mary, Did You Know?"**

Rereading the wonderful story of Christmas in the first chapter of Luke's gospel, I am struck by Mary's humble acceptance of the angel's dramatic announcement that she is to be pregnant. And her child was to be called the Son of the Most High!

After all this fanfare, she simply answers, "I am the Lord's servant. May it be to me as you have said" (1:38). Yes, she may have been a bit confused, or troubled, but she apparently did not need to know all of the minor details and long-term implications, as I usually do. God said it, and that was enough. Such child-like faith is a lesson I often need to relearn.

I think any of us can learn much from Mary. We don't normally receive angelic visitations, but we do often experience God moving in ways we do not understand. And this is where we can remember Mary's example. Rather than trying to understand the big picture all at once, we can simply take the next step with God.

Dear Lord and Master, *thank You so much for Mary and the many other biblical role models You've given me, that I may lead a life pleasing to You. I too am Your servant. So help me live with simple, child-like faith in Your good will and guidance in my life. In the name of the Father, the Son, and the Holy Spirit, I pray. Amen.*

Elizabeth's Joy and Faith

As soon as the sound of your greeting reached my ears, the baby in my womb leaped for joy (Luke 1:44).

Scripture: Luke 1:39-45
Song: "My Faith Looks Up to Thee"

We can hardly imagine the joy that Elizabeth felt when Mary visited her. She who had been childless during her normal child-bearing years was now pregnant. She must have been overjoyed when she immediately recognized that her relative, Mary, was also pregnant in a miraculous way. Elizabeth's joy in the autumn of her life must have been especially sweet.

Yet through all those childless years, Elizabeth kept her strong faith in God. She was upright in the sight of God. She observed all of the commandments and regulations blamelessly. Later, she believed that the One who made the promise would keep the promise. Simply put, she kept the faith.

Many of us have dreams that remain unfulfilled, causing us, at times, to doubt God's goodwill toward us. Yet, like Elizabeth, we need to keep the faith, because our faith is more important than our dreams. As writer Henry Thoreau once said: "The smallest seed of faith is better than the largest fruit of happiness."

Dear Lord, strengthen my faith. Help me to remain true and faithful even when I have no visible evidence, like Elizabeth during her childless years. Help me to keep the faith so I may also experience joy as Elizabeth did. In Jesus' name I pray. Amen.

Mary's Song of Praise

My soul glorifies the Lord and my spirit rejoices in God my Savior (Luke 1:46, 47).

Scripture: **Luke 1:46-56**
Song: **"How Majestic Is Your Name"**

I am humbled by Mary's song of praise in these ten verses, traditionally called the *Magnificat*. After a spontaneous outburst of praise for her personal blessing, she continues to praise God for His mercy, power, and goodness in the past as well as the present.

I must confess that far too often I do not praise God and give Him the glory for the small, and sometimes even the larger, blessings in my life. Oh yes, I pray on a daily basis like many other Christians. But my prayer requests often far outnumber my praise items. Obviously, Mary had many personal prayer needs at this time, but none of them are included in this short song of praise.

Study of this song has convinced me to make a deliberate, personal effort to include more and more praise in my prayer life. In fact, I hope it will become a spontaneous and constant part of my relationship with God. After all, prayer is primarily an opening of hearts up to God, just as Mary did. Sometimes it is simply a wordless adoration or a period of silent listening for Him. But couldn't many of us use a little boost to our prayer lives by adding small songs of praise to our daily devotional times?

Dear Lord, You are so good! Help me to praise you spontaneously and sincerely this day. In Your holy name I pray. Amen.

Messengers

See, I will send my messenger, who will prepare the way before me (Malachi 3:1).

Scripture: **Malachi 3:1-4**
Song: **"If Jesus Goes With Me"**

When I feel unimportant, I recall the words I once heard a minister preach: "You may be the only Bible some people will ever read." John the Baptist must have understood this thoroughly. He was the messenger God chose to prepare the way for Jesus' arrival.

On the face of it, John was unimpressive. He lived in the wilderness, ate bugs, and wore strange clothes. Yet people flocked to hear the message of repentance he preached. They came, not because John was attractive, but because he was a faithful messenger, telling the people what God wanted them to know.

We may never know the impact we have on the people we encounter, day in and day out. A kindness done to a stranger, a hug given a stressed-out coworker, or time spent with a little child may seem like simple, unnoticeable acts. But to God, they are a witness to the world of Christ's love. When we allow God to use us as messengers of the gospel, we may even amaze ourselves.

Lord, I feel so unworthy of the calling to be a messenger of Your good news. Help me be faithful, in word and deed—and be on the lookout for those in any kind of need. In the name of Christ I pray. Amen.

December 10–16. **Lisa Konzen** works for United Way in Janesville, Wisconsin. She also writes health articles for seniors in her local newspaper, *The Janesville Gazette*.

Standing Up

But his mother spoke up and said, "No! He is to be called John" (Luke 1:60).

Scripture: **Luke 1:57-61**
Song: **"Stand Up, Stand Up for Jesus"**

I used to be quite a pushover. If my food was served cold at a restaurant, I'd meekly eat it instead of sending it back. If I wasn't satisfied with something I bought, I'd stash it away in my closet instead of returning it to the store for a refund.

But not anymore. What made the difference? The day I realized that some things are worth standing up for. My father was in the hospital, and because he had many health problems, full and complete information about his status wasn't always communicated very well. I had to approach doctors and nurses rather assertively for the answers I needed.

It taught me a valuable lesson: Sometimes, you just have to be tough. Not unkind, and certainly not violent. But tough. It all depends on what you're standing up for. I imagine Elizabeth trembled a little when her relatives challenged her decision to name her son John. But she knew that was what God wanted her to do. So, despite being a woman in a society that did not highly value a woman's opinion, Elizabeth stood up for God.

Holy God, too often I've been timid when I should have been bold. Yet You are the source of all my courage. Fill me with Your presence to the extent that I have no room left for fear. In the name of Jesus, amen.

Tongue Un-Tied

Immediately his mouth was opened and his tongue was loosed, and he began to speak, praising God (Luke 1:64).

Scripture: **Luke 1:62-66**
Song: **"Praise the Savior"**

Have you ever been tongue-tied when trying to talk about your faith? You know you should say something, but it's so difficult. Maybe you're going through a rough time, and bearing witness for God seems to require more faith than you feel you have.

Zechariah knew about being tongue-tied. When the angel Gabriel told him his elderly, barren wife Elizabeth would bear a son, he asked for proof. His lack of trust was met with a stern promise from Gabriel that Zechariah would not be able to speak until the child was born. And sure enough, Zechariah was mute until the day he said, "His name is John" (1:63).

I think we can learn a lesson from Zechariah. His lack of trust in God led him to mute ineffectiveness. Similarly, when our faith falters, we may find it difficult to speak about the good news of the gospel. But the same Holy Spirit who loosened Zechariah's tongue and restored his faith can do the same for us. Our simple willingness to be used by Him is the first movement toward a full-bodied trust that won't falter.

Word of God, speak through me. My tongue is dry, and my heart is empty without You. But when You dwell in me, rivers of blessings pour forth from my lips as I sing Your praises! In the name of Jesus, amen.

Without Fear

He has raised up a horn of salvation . . . to rescue us from the hand of our enemies, and to enable us to serve him without fear (Luke 1:69, 74).

Scripture: **Luke 1:67-75**
Song: **"All Your Anxiety"**

You've probably heard of the fight-or-flight response. It's the wonderful system God designed in our bodies that helps us react to dangerous situations. When we're in crisis, the hormone adrenaline is released. For example, a grizzly bear challenges us in the woods. We can either try to tackle him to the ground or . . . run away. Fast!

We rarely face grizzlies in modern living today. Yet, our bodies react the same way when we feel under pressure day after day, or experience even a minor conflict with a coworker or spouse. Adrenaline still shoots into our hearts; we react with fear—and fight or flee.

Problem is, when the crisis passes, many of us can't seem to turn off the response! Chronic fear can contribute to the development of generalized anxiety, depression, and a host of physical maladies, including heart disease. Our hectic lives have turned what was once a blessing from God into a curse.

But it doesn't have to be that way. In Christ, we are set free. We'll still face stress, but as we cast our cares upon our Savior, we can let go and let God rescue us.

Dear God, it's so easy to become afraid these days. But You asked me to cast my cares upon You, so that's what I'm going to do. Through Christ, amen.

Knowing the Word

To give his people the knowledge of salvation through the forgiveness of their sins (Luke 1:77).

Scripture: **Luke 1:76-80**
Song: **"More About Jesus"**

The minister of my church is a strong believer in Bible study, and with good reason. Because he is so faithful in teaching the truth of God's Word, we know the history and mystery of our faith. History, because he painstakingly presents the narrative of the Scripture, exploring the time lines and themes.

But he goes way beyond that, teaching us the mystery of the grace of our Savior, Jesus Christ, and the way His life, death, and resurrection free us to serve Him joyfully.

And serve Him we do. From hunger walks to "Christmas in July" fund raisers for the local food pantry, our church practices what our minister preaches. New ministries inside and outside of the church are continually springing up. But if all this sounds like bragging, that's because it is. Not about our members, or even about our minister. We're just responding to the gift of salvation freely given that we learn about as we study Scripture. All the praise, glory, and honor go to Jesus, the Word of Life who writes His gospel across the lives of His people. For without Him, we can do nothing.

O Lord, help me to rededicate myself to studying the Scripture each day. I want to be knowledgeable so I can share the treasures of Your truth with every open-hearted person I meet. In Jesus' name, amen.

Pedigree or Mutt?

Do not begin to say to yourselves, "We have Abraham as our father." For I tell you that out of these stones God can raise up children for Abraham (Luke 3:8).

Scripture: **Luke 3:7-14**
Song: **"A Child of the King"**

All my life we've had dogs. I remember Bagel, so named because we were told she was a beagle, only to learn later that she was a Pit Bull mix. Peggy, a black Labrador retriever, who was so smart and loving. And Princess Su Linn, a Lhasa Apso who was the only pure-bred dog our family ever had.

Pedigreed or mutt, it really doesn't matter. What matters with dogs is not who their parents were, but the love given by their owners. A dog won't snub us because his sire was a best in show. Dogs stand on their own four paws, protecting and loving us because they're part of our family.

We can learn a lot from our pooch pals. It doesn't matter what our name is, where we're from, or how much money sits in our bank account. What matters in the church is that we're all part of God's family. It has nothing to do with any effort on our part. God adopted us and calls us to love each other as brothers and sisters in Christ.

Heavenly Father, *thank You for adopting me into Your family as a precious child. Help me to remember the pure grace that made it possible—and therefore to love unconditionally all my siblings in the faith. I pray this prayer in the name of Jesus, my merciful Savior and Lord. Amen.*

Proud to Be Humble

John answered them all, "I baptize you with water. But one more powerful than I will come, the thongs of whose sandals I am not worthy to untie" (Luke 3:16).

Scripture: **Luke 3:15-20**
Song: **"The Unveiled Christ"**

Have you ever heard someone complain about having to play second fiddle? Perhaps it was an employee whose co-worker was just promoted. "I hate playing second fiddle to him," the disgruntled worker might grumble. Playing second fiddle means you are not the one in charge, not the one getting all the attention.

But have you ever wondered what the phrase literally means? An orchestra has sections and subsections. Within the strings are violins, in subsets of first and second violins (violins being the dressed-up name for fiddles). The role of the second violins is to support the work of the first violins, enhancing them with glorious harmony.

John the Baptist wasn't ashamed to play second fiddle to Jesus. He knew he had a job to do, and he wasn't in it for the limelight. For him, playing second fiddle was right because he knew Jesus was the Savior whose sacrifice would save him and the world. Perhaps next time we're asked to serve in the shadows, we'll remember the prophet in the wilderness who was proud to be humble.

Dear God and Father, may my thoughts, words, and actions take the spotlight off me and glorify You. Let me bring harmony to Your kingdom. Through Your precious Son, Jesus Christ, I pray. Amen.

December 17

Making It a List

Sing to the Lord a new song. . . . Splendor and majesty are before him; strength and glory are in his sanctuary (Psalm 96:1, 6).

Scripture: **Psalm 96:1-6**
Song: **"Glorious Is Thy Name"**

I'm a year-round list-maker. Lists keep me focused—especially at Christmas time. Let's see, what do I need to do in order to be ready? Cards, decorations, gifts, parties, programs . . . and on it goes.

I do something similar when I study God's Word. If I come to a passage that includes a list of God's attributes or commands, I love to list them in my journal. Then I might use a Bible dictionary to jot some definitions next to each item. Even the subtle differences I find between quite similar words give me much food for thought. The next step is to consider how to apply what I've learned.

A particular favorite this time of year is the list of names in Isaiah 9:6: Wonderful Counselor, Mighty God, Everlasting Father, Prince of Peace. Even today's passage lends itself to such a word study with phrases like: praise His name, proclaim His salvation, declare His glory, splendor and majesty, strength and glory. What do each of these mean to you?

Lord, Your Word is so rich. May I pause at even familiar words and find in them a new song to sing Your praise. Through Christ my Lord, amen.

December 17–23. **Susan Miholer,** a grandmother and special education assistant, owns Picky, Picky Ink, her editorial service in Salem, Oregon.

The Trinity of the Slide

Give him the name Jesus, because he will save his people from their sins (Matthew 1:21).

Scripture: **Matthew 1:18b-21**
Song: **"The Name of Jesus"**

"Grandma, come get me!" Four-year-old Nicholas was at the top of the slide at a fast-food restaurant, too scared to come down. I assumed some uncomfortable positions as I crawled through the not-quite-adult-sized tunnels to get to him, and then I rode down the slide with him. Not my most dignified grandmotherly moment! He, on the other hand, thought it was great fun. I kept envisioning the newspaper headline: "Grandmother Stuck—Fire Department Summoned."

I didn't feel very god-like that day; in fact, I was glad there were few witnesses to my actions and attitude. But later I saw the whole episode as a picture of what God did for us. As the Father, He saw our need of a Savior. As the Son, He assumed the uncomfortable positions of the Incarnation to rescue me. And as the Holy Spirit, He rides with me through the twists and turns of this slide-ride we call life.

Jesus. There's just something about that name— something that tells us so much about God that we can never comprehend it all.

Heavenly Father, *when I consider how You reached down through Your Son, I'm humbled that You included me in Your great plan of salvation. Thank You for the sacrifice of the Incarnation! In Jesus' name, amen.*

A New Chapter

So Joseph also went . . . to Bethlehem. . . . He went there to register with Mary (Luke 2:4, 5).

Scripture: **Luke 2:1-5**
Song: **"O Little Town of Bethlehem"**

During the last few weeks of my pregnancies, waddling anywhere was a challenge. Travel for any reason other than essential errands and appointments was pretty much out of the question.

Mary probably wasn't eager to travel from Nazareth to Bethlehem in her condition. But regardless of the discomforts involved, she was no doubt relieved to be getting away from the whispers and judgmental stares in her old neighborhood. She was probably both exhilarated and frightened about her new role as mother too—a new chapter in her life. Bethlehem might well provide a clean slate for her and Joseph.

When God ushers in a new chapter in our lives, we often experience the same emotional mix—the exhilaration, yet the questions about what is happening and why things are unfolding the way they are. And, like Mary, we can face the challenge with a similar response: "May it be to me as you have said" (Luke 1:38).

Facing a life-change in this season of your life? Look to God as He leads you into a new chapter.

*Thank You, **God,** that You have gone before me into the unknown of my life. Allow me to trust You for the grace, strength, and wisdom to face today's challenges. In the name of Jesus, my Savior, I pray. Amen.*

No Room in the Family?

There was no room for them in the inn (Luke 2:7).

Scripture: **Luke 2:6, 7**
Song: **"No Room in the Inn"**

At the birth of my first grandchild, we grandparents practically elbowed each other out of the way to be first in the room to see our new baby boy. But Scripture is strangely silent about Mary and Joseph's families. I would think that several members of Joseph's family would have been in Bethlehem. Didn't they have to go there to register as well? If this was Joseph's ancestral home, I'd expect there may have been relatives in Bethlehem with whom they could have stayed. But they seemed so alone in that place.

I know Scripture doesn't give us all the details, but I'm wondering if Mary's circumstances had ostracized Joseph and Mary so much that even close family members wouldn't extend hospitality to them—or at least some loving concern. That would take the phrase "no room for them in the inn" (2:7) to another level, wouldn't it? Not only was there no room in the inn, there may have been no room in the family circle.

Yet Jesus' earthly parents model for me the response I should have when I feel cut off from others. Follow God anyway.

Father, I sometimes feel there's no room for me in certain situations because I've chosen to follow You along the narrow way. At those times, may I rest assured that You are always with me. Through Christ, amen.

Creative Announcement

Today in the town of David a Savior has been born to you; he is Christ the Lord (Luke 2:11).

Scripture: **Luke 2:8-14**
Song: **"Angels We Have Heard on High"**

People have gotten creative with birth announcements lately, as the computer provides all kinds of new ways to announce a baby's entrance into the world. Families design entire websites to share the news. I've even seen custom-printed wrappers that slip over a regular chocolate bar. The front of the label (and its color) let people know the baby's vital statistics. And the parents' names replace the standard ingredients label.

But the most creative of all birth announcements occurred on a hillside over 2,000 years ago as a bunch of ordinary (and probably scruffy) shepherds settled their sheep and themselves for the night. As they adjusted their cloaks to ward off the evening chill, and breathed that last relaxed sigh of impending sleep, an angel amid the glory of the Lord delivered awesome good news. And then the sky seemed to explode as the heavenly host underscored the grand message.

No other birth in history has been announced in such magnificent style. Nor has any other birth in history had the same eternal consequences. No wonder the angels praised God!

Eternal God, *may I, like the angels, praise You and say, Glory to God in the highest! In the name of the incarnate Christ I pray. Amen.*

Different Reactions

Mary treasured up all these things and pondered them in her heart (Luke 2:19).

Scripture: **Luke 2:15-20**
Song: **"O Come, Let Us Adore Him"**

Different people react differently to good news. Some clap, some cry, some dance, and some just stand there looking surprised. I've done all four—and sometimes two or three at the same time.

Recovering from the spectacle of God's glory and the good news of Christ's birth, the shepherds couldn't get to Bethlehem fast enough. Having seen the baby, their exuberance bubbled over as they told everyone of the angel's announcement and what they had seen. People were astonished. Even without e-mail, the news traveled quickly. But Mary, precious Mary, the one who had known for months whose child this was, quietly pondered what was happening, filing away memories of her Son.

Emotions run high at Christmas time. Like the shepherds, we may push and shove to get there first. We may be so excited about the good news of Christmas that we sing the familiar carols with new enthusiasm, astonished by the discovery of new facets in the familiar story. But like Mary, I also want to carve out times of quiet reflection upon who Jesus really is—my Lord and my God.

Dear Father, *the birth of Your Son changed the course of history. May I understand a piece of the Christmas story in a new way this year. Keep my focus on who Christ is and why He came. In His name I pray. Amen.*

Who's the Author?

Ascribe to the LORD the glory due his name; bring an offering and come into his courts (Psalm 96:8).

Scripture: **Psalm 96:7-13**
Song: **"Creation's Lord, We Give Thee Thanks"**

We don't use the word "ascribe" very often anymore. The dictionary says it suggests an "inferring or conjecturing of cause, quality, or authorship." If you're a Shakespeare scholar or an expert on Picasso, you know what to look for in a specific play or work of art to indicate its creator. Sometimes, though, even the experts don't agree as to whom a particular work ought to be ascribed.

But there is no disagreement in today's passage about who is responsible for, who is the author of, all the beauty in nature. Every aspect of the natural world—the seas, the hills, the forests, even the living beings—point us toward their creator. And that same author is the author of our salvation, the baby whose birth we celebrate at this time of year.

Born in obscurity, He is the author of this world and everything in it. And if anything good and admirable blossoms within our hearts . . . He is the author of all of those virtues too. For our heart is the place He has chosen to make His dwelling place. Ascribe glory to Him!

My Father in Heaven, Your Son came to the earth to be the author of my salvation. Thank You, from the bottom of my heart. I want to worship You in the same spontaneous way Your creation does, pointing others to You. In the name of the Father, the Son, and the Holy Spirit, I pray. Amen.

The First Christmas Gift-giv

That you may bring my salvation to the ends of the ...t (Isaiah 49:6).

Scripture: **Isaiah 49:5, 6**
Song: **"It Came Upon the Midnight Clear"**

Our familiar white-bearded Santa harks back to a third-century bishop born in Turkey. Renowned for his humility and generosity, Nicholas became the patron saint of many nations, causes, and groups, including sailors and children. A body of legend grew around his person, including the idea that he dressed in red and gave gifts at Christmas time.

Poet Clement Moore leaned on such legends as he wrote the whimsical, "A Visit from St. Nicholas" in 1832 to amuse his children. But the reindeer-powered Christmas Eve trip around the world was Moore's unique idea. His poem gained immediate fame and imposed a curious persona on humble Nicholas that would have amazed him.

We need not fuss about the folklore from many lands that colors our Christmas celebrations. But tree lights, holly, and mistletoe must not overshadow the manger, where the true Gift-giver was born. He offers His gift to the ends of the earth, not once a year, but every day—and throughout all generations to every tribe and tongue.

*Thank You, **Lord,** for offering Your gift of eternal life to all, whether they have been naughty or nice. All praise to You, in Christ's name. Amen.*

December 24–30. **Lloyd Mattson** is a retired minister and author of Christian camping books. He and his wife, Elsie, live in Duluth, Minnesota.

Poor Joseph and Mary!

Joseph and Mary took him to Jerusalem to present him to the Lord . . . and to offer a sacrifice in keeping with what is said in the Law of the Lord" (Luke 2:22, 24).

Scripture: Luke 2:21-24
Song: "Thou Didst Leave Thy Throne"

Joseph and Mary came to the temple with birds, the sacrifice of the poor. Similarly, throughout His ministry, Jesus depended on others for food and shelter. Yet we seldom think of Jesus or His family as poor. After all, poverty is relative; our poorest seem rich beyond imagining to earth's millions who are starving.

While Jesus placed no premium on poverty, He spoke often about greed. That's why Christmas appeals move us to give to the needy, and we rightly feel good about doing so. The Magi, too, presented gifts, but we can't know the worth of those gifts until we know what they had left.

What do we have left? Our benevolent giving marks us as among earth's most generous people, yet America has little cause for pride. Consider what we keep! The American dream wears a dollar sign, and a good Christmas usually means retailers sold more than they did the year before.

The point is, giving isn't really giving until it costs us something. And at Christmas time we can remember: We celebrate the birth of a man who owned nothing.

Heavenly Father, *that I might embrace Your presence in me to the fullest, please help me loosen my grip on everything else. In Jesus' name, amen.*

A Devout Nobody

Now there was a man in Jerusalem, called Simeon, who was righteous and devout. He was waiting for the consolation of Israel, and the Holy Spirit was upon him (Luke 2:25).

Scripture: **Luke 2:25, 26**
Song: **"Spirit of Faith, Come Down"**

A remarkable man, Simeon. He held no office or honors, yet the Holy Spirit was upon him. How could that be? Pentecost was at least three years away. Was not that the day the Holy Spirit came?

We tend to arrange God's affairs according to our limited understandings, keeping Him safely within the boundaries of our doctrinal preferences. We ought not do that, for the sovereign God works where, when, and among whom He chooses, and that truth abides today.

Simeon came to the temple at just the right time. As far as he knew, it was an ordinary day. Many people, priests, Levites, scribes, and teachers of the law bustled about. Did any of them long for Messiah's coming? But Simeon had a God-ward heart, and the Holy Spirit had given him a remarkable promise.

That day Simeon's longing was fulfilled. And the least of Jesus' followers can draw comfort from Simeon, a devout nobody who longed to see the Christ.

Dear Father above, grant me holy desires this day. And thank You for Your gift of the Holy Spirit, who fulfills the desires of my heart. I pray this prayer in the name of Jesus, my merciful Savior and Lord. Amen.

Take Him to Your Heart

When the parents brought in the child Jesus to do for him what the custom of the Law required, Simeon took him in his arms and praised God (Luke 2:27, 28).

*Scripture: **Luke 2:27, 28***
*Song: **"Into My Heart"***

I once read a little anecdote about a shabby lad who rushed into a department store on Christmas Eve, just before the store's closing. Out of breath, he pled, "Could we borrow your Jesus? Ours got busted." That line was irresistible, and I later wrote a story about a clumsy young man who knocked over a Christmas tree and shattered the porcelain pieces of a nativity scene. The story's theme: We all need our own special relationship with Jesus

Simeon experienced this when Mary came to the temple bearing a precious, six-weeks-old bundle. The baby's humanity and deity wasn't the issue, nor was His transcendent holiness. Moving beyond theology, Simeon simply took the mystery of Incarnation into his arms. For those moments, he had his very own Jesus.

We can take Jesus to our heads and acknowledge His historic reality. That is well and good—and quite necessary. We can assign Him the highest place of transcendence in our doctrines and worship. But day by day, do we keep Him at the center of our lives? Simeon, a simple, devout man, took Jesus to heart—and praised God.

***Father in Heaven,** grant me each day a continuing sense of Your presence in my life, through the indwelling Christ. In His name I pray. Amen.*

Marvelous Pronouncement

The child's father and mother marveled at what was said about him (Luke 2:33).

Scripture: **Luke 2:29-33**
Song: **"My Savior First of All"**

A quiet, elderly woman came to our small church. Though she had had no formal Bible training, she eventually became our favorite Sunday school teacher. One day my wife asked where she had gained such heart-warming, intriguing insights. The woman replied, "Elsie, it takes a lifetime to know the Scriptures." She might have added, "It takes a lifetime—and beyond—to know Jesus."

Joseph and Mary marveled at Simeon's song, and little wonder. They were ordinary folks; how could those things be?

Joseph had taken Mary to be his wife at great risk. Who would believe her story? She had endured birth pangs and held the newborn to her breast in a stable. She had not yet digested the angel Gabriel's mysterious words or the song of her cousin Elizabeth. Now could the new parents not marvel at Simeon's prophetic pronouncement?

We, too, will marvel as we grow in the grace and knowledge of our Lord. There is much, much more to Jesus than our quaint renditions of the Christmas story. It will take a lifetime and more to learn it all.

*Thank You, **Lord,** for the privilege of knowing You. As I open my heart to You daily in prayer, lead me into an ever deeper knowledge of Your presence and purpose in my life. In the name of my precious Savior, I pray. Amen.*

Couldn't Lie to Her

(And a sword will pierce through your own soul also), that thoughts out of many hearts may be revealed (Luke 2:35, *Revised Standard Version*).

Scripture: **Luke 2:34, 35**
Song: **"Grace and Truth Shall Mark the Way"**

I could not bring myself to lie to Mother. I lied easily to my sister, and I could stretch a point with my father, but I could not lie to Mother. A quiet, small woman, Mother seemed able to read my thoughts. I believed that because I knew her character. I could depend on her, and I couldn't imagine her telling a lie. I fully believed lying to her was useless; she would know the truth.

We were not an overtly religious household, and few Christian artifacts hung on our walls. We attended church faithfully, though, and rarely missed a mealtime prayer. The Bible was prominent, faith in Christ was genuine, and Mother was warm and affirming. She embodied what I imagined Jesus to be.

An early memory finds me snuggling close to Mother's breast in an heirloom rocking chair. As we rocked, "Jesus Loves Me" resonated from her. Mother loved me, she loved Jesus, and so did I, even at age three. Yes, even then I understood that nothing was hidden from Mother, nor from God.

Lord, we are all the products of what we've been taught by people we trust. Thank You for my own teachers. May I be trustworthy, so that those who follow me will be following You. Through Christ I pray. Amen.

A Touch from the Old

She was very old . . . . She never left the temple but worshiped night and day (Luke 2:36, 37).

Scripture: **Luke 2:36-38**
Song: **"Beyond the Sunset"**

August was old and dying. I was his young, green minister. He told me one day he had seen Jesus. It seems the Lord was standing in the meadow just beyond a small stream on his old country farm, beckoning. "I will go home soon," August said.

I smiled at the old man's odd vision and prepared to read a psalm. A thin, pale hand slipped over the page. "Read from your heart, my brother." That I couldn't do, and so he led me, verse by verse, through the beloved passage, his words tinged with the gentle accent of his homeland. Within a few days, August died.

Cherish your godly elders! They are wiser and closer to Heaven than younger people can be. Come to think of it, those who have eternal life can never grow old. They will change dwelling places, but they can never age. I think often of August. I'm glad Jesus came to him when he was very old, so he could touch the heart of a young, green minister.

*Thank You, **Lord,** for elderly friends. Throughout the new year, nudge me to spend more time with them, so they can minister to me in their special way. And help me to never look down on those who are close to seeing You, face to face. I pray this prayer in the name of Jesus my Savior. Amen.*

Praise from Deep Within

Praise the LORD from the earth, you great sea creatures and all ocean depths (Psalm 148:7).

Scripture: **Psalm 148:7-14**
Song: **"All Creatures of Our God and King"**

Beneath the ocean's depths exists an amazing world of God's creation that most of us will never see. Yet even nature unseen functions as a testimony to God and offers its praise to the one who sees it, created it, and maintains it. The depths of the earth's oceans, and the creatures contained within, cause us to marvel. So many small creatures, such as jellyfish, sand dollars, starfish, and sea horses. So many grand creatures, such as manatees, dolphins, sharks, and whales. So many shapes and sizes and colors of marine life grace the seas. Even in a fallen world, God's creation is breathtaking.

Like the creatures of the sea, we too praise the one who intricately designed and assembled us, He who maintains us and sustains us. We worship Him who knows us and loves us despite our sin.

The unseen in us? He sees our deepest hurts and cares. And like the rest of creation, we too praise God, especially when we live according to our ultimate purpose on earth: to become more and more like His Son, Jesus.

Sovereign God of all Creation, *I worship You. And as I live each day on earth, may my life reflect Your greatness. In Jesus' name, amen.*

December 31. **Brian J. Waldrop** is a freelance writer and professional copy editor. Originally from Champaign, Illinois, Brian now resides in Mt. Healthy, Ohio.